READINGS
in PHYSIOLOGICAL
PSYCHOLOGY
Learning and Memory

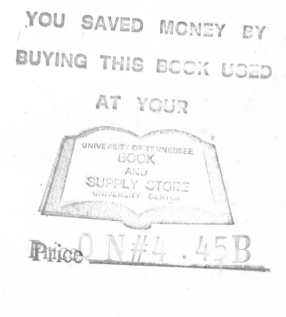

HARPER'S PHYSIOLOGICAL PSYCHOLOGY SERIES
Under the editorship of H. Philip Zeigler

READINGS
in PHYSIOLOGICAL
PSYCHOLOGY
Learning and Memory

EDITED BY **CHARLES G. GROSS**
HARVARD UNIVERSITY

H. PHILIP ZEIGLER
THE CITY COLLEGE
OF THE CITY UNIVERSITY OF NEW YORK

HARPER & ROW, PUBLISHERS
NEW YORK, EVANSTON, AND LONDON

Contents

Preface

The selection of readings for inclusion in these volumes has been guided by certain assumptions on the part of the editors. First, that physiological psychology is not a distinct area of psychology but a method of analysis applicable to many problems; second, that the primary function of a collection of readings is to give the student a concrete feeling for the procedures of physiological psychology and for the diverse ways in which experiments are generated and their results analyzed. Our final assumption is that although the physiological psychologist may use a variety of procedures drawn from physiology, anatomy, or biochemistry, his primary concern is with behavior and his unique contribution is the development of methods for the analysis of its underlying mechanisms.

With the exception of a brief section in the first volume (neurophysiological foundations), the readings have been grouped under three of the major rubrics of contemporary psychology: sensory processes, motivation, and learning and memory. Such a division has advantages for both instructor and student. Few instructors attempt, within the confines of a single course, to cover all important problem areas with equal thoroughness. Instead, they tend to select certain topics for detailed treatment. What is needed, therefore, is a collection of readings that covers a wide enough range to be truly representative and at the same time provides reasonably detailed coverage of each of the problem areas. The present volumes, used singly or in combination, should provide the necessary diversity and representativeness of topics without sacrificing comprehensive coverage of a given problem area. Furthermore, because of the grouping by problem areas, the volumes are usable individually as supplementary readings in courses whose primary focus is on behavioral rather than physiological analysis (e.g., courses in perception, motivation, and learning). In view of the growing interest in physiological mechanisms underlying behavior it is hoped that these volumes will be useful to a variety of workers who do not consider themselves physiological psychologists.

In our selections, we have favored experimental papers that can illustrate some of the methods and procedures used by physiological psychologists. Whenever possible, we have grouped together papers related to a single topic to illustrate the diversity of approaches to the problem or to indicate something of its intellectual history and current status. The editors are jointly responsible for the selection of readings collected in these volumes. Authorship of the introductory comments is indicated in each volume.

We are grateful to those publishers and authors whose permission made it possible to reprint these articles. Since so much of the pedagogical value of a scientific paper resides in its figures, we owe a special debt of gratitude to the many authors who graciously provided us with copies of the original figures.

For their assistance with the tedious but necessary clerical work involved in the preparation of the volumes we are indebted to Mrs. M. Ashby and Mrs. E. Rosenberger (Harvard University) and Mr. R. Valmindez (The City College).

C.G.G.
H.P.Z.

READINGS
in PHYSIOLOGICAL
PSYCHOLOGY
Learning and Memory

INTRODUCTION

Animals and men are affected by their experiences. Experiences, therefore, must produce changes within the organism, presumably in its nervous system. The studies in this volume are concerned with the nature of these changes. The selections in Part I deal with the problem of *when* the changes occur and when they become relatively permanent. The papers in Part II ask *what* is the nature of the changes. The third set of selections deals with the problem of *where* the changes occur. The papers in Part IV illustrate several electrophysiological approaches to learning and memory.

I

THE PROBLEM OF WHEN: CONSOLIDATION THEORY AND RETROGRADE AMNESIA

Like many areas in physiological psychology, the study of
the physiology of learning and memory began with clinical observations.
By the nineteenth century it was realized that head injury affects recent
memories more than older ones. Ribot (1881) formulated this observation
as the "Law of Regression": new or poorly organized memories are
lost before older ones; in recovery from amnesia the memories come
back in the opposite order. Such observations gave rise to the
Consolidation Theory of Memory. As originally proposed by Müller and
Pilzecker in 1900 and more recently championed by Hebb (1949),
Consolidation Theory divides memory into two successive stages. The
first stage consists of transient electrical events, or "reverberating
circuits" and is usually identified with "short-term memory." In the
second, "long-term memory" stage, these electrical events are presumed
to have produced some structural change, such as synaptic growth.
Thus, if the electrical events in the first stage are interrupted, there
will be no long-term "trace." The memory will be lost.

The most compelling evidence for Consolidation Theory still
comes from study of head injury in man. The classic modern account
is Russell and Nathan's (1946) "Traumatic Amnesia" (see page 6).
After a serious head injury there is usually a period of unconsciousness
followed by confusion and impaired consciousness. This period can
vary from minutes to weeks and is known as the period of *Post-
Traumatic Amnesia* (PTA). During PTA it seems as if the "recording
apparatus" of the mind is not working properly. Almost always
associated with even a moderate PTA is a loss of memory of events

before the accident, known as *Retrograde Amnesia* (RA). RA never occurs without PTA, and the longer the PTA the longer the RA is likely to be. The period of RA, which may be months or years, gradually shrinks, but the memory of events that occurred a few moments before the injury seems to be lost forever.

With the introduction of electroconvulsive shock therapy (ECS), it was noticed that patients were not only disoriented immediately after an ECS treatment but also were confused about events immediately before the convulsion. Zubin and Barrera (1941) trained patients on paired-associate lists and noted that ECS given immediately after training impaired retention, but ECS given some hours later did not. Most of the subsequent evidence for a retrograde amnesic effect, and thus for the Consolidation Theory of Memory, has come from animal experiments. Duncan (1949) was the first to investigate the time course of the apparent effect of ECS on memory. In a shuttle-box situation, Duncan showed that ECS 20 sec. after a trial had a deleterious effect on memory. ECS 80 sec. and 4 min. later had smaller effects, and ECS more than an hour later had little or no effect. Thus, "consolidation" seemed to be completed within an hour. In the next ten years Duncan's findings became well known and were often repeated. In fact, anoxia, cooling, anesthetics, and other treatments were soon added to the list of procedures which, when given immediately after a trial, seemed to impair memory of it. Many of these studies are reviewed by Glickman (1961).

In a provocative paper published in 1960, Coons and Miller (see page 23) challenged the entire claim that ECS produces RA by interfering with the postulated consolidation process. They suggested that, instead, ECS acts as an aversive stimulus. Coons and Miller did not simply offer another explanation of Duncan's results or report failure to repeat them. Rather, they repeated Duncan's procedures, obtained his results, and then went on to show experimentally that ECS had an aversive effect which was sufficient to explain the results of Duncan and others.

Although Coons and Miller had clearly demonstrated an aversive effect of ECS, it was still conceivable that ECS also had an amnesic effect, and experiments were soon reported that were difficult to explain otherwise. This controversy was finally resolved by the Chorover and Schiller study (1965) "Short-Term Retrograde Amnesia in Rats" (see page 36). Using a different and simpler behavioral procedure, they elegantly demonstrated both amnesic and aversive effects of ECS and traced their separate time courses. In their situation, consolidation seemed to occur within 10 sec. Soon after, an almost identical study from Miller's group appeared (Quartermain *et al.*, 1965).

How ECS exerts its amnesic effect remains obscure. It may do so by interfering with electrical activity in a specific brain structure. This is suggested by Mahut's (1962) study (see page 46) comparing the effects of intralaminar, tegmental, and cortical stimulation at various times after each learning trial. She found that only intralaminar stimulation immediately after a trial interfered with learning.

In the final selection in this Part, Pearlman, Sharpless, and Jarvik (see page 57) demonstrate that the duration of the period after a trial in which a drug can have amnesic effects differs widely with different drugs; that is, consolidation time depends on the amnesic agent. This is also illustrated in a paper by Flexner, Flexner, and Roberts (1966) in Part II (see page 95). In this study, puromycin given three days after learning produces RA, suggesting at least three days of consolidation.

Where do these different consolidation times leave Consolidation Theory—the idea that temporary electrical changes and the subsequent permanent structural changes constitute the substratum of memory? Clearly this two-stage theory is a great oversimplification. Rather, memory—the fixation of experience—involves multiple processes (some serial, some parallel) with different time constants. Different treatments probably affect different stages and processes of memory. There appears to be a continuum of retroactive amnesic effects reflecting the series of processes involved in memory. At the briefest end are phenomena such as visual masking and metacontrast, where the interference comes milliseconds after the event. Up to seconds or minutes after an event, ECS, spreading depression, and certain anesthetics interfere with memory, probably by interfering with electrical activity. Other drugs such as puromycin can affect memories that are hours or a few days old. They may do so by structural alterations. Finally, at the other end of the continuum, brain damage can affect memories that are years old.

One aspect of experimentally induced retrograde amnesia that has received little attention is its permanency. Perhaps some of these experimentally produced RA's shrink with time as RA in man usually does.

C.G.G.

REFERENCES

DUNCAN, C. P. The retroactive effect of electroshock on learning. *J. Comp. Physiol. Psychol.*, 1949, **42**, 32–44.

GLICKMAN, S. E. Perseverative neural processes and consolidation of the memory trace. *Psychol. Bull.*, 1961, **58**, 218–230.

HEBB, D. O. *The organization of behavior: A neuropsychological theory.* New York: Wiley, 1949.

MÜLLER, G. E., & PILZECKER, A. Experimentelle Beiträge zur Lehre vom Gedächtnis. *Z. Psychol.*, 1900, suppl. 1.

QUARTERMAIN, D., PAOLINO, R. M., & MILLER, N. E. A brief temporal gradient of retrograde amnesia independent of situational change. *Science*, 1965, **149**, 1116–1118.

RIBOT, T. A. *Les maladies de la mémoire.* Paris: Ballière, 1881.

ZUBIN, J. & BARRERA, S. E. Effect of convulsive therapy on memory. *Proc. Soc. Exp. Biol. Med.*, 1941, **48**, 596–597.

Traumatic Amnesia

W. Ritchie Russell
and P. W. Nathan

INTRODUCTION

The disturbances of memory associated with head injury are varied and worthy of special study. The most obvious clinical abnormality which accompanies many head injuries is an instantaneous paralysis of brain function—motor, sensory, reflex and mental. The term *concussion* is often used to describe this phenomenon. It is obvious that during the period of brain paralysis there can be no registration of surrounding incidents and accordingly there is subsequently a permanent amnesia for events occurring during this time. As consciousness returns the mental functions recover as after an anæsthetic, the more complex being the last to return to their normal state. While in slight injuries the stages of recovery occupy only a few minutes, after severe trauma recovery of brain function may occur very gradually during a period of several days or weeks. The stages of recovery, however, are often similar whether they run a brief or prolonged course. The function of memory is usually regained at about the same time as the last trace of confusion disappears, and the period of post-traumatic amnesia (P.T.A.) is then at an end. The duration of the P.T.A. can be roughly ascertained, as Russell (1932) has pointed out, by asking the patient at any time *after* he has finally emerged from the state of confusion, when he "came to himself". This endpoint, however, is sometimes ambiguous, for as Symonds has emphasized, the patient's first memory after the injury, though clearly described, may be followed by a further period of amnesia for hours or days. In such cases the patient is usually able to record the time or date from which he has continuous memory, and this has been used by us for the measurement of the P.T.A. in the cases to be described. It is thus only in the later stages of mental recovery that the patient becomes sufficiently aware of his surroundings to commit them to memory and thus to end the period of post-traumatic amnesia.

From *Brain*, 1946, **69**, 280–300. Reprinted with permission of the publisher and authors with whose approval certain material has been omitted.

POST-TRAUMATIC AMNESIA (P.T.A.)

The duration of post-traumatic amnesia (P.T.A.) can only be estimated with accuracy after the patient has recovered from even slight degrees of confusion. This duration of P.T.A. will then usually remain relatively constant and will form a permanent index of the duration, not of unconsciousness, but of impaired consciousness. The P.T.A. therefore provides a useful clinical guide for the physician who may enquire into the case for the first time long after the injury occurred. It is obvious that the duration of P.T.A. will provide some indication of the severity of the general brain commotion caused by the injury, and studies by Symonds and Russell (1943) indicated its usefulness in prognosis. We have again analysed these Service cases with reference to subsequent fitness for *full duty* in a series followed up successfully through the Unit medical officers. The results are given in Table 1 and indicate clearly that the prospects of good recovery of efficiency diminish rapidly as the P.T.A. lengthens.

Table 1   Follow-up[a]

DURATION OF P.T.A.	TOTAL CASES ADMITTED TO HOSPITAL	RET. TO DUTY FROM HOSPITAL	"FULLY DUTY EFFICIENCY" ON FOLLOW-UP	PERCENT OF TOTAL
Nil	29	28	25	86
1 hour	92	90	80	87
1–24 hours	73	70	54	74
1–7 days	39	34	23	59
7 days	41	26	7	17
No record	2	2	1	
Total	276	250	190	69

[a] Duration of post-traumatic amnesia compared with future fitness for *full duty*—based on follow-up of surviving cases six to twenty-four months after discharge from hospital. Cases were those admitted in the acute stage and therefore relatively unselected. Only those followed up successfully are considered.

Duration of P.T.A.

This analysis in Table 1 is concerned with accidental blunt injuries in which the rate of change of velocity to which the skull is subjected probably determines the degree of brain damage (Denny-Brown and Russell, 1941). In gunshot wounds, on the other hand, the brain is often submitted to little acceleration, and as in other penetrating injuries the damage is often quite local. Thus in Table 2 the duration of P.T.A. is compared in a series of accidental injuries and of gunshot wounds of the head with dural penetration or skull fracture. No less than 32 per cent of the gunshot wound cases have no amnesia, and this must be due to a failure of many of these missiles (which include small bomb fragments) to concuss the brain as a whole. There is also

Table 2[a]

| | TOTAL | DURATION OF POST-TRAUMATIC AMNESIA | | | | | |
		Nil	< 1 hr.	1–24 hr.	1–7 days	> 7 days	No record
"Accidental" head injury	1,022	99	208	312	231	167	5
	—	10%	20%	31%	23%	16%	$\frac{1}{2}$%
Gunshot wounds of the brain	200	64	40	22	42	24	6
	—	32%	20%	11%	21%	12%	3%

[a] Duration of post-traumatic amnesia in a consecutive series of surviving "accidental" and gunshot wound cases admitted to a Military Hospital for head injuries.

a remarkably small proportion of cases of gunshot wound with P.T.A. of one to twenty-four hours. This is in striking contrast to the "accidental" group and indicates that when gunshot wounds do cause loss of consciousness the latter is likely to be either of very short or of much prolonged duration. This can probably be explained by the assumption that when such wounds are of sufficient severity to cause severe general commotion the associated brain destruction will ensure by its extent or its complications that the P.T.A. is prolonged.

Table 3[a]

| | TOTAL | DURATION OF P.T.A. | | | | | |
		Nil	< 1 hr.	1–24 hr.	1–7 days	> 7 days	No record
Military Hospital cases.	331	34	115	91	45	43	3
Percent		10	35	27	14	13	1
Russell's (1932) cases. Edinburgh	184		80	57	47		
Percent			43	31	25		
Gutmann's (1943) cases. Oxford	179		118	39	19	3	
Percent	—		66	22	11	2	

[a] Duration of post-traumatic amnesia in a series of surviving cases admitted to hospital in the acute stage and therefore relatively unselected.

Table 3 gives the number of cases in the various P.T.A. groups in an unselected series of acute hospital admissions. The cases were admitted to a Military Hospital for Head Injuries, and were those admitted in the acute stage only; they are compared with figures for general hospitals published by one of us (W. R. R.) and also by Gutmann. There is a close similarity between the figures in the first two groups of cases, while those in Gutmann's series have a larger proportion of slight injuries.

It is now generally agreed (Symonds, 1932; Russell, 1932; Greenfield, 1938; Jefferson, 1942) that the disorders of consciousness following head injury are usually dependent on neuronal trauma and are rarely due to vascular complications such as hæmorrhage, œdema or increased intracranial pressure. Study of the duration of amnesias following injury carries us a step further, for this makes it necessary to postulate many degrees of neuronal commotion which, for example, may recover fully in ten minutes or may "feel their way" gradually to recovery in ten days.

Reduction of P.T.A.

Though the duration of P.T.A. is usually more or less permanent and unchanging, there are exceptions. Occasionally it becomes reduced spontaneously as in the following case:

> Fus. R. sustained a head injury on July 19, 1942. On August 4 he had a momentary retrograde amnesia (R.A.) and a P.T.A. of six days with an "island" on the fourth day. Ten weeks after the accident he regained spontaneously another island in the P.T.A., for while sitting quietly in bed he suddenly remembered being on the floor of a moving truck, and this was, in fact, the way he was brought to hospital.

Cases of reduction in P.T.A. under barbiturate hypnosis are described later. These recoveries of things forgotten are reminiscent of hysterical amnesia and yet there is no reason to suppose they are hysterical.

Delayed P.T.A. and Lucid Interval

In some few cases of accidental head injury all details of the injury and of events which closely followed it are clearly recalled, but there follows later a period of confusion and amnesia. This can be referred to as *delayed post-traumatic amnesia*. In most cases, especially in gunshot wounds of the brain, the delayed P.T.A. probably indicates that vascular complications of the wound are responsible for the delayed amnesia. 2.5 per cent of 1,029 cases of accidental head injury had delayed amnesia, while the figure for gunshot wounds of the skull and brain was much higher, being 14 per cent in 372 cases. In a very few cases of relatively slight injury the short lucid interval seems to correspond with a period of intense stimulation for the patient which may "keep him awake" for a time. For example, a cyclist whose motor-cycle caught fire after the accident remembers trying to put out the fire and then no more for many hours. Or again an airman after a crash remembered turning off the petrol before his P.T.A. developed. In this type of case the disturbance of consciousness is relatively slight and a strong stimulus may lead to registration of an event so well that it can be subsequently recalled.

The phenomenon of a lucid interval has for long been recognized as a clinical feature in the diagnosis of extradural hæmorrhage. It should be noted, however, that it is only those cases which have little initial concussion which show this well-developed lucid interval before cerebral compression supervenes. It is equally important to note that there may be a lucid interval followed by delayed confusion in the absence of any gross intracranial complication such as hæmorrhage. This is usually easy to distinguish clinically from the progressive stupor and coma of cerebral compression. These slight degrees of delayed confusion appear sometimes to be due to subarachnoid hæmorrhage, or to minute intracerebral hæmorrhages in the brain-stem (Denny-Brown, 1941).

Islands of Memory in P.T.A.

The loss of memory for all events during the time covered by the P.T.A. is not always uniformly complete. In some cases islands of memory emerge which are often concerned with special events such as an operation or the visit of a relative. They are liable to appear when confusion is slight and the patient able to converse and behave in a sensible way. In 13 cases showing an early island in the P.T.A. the final duration of amnesia was one to twenty-four hours in 4 cases, one to seven days in 4 cases, and over seven days in 5 cases. In most of these cases of early islands in the P.T.A. the underlying factors are probably the same as in the cases of delayed amnesia already referred to, but the injury being more severe there is immediate loss of consciousness, then partial recovery or lucid interval corresponding to the "island", and then the delayed amnesia due to vascular complications. As with cases of delayed amnesia, the "island" with subsequent deterioration does not usually indicate that a serious degree of cerebral compression is developing. These islands, when they occur, cannot be localized, for they concern an isolated happening unconnected with the normal chain of memories—restricted paramnesias as Bannister and Zangwill (1941) term them. A special occasion may sometimes appear to be responsible for the return of continuous remembering and the end of the P.T.A. The suddenness with which the patient may "come to himself" is often a striking feature, and is of interest in considering the physiology of P.T.A.

Behaviour During Period of P.T.A.

During the stages of recovery of consciousness many remarkable abnormalities are observed. In the first place the patient's behaviour may closely approximate the normal, and many football players have continued the game and have even played well after a head injury, though they subsequently remember nothing of that part of the game which followed the concussion. Their behaviour may be such that their friends notice nothing amiss, but in other instances there is obvious confusion, as for example the football player who after a head injury plays towards the wrong goal.

Similar abnormalities are sometimes observed after epileptic fits, where again the patient's inability to recall his actions is a striking feature. The term *automatic behaviour* is used to describe this condition, but it must be stressed that the term may refer to behaviour which is obviously confused, or on the other hand to behaviour which is outwardly normal and rational, but in which only the loss of recall indicates that a high level of cerebral function is in abeyance.

Conversation During Period of P.T.A.

Many interesting aphasic phenomena occur during recovery from concussion, but these will not be considered here. When the patient is still severely confused he may occasionally give information regarding his injury which is subsequently quite forgotten. Burton (1931) has found that this information may be correct, but care must be taken not to be misled by confabulation.

CASE OF MEMORY REGARDING ACCIDENT DURING PERIOD OF
CONFUSION WHICH WAS LATER FORGOTTEN WITHIN R.A.:
CONFABULATION AND FALSE ACCUSATION

W. D. (*Case* P 91), an electrician aged 38, had a motor-cycle accident on 8.8.33, while swerving to avoid a dog. There was a laceration in the left frontal region and a linear fracture of the middle fossa of the skull. Two days after the injury he repeatedly said "It was a dog!" He was however quite confused, and gave the date at February, 1933. He gradually became more alert and confabulated aggressively regarding this early memory, and some information probably derived later from his wife. On 16.8.33 he gave the date and place correctly and said he had been in hospital for a week. "I'm supposed to have had a smash up, but it wasn't my fault—dog flew at me and I flew at it—a big black dog with a white spot on its chest. Farmer's son turned on me and smashed me with an instrument in his hand for damaging him. He is getting arrested to-day—plain clothes officer told me he had been arrested—that is one of the charges I have against him. I've the money to fight the case. I can prove what I said. . . . The police have found the instrument, and everything is turning out as I said. Marks on the instrument and everything . . . the dog did not harm me . . . it was the man that hurt me . . . etc."

The condition improved steadily and he was discharged home about three weeks after the accident and resumed work two months after leaving hospital. When re-examined on 9.1.34 he had no recollection of his period in hospital except the last four days (P.T.A. sixteen days). The R.A. was two days, and those two days were a "complete blank". He was quite fit with no headache or giddiness and he considered his work capacity and memory to be as good as ever.

A witness, who was near when the accident occurred, said it was due to his swerving to avoid a large, black dog with white spots belonging to the adjacent farm. The farmer's son accompanied the patient to hospital in the ambulance, but the patient now has no idea even what the farmer's son looks like.

Occasionally the P.T.A. lengthens in the early days after recovery of consciousness as though the memory of events soon after recovery of consciousness is not retained with sufficient firmness for recall at a much later date. Barbiturate hypnosis may facilitate recall as in the following case:

CASE OF LENGTHENING P.T.A. SUBSEQUENTLY REDUCED BY BARBITURATE HYPNOSIS

SPR. C. had a R.A. of a few seconds. When questioned *seven* hours after the accident his first memory was of being lifted on to a stretcher. From the account of a witness of the accident this was half an hour after it occurred. Then he remembered nothing more until he heard someone saying that he needed two stitches in his lip: this was half an hour later. When questioned again *one week* after the accident, his first memory of being lifted on to a stretcher had gone, and the earliest memory now was someone saying he needed two stitches. The memory of the entire day of the accident was then vague, whereas it had been quite clear at the first examination. A fortnight after the accident his remembrances were unchanged but his memory of the day of the accident had become even more vague, and he could not give a satisfactory account of his medical examination on the day of admission. Under pentothal, however, he remembered being lifted on to the stretcher, and he also remembered an old lady saying: "Lift him carefully; he's badly injured". (This remark was confirmed by the police.) He now remembered part of the journey in the ambulance, but thought he must have gone to sleep for the last part of it, as he remembered nothing more until he was being stitched. His memory of his medical examination on admission remained, however, as vague as before.

"Visions" Relative to the Injury

A curious phenomenon which seems allied to those described above is occasionally described by the patient after full recovery of consciousness. This consists of a transient and sometimes repeated "vision" of something seen just before the accident, though events concerning the vision cannot be recalled in the usual way and fall within the R.A.

One of us (Russell, 1935) described a case of head injury in which for a period of one week only after recovering consciousness (P.T.A. twelve hours) the patient frequently had a sudden vision of the huge tyre of a motor lorry bearing down on him. Though the retrograde amnesia was only a few seconds and the injury was actually due to a motor lorry knocking him down he was never able to remember seeing the lorry which in fact could only have been visible to him for a moment before the injury occurred.

We have recently observed similar cases which were investigated under pentothal hypnosis without restoring any memory of the events relative to the hallucination:

DRIVER T.'s first memory on coming round in hospital was of seeing a horse as in a cloud. He had a very clear idea of the horse; it was a brown cob, and he had a side-view of it. It was galloping with its head up, coming from right to left. There was no cart attached to it; he was unaware of any background of road or surrounding scenery or people or noise. He was unaware of being frightened or of any feeling that an accident was about to occur. This vision at once passed and he was aware of two nurses making his bed. He asked them what had happened, and they told him he had had an accident. He then asked them whether it was anything to do with a horse, and they told him they did not know, but that he had already told them that it occurred through a horse. He himself had no recollection of having told them this. This story of the accident has been confirmed: he did collide with a runaway horse.

[Description of two additional cases has been omitted.]

These rare cases suggest that during the period of confusion isolated and dramatic events preceding the injury may be registered and retained which cannot be recalled in the normal way, but only in the form of "vision".

Confabulation

During the period of confusion following concussion which falls within the P.T.A., speech and behaviour may be so nearly normal that confabulation misleads the unskilled observer. The subject matter for confabulation is usually unconnected with the injury, but in some instances the patient apparently realizes he has had an accident and confabulates with regard to it. This may lead to the patient making false accusations regarding the cause of the injury, as has been reported by Russell (1935) and Symonds (1937). The hallucinations referred to in the last paragraph may play a part in the confabulation in some cases.

The confabulation may be rational and yet the period of abnormality usually falls within the P.T.A. In such cases the mental activity approximates to normality but there is a loss of continuous remembering, and the context of the confabulation is forgotten.

Secondly there are cases in which the confabulation is subsequently remembered, as may occur after alcoholic intoxication or psychosis of Korsakoff's type. In these instances the faculty of continuous remembering has recovered while the confabulation persists, as in the following case:

CASE OF PROLONGED CONFUSION WITH MEMORY OF ABNORMAL
BEHAVIOUR AFTER RECOVERY OF FULL CONSCIOUSNESS

R. D. (*Case* P 150) had a severe motor-cycle accident on 3.5.31. When seen a few hours later he was stuporose and very restless. On 4.5.31 he was violent and required forcible restraint for several days. His speech was at first meaningless, but gradually he became very talkative, emphasizing all he said with powerful gestures. He talked incessantly of his ability as a sheep-shearer and fisher, and promised money to Sister and Doctor if they would let him go home. This continued until about 23.5.31 when his behaviour and conversation became normal, and he was most apologetic for his abnormal behaviour. He remembered many events during his confusion, especially during the last week. He had a clear recollection of being strapped in bed, refusing medicine and struggling with the nurses. The R.A. was momentary.

When re-examined nine months after, he was back at work and had made an excellent recovery. He was more talkative than before the injury, but said his memory was excellent, except that he had no idea of the number of sheep he counted six hours before the accident. He was driving his motor-cycle as fast as ever.

The abnormality of localization of islands of memory may contribute considerably to confabulation, as in the case of a fitter, who had an accident on October 10, 1941, while walking in Norwich, and who gave his story on October 28 in such a way that it was clear that though he gave some particulars correctly, he was confusing his injury with an accident near Epsom which he had two years previously. The confusion was clearly due to failure to localize his memories of the more recent injury.

A similar disturbance of localization has been produced by Flescher (1941), by giving schizophrenics various material to remember before electric shock therapy. He was able to show that though much was correctly remembered it was often localized quite incorrectly in time.

RETROGRADE AMNESIA (R.A.)

The curious phenomenon of retrograde amnesia which is so well known in head injury is also found after electric convulsion therapy, status epilepticus, meningitis and acute cerebral anoxia as in hanging, CO poisoning and severe loss of blood. R.A. is for events which occurred before the injury while the patient was still fully conscious. The events occurring during this period were often dramatic and must have been registered by the normally acting sensorium, yet the injury intervenes and these events are thereby prevented from being retained, or if they are retained they cannot be recalled. The clinical features of R.A. present many interesting variations.

Duration of R.A.

The R.A. is in most cases for a few moments only. The motorist remembers approaching the cross-roads, the cyclist remembers losing control on a steep hill, or the window-cleaner remembers losing his balance. This momentary

Table 4[a]

DURATION OF R.A.	Nil	< 1 hr.	1–24 hr.	1–7 days	> 7 days	No record	Total
			DURATION OF P.T.A.				
Nil	99	23	9	2	0	0	133
Under 30 minutes	—	178	274	174	80	1	707
Over 30 minutes	—	3	16	41	73	0	133
No record	—	4	14	14	15	9	56
Total	99	208	313	231	168	10	1,029

[a] Duration of P.T.A. and R.A. compared in 1,029 cases of "accidental" head injury (gunshot wounds excluded).

Table 5ᵃ

DURATION OF RETROGRADE AMNESIA	DURATION OF POST-TRAUMATIC AMNESIA				
	< 1 hr.	1–24 hr.	1–7 days	> 7 days	Total
Nil	9	1	1	—	11
1 minute	34	35	15	12	96
1–30 minutes	6	13	21	18	58
½–12 hours	1	1	9	6	17
½–2 days	—	—	3	7	10
2–10 days	—	—	1	6	7
Over 10 days	—	—	—	1	1
Total	50	50	50	50	200

ᵃ Detailed comparison of duration of P.T.A. and R.A. using 50 consecutive cases from each P.T.A. group.

R.A. is observed after injuries of all degrees of severity and presumably has a clear and uniform physiological basis. In cases of prolonged R.A. other factors require consideration.

In Table 4 the R.A. in 1,029 cases is roughly estimated, and compared with the P.T.A. In Table 5, fifty consecutive cases from each P.T.A. group have the R.A. recorded in greater detail. These tables indicate how very constant some period of R.A. is in all injuries which disturb consciousness sufficiently to produce even a short P.T.A. These records were made by many observers, and some errors there must be. It is common, for example, in street accidents for the victim to remember being struck by a vehicle but nothing more. His head injury may, however, have been due to his striking the ground a second or two later, and this would be recorded according to our standards as a momentary R.A. Such cases may easily be entered in error as R.A.: nil. However, there is no doubt that certain cases of accidental concussion with a short P.T.A. clearly remember the head injury, and in Table 5 there are 11 cases of this type in 200 cases. On the other hand in 186 cases of G.S.W., brain or skull, with a definite period of P.T.A., there were no fewer than 65 with no R.A., that is to say the patient remembered his head being struck by the missile.

CASE OF ACCIDENTAL HEAD INJURY FROM A FALLING STONE WITH R.A.: NIL, AND P.T.A.: TWENTY-FOUR HOURS

A. M. (P 203), a quarryman, was injured by a falling stone, which was about the size of a man's fist. The stone fell from a height of about 60 feet, and striking his head caused a fissure fracture of the skull in the parieto-occipital region. When questioned ten days after the injury he said that he remembered hearing the stone falling, and he ran to get out of the way. Then he remembers clearly a dull, crushing sensation in his ears, but nothing more until he came to himself in hospital twenty-four hours later. He did not remember falling to the ground after being struck, but the ground was soft, so that it is unlikely that he had a second injury while falling.

ACCIDENTAL HEAD INJURY: P.T.A.: ONE HOUR, R.A.: NIL. A. M. (MRC 876) was playing goal in a football match. He remembers diving at the feet of the opposing centre forward, and deflecting the ball. He then remembers seeing a boot coming towards his face, then a blinding flash, but has no memory of the impact. He came to himself in hospital over an hour later.

While cases of this type with no R.A. are common in gunshot wounds, they are, as has been shown, uncommon in accidental injuries. In the two examples given above, however, it is noteworthy that the accidental injury was of the type which is likely to cause focal brain injury as they were due to a fast moving object striking the skull. They were in some ways, therefore, similar to the wounds caused by the high velocity missile.

Absence of R.A.

The absence of R.A. with definite P.T.A. in gunshot wound cases must be connected with the more focal type of injury. Certainly the immediate loss of memory after the wound occurs too quickly for it to be explained on a vascular basis, and these cases must be clearly distinguished from the delayed amnesias already referred to. Perhaps some diaschisis effect causes the disturbance of consciousness and, if so, the memory of the injury is registered and retained before the trans-neuronal shock effect spreads to prevent further remembering.

Shrinkage of R.A.

During the gradual recovery of consciousness, while there is still some confusion, the R.A. is often very long. This may be so marked that the patient gives the date as several years previously with a corresponding reduction in his age. For example, a Polish airman, who crashed in 1941, when questioned three weeks later, was still confused and said it was 1936, and when asked about war with Germany replied "We are not ready yet."

A case previously described (Russell, 1935) was that of P. A. S. (P 234), a green-keeper, aged 22, who was thrown from his motor-cycle in August, 1933. There was a bruise in the left frontal region and slight bleeding from the left ear, but no fracture was seen on X-ray examination. A week after the accident he was able to converse sensibly, and the nursing staff considered that he had fully recovered consciousness. When questioned, however, he said that the date was in February, 1942, and that he was a schoolboy. He had no recollection of five years spent in Australia, and two years in this country working on a golf course. Two weeks after the injury he remembered the five years spent in Australia, and remembered returning to this country; the past two years were, however, a complete blank as far as his memory was concerned. Three weeks after the injury he returned to the village where he had been working for two years. Everything looked strange, and he had no recollection of ever having been there before. He lost his way on more than one occasion. Still feeling a stranger to the district he returned to work; he was able to do his work satisfactorily, but had difficulty in remembering what he had actually done during the day. About ten weeks after the accident the events of the past two years were gradually recollected and finally he was able to remember everything up to within a few minutes of the accident.

R.A. AT FIRST FOR SIX MONTHS—SHRINKING TO A FEW MINUTES. P.T.A. TWO MONTHS

GNR. J. W. T. (MRC 516) was injured in an air-raid on 28.11.40. When first seen he was deeply comatose with flaccid limbs. Recovery of consciousness was very slow, and he did not begin to talk until a month later. On 11.3.41 his mental state was still greatly retarded. The R.A. was for about six months, and he had no recollection of three months in the Army. He now remembered coming to himself in hospital in January, 1941, when he found two women and a man sitting at his bed. These people told him they were his wife, mother and a close friend. He remembers arguing with them and saying he was not even married, and that he was certain he had never seen the man before. He was now correctly orientated, but was still very uncertain of the main facts concerning himself. He did all intelligence tests badly, and had difficulty in reading. He was very cheerful and friendly.

By 16.4.41, the R.A. had shrunk to a few minutes, and he remembers standing by the guns on the night he was injured, and that a few shells had been fired, but he does not remember any bombs: the P.T.A. was for about two months. He remained popular with the patients, but childish and slow in his movements with periods of irritability. He was invalided in May, 1941, and returned to light manual work in February, 1942. He found his right leg and arm "untrustworthy", and his relatives said he was forgetful and hesitated in his speech.

In one of this group of cases in which the patient, while still slightly confused but orientated, had a dense R.A. of about a year's duration, amytal was given in an attempt to recover the amnesia but without any improvement.

In these cases of slow shrinking R.A., the P.T.A. terminates long before the R.A. shrinks to its final duration. While the R.A. extends over many months or years the patient may, to careful testing, be slightly confused, but he has often recovered sufficiently to have continuous memory and to behave in a rational way.

During this period of shrinking amnesia the patient is unable to recall an important group of memories which, as later recovery shows, were well registered. The recovery occurs not in order of importance but in order of time. Long-past memories are the first to return, and the temporary blocking of relatively recent memory may be so marked that several years of recent life may be entirely eliminated. For a limited time the patient may re-live his childhood, a state of affairs reminiscent of the case of senile dementia.

During recovery the R.A. shrinks at a varying rate to a point where memory of subsequent events ceases abruptly. This usually leaves the duration of R.A. clearly indicated, but this can only be estimated accurately after full recovery of consciousness.

By the time the R.A. has shrunk to a few minutes or less the patient has usually fully recovered consciousness, and indeed a brief R.A. is often an accurate indication of mental normality.

Table 5 shows the increasing proportion of cases with a permanent long R.A. as the P.T.A. lengthens, though as has been mentioned the R.A. may be very short in severe injuries. In some cases this matter can be explained very simply, for in attempting to estimate the R.A. the patient who has emerged from a long P.T.A. endeavours to remember events which occurred perhaps over a week previously. Many uninjured individuals are unable to describe what happened a week ago, unless there is some special experience to remind them.

Prolonged R.A.

This simple explanation does not, however, explain the long R.A. in many cases, especially those in which events of importance to the individual were forgotten. It has already been suggested that the common momentary R.A. is due to a physiological effect of the injury which blocks the retention of events seen or heard in the moments before the concussion. Some very different explanation is required for the relatively long R.A. which may be recorded in severe cases with a long P.T.A. In Table 5, 14 per cent of the cases with P.T.A. over seven days reported R.A. of over two days. These periods of R.A. are completely blank to the patient and often cover important events.

An example of important memories lost during an R.A. lasting several days is the following case kindly provided by Sir Charles Symonds:

> FLIGHT-LIEUTENANT T., aged 31, was seen on February 7, 1936. Following a head injury when flying in 1934 he had been posted to ground duties which he had performed inefficiently, and was charged with being unable to account for stores to the value of £100. On examination he was orientated, voluble, facile and dysarthric. He could not retain more than six digits, showed three errors in repeating name, address and flower after five minutes, and failed in simple mental arithmetic. His face was expressionless with weakness of the left facial muscles. There were no other abnormal physical signs.
>
> The head injury occurred in a crash on April 15, 1934, and there was a P.T.A. of twenty-one days. He came to himself in an eight-bedded ward which he describes in considerable detail, and has a consecutive memory of subsequent events. The story of his R.A. is as follows: The injury occurred on a Monday, and he had joined his unit eight days previously on a Sunday. He remembers arriving on the Sunday night and noticing that his room was of a different type from any he had slept in before. He has an isolated memory of firing at a ground target the following day, and of visiting a café sometime on that day, but has no recollection of the subsequent week. During this period he was on flying exercises of a kind he had not done before in an aircraft to which he was accustomed, doing several trips a day. He had studied his log book giving the details of these exercises over and over again in a fruitless attempt to recall the memory of these days. On May 21, 1927, he had had a head injury with a permanent R.A. of fifteen minutes and P.T.A. for three days followed by a headache for several days.

Islands in R.A.

It is clear that severe head injury may have a specific effect on very recently acquired memories, and this will be discussed later. A long R.A. with a P.T.A. of only twenty-four hours is very unusual, but the following case illustrates this:—

CASE OF R.A. WITH ISLANDS FOR OVER 24 HOURS.
P.T.A. 24 HOURS. INVESTIGATION OF R.A. UNDER
AMYTAL HYPNOSIS MADE LITTLE ALTERATION

CPL. G. W. (MRC 2039) was thrown from his horse on 20.7.41. He came to himself twenty-four hours later, and his memory thereafter is quite clear. When examined on 22.8.41 his memory of events before the injury was normal up to the morning of the day before the injury (19.7.41). On this day, over twenty-four hours before the injury, he remembers reporting sick at about 9 a.m. with synovitis of the knee. He was excused duties, but remembers little more of that day—he does not even remember leaving the M.I. room. His wife came to meet him that evening, but he has no memory at all of her visit except that he remembers getting into a bus with her, to see her home, and later being at a station near where she was staying. For the day on which the accident occurred he has no memory except one island—he remembers tying up his horse at the gate where his wife was staying, going to the house and being told his wife was out. From 9 a.m. of the previous day, therefore, there was complete amnesia, except for three short islands. When he came to himself on 21.7.41 his first memory was of tying the horse to the gate.

Under the influence of sodium amytal he became sleepy, euphoric and talkative. Repeated attempts were made to reduce the R.A. and P.T.A. or to increase the islands in the R.A., but without success, except that one further island appeared—he now remembered leaving camp on the evening of 19.7.41, and walking with his friend, Bill, past some sentries.

He made a good recovery, and went to a Convalescent Depot on 2.10.31. Eighteen months later he was Category A, and was then serving efficiently in the Middle East.

In most cases of persistently long R.A. the P.T.A. has also been long.

[Description of two additional cases has been omitted.]

In these cases there is clear inability to recall important events which must previously have been well registered, retained and recalled before the injury. This type of amnesia is obviously different from the R.A. for events occurring a few moments only before an injury. When important events are obliterated from memory after head injury they are usually for relatively recent happenings. Recent memories are therefore more vulnerable than those that are remote, but it is remarkable that recent memories for important events should be so completely obliterated from memory as they often are. This long R.A. differs from the memory disorders of organic dementias. In both conditions recent memories are lost, but in the traumatic cases the ability to recall events since the injury has recovered well.

In the case of permanent long R.A. the memory loss resembles that which, as has been mentioned, is often observed during recovery from traumatic confusion, before the R.A. has shrunk down to its final length. In both types of case the relative vulnerability of recent memory is very evident. The retention of recent memories is evidently less firmly established and may, as in these last cases, be abolished permanently by the physical effects on the cerebral neurones of a severe head injury.

Association of ideas may assist the reduction of R.A., as in the case of a soldier who, after recovering consciousness, had an R.A. of over an hour— his last memory was setting out on his journey driving a truck in the dark. Some months later at the cinema he was watching the picture of an aeroplane crashing with the appropriate sounds. The patient found this a very upsetting experience, and suddenly the noise brought back to his mind the noise he heard as his truck crashed.

This type of case bears a remarkable resemblance to the behaviour of a repressed complex, in that an experience which had been registered and retained was not recalled except through an association of ideas, and this experience caused an emotional response which was appropriate to the forgotten material.

[A section entitled "Effect of Barbiturate Hypnosis on R.A. and P.T.A." has been omitted.]

TRAUMATIC AMNESIA AND TRAUMATIC INTELLECTUAL IMPAIRMENT

In cases in which the P.T.A. exceeds seven days some loss of intellectual capacity is a common permanent disability. In these cases the general blunting of memory may contribute slightly to the loss of memory of events before the injury. In considering a general traumatic impairment of memory one is presumably studying the same cerebral mechanism which is disturbed so grossly during the period of R.A. and P.T.A., and it is noteworthy that trauma sufficient to cause a long R.A. and long P.T.A. will also, in many instances, lead to a permanent impairment of the faculty of remembering.

SUMMARY AND DISCUSSION

It is naturally important to discuss the significance of the phenomena described above in so far as they may throw light on cerebral mechanisms. In the first place it is clear that traumatic loss of consciousness prevents remembering, and that this inability to remember events persists in most cases until full consciousness has returned. In other words, the recovery of continuous remembering coincides with a late, if not a last, stage in recovering consciousness.

It may also be affirmed that a single blow of varying severity can disturb remembering, as it does consciousness, for very varying periods of time, and that the duration of this period depends usually on the severity of the initial neuronal commotion.

The almost constant occurrence of R.A. indicates that the injury, though it cannot have time to prevent what is last seen or heard from reaching the sensorium, does completely prevent its retention for future recall. The latter process presumably requires a few seconds of time for completion.

The occasional occurrence of a vision of events within the R.A. indicates that in these cases some form of registration has occurred with great vividness which, though it can never be properly retained for later recall, can reproduce itself from a relatively low level in the form of a momentary "vision." This appears to be a striking illustration of different levels of activity in the Hughlings Jackson sense. The injury in such a case appears to have blocked the process of retention half-way.

The variations in the R.A. during recovery of full consciousness seem to be specially significant. Distant memories return first and loss of memories for the previous few years may, for a time, be so complete that the patient believes himself to be several years younger. After severe injuries there may be a permanent R.A. of several days' duration which may include events of great importance to the patient.

General brain trauma therefore has an effect on *recent* memory which is much greater than its effect on remote memory, and this fact must be closely linked with the physiology of remembering. It is clear that the events forgotten are often of importance to the individual, yet for a time, and sometimes permanently, they are completely erased, while distant memories of little importance are returning freely.

The recovery of this type of memory loss is by shrinkage towards the present time. The long amnestic period recovers not so much according to the relative importance of events forgotten as according to the time before the injury that the events occurred. There is thus a vulnerability of memories which depends directly on their nearness to the injury.

We are thus forced to the conclusion that as memories become older they become more strongly established irrespective of their importance to the individual, while recent memories are relatively liable to traumatic extinction, however important they may be.

Further it is clear that a long R.A. is almost always associated with a long P.T.A. We have good evidence that a long P.T.A. usually means a very severe injury, hence a long R.A. is observed when severe general neuronal commotion has occurred. It can thus be concluded that a long R.A. whether temporary or permanent, occurs after severe neuronal commotion, and that severe neuronal commotion has a much more damaging effect on erasing recent than remote memories.

In the cases with long R.A. which recover spontaneously it is evident that the effect of this neuronal commotion is reversible, but in some cases the effect is permanent.

In either case the observation demands a physiological explanation. It seems likely that memory of events is not a static process. If it were, then distant memories would surely fade gradually and would be the more vulnerable to the effects of injury. On the contrary, when the brain is injured, these distant memories are the least vulnerable. It seems that the mere existence of the brain as a functioning organ must strengthen the roots of distant memories. The normal activity of the brain must steadily strengthen distant memories so that with the passage of time these become less vulnerable to the effects of head injury.

The patient with senile dementia may show a very similar loss of recent memory. She may forget the visit of her favourite grandchild within twenty minutes, yet she remembers an unimportant escapade of fifty years before in every detail. The distant memory shows no sign of fading and this suggests that it has received continual reinforcement and has survived not because it was important but because the brain throughout the decades has strengthened it automatically till it has become highly resistant to cerebral degeneration.

It is tempting to speculate on the possible physiological processes concerned in remembering which could behave in this way. The brain works through chains and circuits of neurones which can set a pattern for automatic responses of infinite variety. Presumably the synapses of such a chain pattern are " opened " to allow the least possible delay and to avoid diversions in other directions. The neuronal system concerned with a certain memory, if it is to behave with the passing of years in the way it does, must then be automatically strengthened or more strongly canalized by the normal activity of the brain, and perhaps indeed this facilitation of the circuit is carried out by the spontaneous rhythm of the neurones concerned.

The recall under barbiturate hypnosis, or occasionally in the state of traumatic confusion, of events which cannot be remembered in the normal state of consciousness is of considerable interest. It seems as if under certain conditions clinically manifest as clouded consciousness, and physiologically determined by impairment of function at Jackson's highest level, pathological recall may occur as a release phenomenon. The twilight states of dreaming and toxic or infective delirium are analogous, and in these also there may be recall of experience not available in the state of clear consciousness.

ACKNOWLEDGMENTS

Sir Charles P. Symonds, *K.B.E.*, C.B., M.D., F.R.C.P., has helped greatly with this paper at all its stages. Most of the cases were seen at the Military Hospital for Head Injuries, Oxford, and careful notes by many medical officers made the study possible, while the Medical Research Council provided Secretarial Assistance for head injury research. The Director-General of the Army Medical Services has granted permission for publication.

REFERENCES

BANISTER, H., & ZANGWELL, O. L. (1941), *Brit. J. Psychol.*, **30**, 32.
BURTON (1931), *Proc. Roy. Soc. Med.*, **24**, 1405.
DENNY-BROWN, D. (1941), *Lancet*, **1**, 371.

DENNY-BROWN, D., & RUSSELL, W. R. (1941), *Brain*, **64**, 93.
FLESCHER, G. (1941), *Schweiz. Arch. Neurol. Psychiat.*, **48**, 1.
GREENFIELD, J. G. (1938), *Proc. Roy. Soc. Med.*, **32**, 43.
GUTMANN, E. (1938), *Brit. Med. J.*, **1**, 94.
HOOPER, R. S., MCGREGOR, J. M., & NATHAN, P. W. (1945), *J. Ment. Sci.*, **91**, 458.
JEFFERSON, G. (1942), *Glasg. med. J.*, **20**, 77.
RUSSELL, W. R. (1932), *Brain*, **55**, 549.
RUSSELL, W. R. (1935), *Lancet*, **2**, 762.
SYMONDS, C. P. (1937), *Clin. J.*, **66**, 397.
SYMONDS, C. P., & RUSSELL, W. R. (1943), *Lancet*, **1**, 7.

Conflict
Versus Consolidation
of Memory Traces
to Explain
"Retrograde Amnesia"
Produced by ECS

Edgar E. Coons
and Neal E. Miller

Clinical observations by Janis (1950) and Russell (1946) on retrograde amnesias induced by electroconvulsive shock (ECS) or other trauma suggest that recently formed associations are especially subject to disruption. If true, this is of basic importance to learning theory. It suggests that there is a process of fixating memory traces which operates for a period after each learning

From *Journal of Comparative and Physiological Psychology*, 1960, **53**, 524–531. Reprinted with permission of the publisher and author. This investigation was supported by a research grant, M647, from the National Institute of Mental Health of the National Institutes of Health, U.S. Public Health Service, Bethesda, Md. The findings were presented in part at a meeting of the American Psychological Association by Miller and Coons (1955).

episode and that the memory trace is especially vulnerable to disruption the earlier the trauma occurs during this period. Although this interpretation is relevant for any theory of consolidation, it has most often been related to Hebb's (1949) hypothesis of a neural reverberatory process which persists for a while after the original association and helps in the formation of a more permanent engram. However, a consolidation hypothesis should not rest its case too exclusively upon clinical data since the amnesias reported may be an artifact of repressive processes produced by unpleasant associations formed between the trauma and the thoughts about events immediately preceding it (Dollard & Miller, 1950).

In addition to repression, two related sampling artifacts may contribute to clinical impressions of a temporal gradient of retrograde amnesia. Memory for events immediately before the trauma is likely to be sampled in class intervals of time which are shorter than those used for memory for earlier events. For example, an S with a seriously impaired memory will have many more opportunities to recall some major events from the whole previous day before the fateful one, than from the 15 min. before the traumatic incident. Furthermore, when questioning (e.g., before and after ECS treatments) covers memories from a period of many days or years, the earlier remembered events are likely to be more highly selected for resistance to forgetting than the later ones.

Evidence more appropriate to the consolidation hypothesis has been sought by Gerard (1955), Thompson and Dean (1955), and Duncan (1949) in experiments which measure learned performance as a function of the interval between an animal's learning trial and a subsequent ECS. As a specific example, Duncan (1949) trained rats to avoid a grid-shock to their feet by running from a dark to a light compartment. Eight different groups received ECS at different intervals ranging from 20 sec. to 14 hr. after each training trial. Groups which were convulsed an hour or more after a trial did not differ from a no-ECS control group, while groups convulsed sooner showed slower learning the shorter this interval. These results are consistent with the consolidation hypothesis.

However, in the experimental designs of Duncan and the others any fear or conflict produced by the avoidance response's association at the shorter intervals with some aversiveness of the ECS itself would produce the same effects as any amnesia. In an attempt to control for this possibility, Duncan gave to Ss in a series of control groups a shock from the ECS source but applied to the hind leg after some of the same intervals used for the experimental groups. The controls showed a decrement in learning only at the 20-sec. interval; a delay of 60 sec. apparently produced no such decrement. This marked difference in the temporal gradients between experimental and control groups Duncan took as evidence against use of fear and conflict to explain the effects of the ECS. As additional evidence against the "fear" alternative, he noted that, unlike animals receiving leg-shock, the ECS group would lie passively in the hand while the clips for delivering ECS were being applied. While Duncan used 10 Ss in each experimental group, he used only 5 in each control group and reports no reliabilities of differences between the experimental and control groups.

Others have reported contradictory findings. Leukel (1957), in a similarly conducted leg-shock control test with 10 Ss in each group, did find that a shock to the feet after a 60-sec. delay had a significant effect on maze errors. His results suggest that the apparent difference between the experimental and leg-shock control gradients in Duncan's experiment may be a sampling error. Moreover, Hayes (1948) reports that animals in a maze experiment developed conflict and emotional behavior toward the goal box where they not only received food but, 30 sec. later, also ECS. He mentions, like Duncan, that restraint was unnecessary in applying ECS clips to experimental animals but qualifies this with the observation that the animals usually crouched motionless in a manner having the semblance of terrified apprehension, often urinating and defecating while the clips were being attached. Furthermore, Gallinek (1956), in a study of 100 human patients undergoing a series of ECS treatments, found that 67 of these gradually developed marked degrees of fear of the treatments, not reputedly of any pain involved, but of the intense disorientation which they experienced immediately following ECS. This fear occasionally lingered on after treatment to such an extent that the patients, even when completely recovered, liked to avoid the street in which the hospital or the doctor's office was located. These observations imply that fear and conflict as factors explaining "retrograde amnesia" produced by ECS have not been properly eliminated. Furthermore, there is no assurance that the aversiveness of the leg-shock used as a control in those experiments is equal to that of the ECS.

Finally, we failed to obtain results consistent with Duncan's interpretation in a preliminary experiment designed so that any aversive effect of ECS would not summate with, but instead oppose, any effects of retrograde amnesia. In a pretest period 28 Sprague-Dawley male albino rats approximately 90 days old were habituated to having attached to the ears the alligator-clamp electrodes through which ECS would later be delivered. Then, all animals were given several days of massed training trials to run a 4-ft.-long straight alley for pea-sized pellets of wet mash while food-deprived. Subsequently, the animals were divided into six groups equalized with respect to speed scores recorded during training. In the test period that followed, all rats were retained on a food-deprivation schedule and still required to run the alley for food. Trials were administered once a day for eight consecutive days. Four of the six groups were given, through a series resistor of 250,000 ohms, a grid shock to the feet immediately upon reaching the food. The strength of shock on the first testing day was 112 v. of 60-cycle a.c. It increased 56 v. each additional day to 508 v. on Day 8. Three of these four groups received ECS 20 sec., 60 sec., or 1 hr., respectively, after each grid shock. The fourth group was a control for the aversiveness of grid shock alone. The two remaining groups were never shocked via the grid but received ECS 20 sec., or 1 hr., respectively, after reaching the food goal, as controls for the aversiveness of ECS alone and its possible general debilitating effects. Whereas the amnesia hypothesis predicted that the animals receiving ECS treatment at the shorter intervals should develop the least avoidance of the shock introduced at the food goal, the actual data suggested that the opposite was the case. The rats receiving the ECS sooner after the grid shock were not retarded in learning to stop running to the goal; in fact, the difference was in the opposite direction although not statistically reliable. Furthermore, the rats receiving no grid shock but ECS sooner after the goal were slowed down more than those receiving the delayed ECS, although this difference also was not statistically reliable.

As a consequence of this preliminary experiment, we decided to repeat the essentials of Duncan's original experiment to show that we were replicating his procedures well enough to replicate his results and then to perform a second experiment as similar to his as possible but designed so that, instead of summating with each other, any aversive and amnesic effects of the ECS would oppose each other.

EXPERIMENT 1

Method

SUBJECTS

The *S*s were 37 naive male albino rats of the Sprague-Dawley strain approximately 120 days old.

APPARATUS

The apparatus in which the *S*s were run consisted of a box with inside dimensions 14 in. long, 10 in. wide, and 9 in. high. This box was divided by a partition into two distinctively different but equal-sized compartments labeled "dark" and "light." These were connected by a 3-in. by 3-in. doorway. Both had grid floors composed of $\frac{3}{16}$-in. stainless steel rods spaced at gaps of $\frac{1}{2}$ in. However, the dark compartment's grid slanted 15° to the horizontal. Moreover, all its surfaces, including the underlying feces tray, were black. In contrast, three walls and the top of the light compartment were Plexiglas. Its partitioning wall and feces tray were white. In addition, a 100-w. bulb was placed 2 in. from one Plexiglas wall but at a position shielding it from shining directly through the doorway into the dark side.

The equipment measuring latencies to escape from the dark compartment and governing the length of an initial "shock-free" period consisted of an electronic relay wired to the dark grid, a 60-sec. Springfield timer, an electronic timer, and a manual switch operated by *E* at the completion of an escape. A variable voltage divider delivered shock to the dark grid through a 250-K resistor in series with the rat. The ECS apparatus was set to administer approximately 50 ma. of 60-cycle a.c. through an average rat resistance of 2.5 K for a duration of .2 sec. This was applied by means of two gauze-padded alligator-clip electrodes that were soaked with saline before being attached to the ears of an *S*.

PROCEDURE

HABITUATION. Prior to the experiment, all animals, while four days thirsty, were habituated to having electrodes clamped to their ears for brief intervals by pairing each electrode application with a water reward from an eye dropper. This habituation, lasting four days of from two to five applications daily, was done to reduce the struggling and tension which, when combined with ECS, may partially account for the high initial fatality rates that often occur. After habituation, all *S*s were maintained on ad lib. food and water for the rest of the experiment.

ASSIGNMENT TO GROUPS. Each animal was weighed on the fourth day following habituation. On the basis of these weights the animals were evenly distributed through four testing groups distinguished from one another during testing by the different intervals at which, after each trial, they received ECS or the similar but mock treatment (pseudo-ECS) of having the electrodes briefly attached without being subjected to a convulsion or any passage of current. These intervals were 20 sec., 60 sec., and 1 hr. for the 3 ECS groups and 1 hr. for a pseudo-ECS group. They initially contained 10, 8, 9, and 10 *S*s, respectively. One paraplegic casualty in the Hr-ECS group was the only loss sustained during the experiment. However, to enable the *E* to perform analysis-of-variance trend tests requiring equal *N*s, two *S*s each were randomly eliminated from the 20-sec.-ECS and the pseudo-ECS groups. It is on the remaining 32 *S*s that the results to be reported are based.

TESTING. Testing covered 27 consecutive days. Each *S* received one trial per day of being placed in the "dark" compartment where the 112-v. shock came on after 10.6 sec. and stayed on. The *E* timed the avoidance or escape responses by pushing a switch as soon as the *S* had at least three legs over the "light" side of the doorsill. After escape, each animal remained 10 sec. in the "light" compartment and then was removed. All except the 20-sec-ECS group waited out the appropriate interval in their home cages before receiving their treatment.

All *S*s' performance during this testing phase was recorded in terms of both the number of anticipatory escapes made and the log-latency of all escapes whether anticipatory or not. Other measures were also taken. A day-by-day urination-defecation count, as a possible index of fear, was introduced on Day 7 of testing. Each *S* was observed for urination and/or defecation while being carried from its home cage to the "dark" compartment for its daily trial. A defecation (irrespective of the number of feces passed) and a urination each rated as 1 point. The maximum score obtainable for each *S* per day was 2. Besides the initial pretest measurements, each *S* was weighed on Days 10 and 20 of testing.

Results

Figure 1 presents curves for learning as measured by the percentage of anticipatory avoidance responses. It can be seen that the sooner a group's ECS came after each trial, the worse was its performance during learning. To test for the significance of this trend among the experimental groups, each S was assigned a score representing its total anticipatory escapes from Days 2 through 27. Since the within-group variances increased systematically from the 20-sec- through the Hr-ECS groups, an arc-sine transformation of the scores was used to achieve the homogeneity required for the

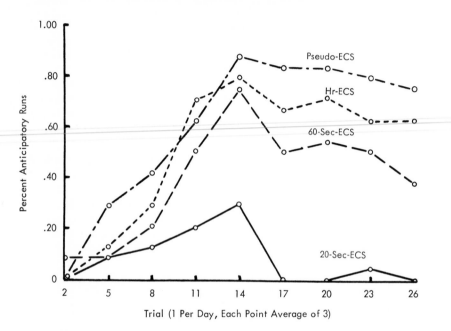

Fig. 1. When any effects of either amnesia or conflict would hinder learning to make anticipatory runs, learning is poorer the shorter the interval between each training trial and the ECS.

F test. A linear form of this trend was tested by weighting each group total by numbers proportional to the reciprocal of its trial-ECS interval. This linear trend was found to account for virtually all the between-groups variance ($F = 19.27$ at 1, 21 df; $p < .001$). In addition, F ratios for specific comparisons of the 20-sec-ECS group with each of the 60-sec-, Hr-, and pseudo-ECS groups were all significant well beyond a p of .01. Comparisons between the 60-sec-, Hr-, and pseudo-ECS groups did not achieve the .05 level of significance. This failure to attain significance was repeated in a separate analysis of variance upon only the last 10 trials of the experiment, a period during which all the groups seemed to have been more stable.

The profile of group means based upon log-latency to escape paralleled that of the means based on the percentage of anticipatory escapes. However, under the conditions of this experiment, log-latency was not a sensitive measure. The fact that the grid-shock at the end of the 10.6-sec. "free" period immediately forced any escape to occur that was not made earlier, placed an upper limit on escape latencies. The narrowness of the range defined by this limit severely reduced the opportunities for groups to differ from one another and so tended to equalize the groups falsely. Moreover, the length of latencies of less than 10.6 sec. varied widely among all groups, producing a relatively large within-group variance. This may explain in part the fact that few of the log-latency differences between groups were reliable. Only F tests comparing the 20-sec-ECS versus the Hr-ECS groups and the 20-sec-ECS versus the pseudo-ECS group yielded significances beyond the .05 level.

Whereas those groups receiving ECS in close association with each day's trial were lower on the measures just discussed, they were higher in the frequency with which they defecated and/or urinated. Out of a possible mean daily score of 2.0, the 20-sec- and 60-sec-ECS groups tallied .81 and .84, respectively, while the Hr-ECS group obtained only .40 and the pseudo-ECS group .04. An F test on the over-all between-treatment differences was highly significant, confirming previous results suggesting that one effect of ECS is to

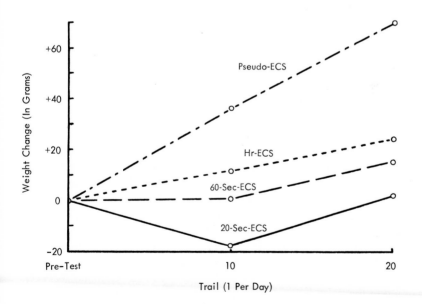

Fig. 2. The relationship between weight change and the interval between each training trial and the ECS.

increase general emotionality. However, within the experimental groups, comparisons between the Hr-ECS group and each of the two others were also significant ($p < .01$), indicating that closeness of association between the trial and ECS was also an important factor. Only the slight difference between the 20-sec- and 60-sec-ECS groups was not found to be statistically reliable.

The means of the weight changes that occurred within the various groups over the course of the experiment are plotted in Figure 2. The group receiving no ECS showed the fastest and the most constant rate of gain while the rates of the experimental groups were considerably depressed. Over the first 10 days the 20-sec-ECS group actually showed a loss. According to an F test, the difference between the pseudo-ECS and the experimental groups is reliable beyond the .001 level. On Day 10 the linear-trend effect of treatments on the weight changes of the experimental groups is significant at $p < .025$ but disappears thereafter. However, a trials-by-experimental groups interaction over all days of weight measurement is again reliable at $p < .025$.

Discussion

In this first experiment the results on frequency of anticipatory escapes and log-latency to escape confirmed most of Duncan's results. Trend tests sustained Duncan's findings of a greater decrement in learned performance the earlier after each trial the ECS occurred. Specific comparisons supported the reliability of the difference between his 20-sec-ECS group and the other groups. However, these comparisons failed to confirm the significance of the difference between the 60-sec- and Hr-ECS groups that he had obtained. This failure probably arose from some departure from Duncan's conditions. However, it is worth noting that the temporal gradient of the present ECS results as they stand are more consistent with the temporal gradient of Duncan's leg-shock control data and suggest that the processes producing the two gradients may not be so fundamentally different.

The data on emotionality reinforce this possibility. The observations of greater urination and defecation connected with shorter intervals before ECS is evidence for fear being conditioned to the test situation by ECS. This implies both that ECS is aversive and that the immediately preceding traces with which it is associated do survive its effects. If so, then it is not completely dissimilar to leg-shock and should, perhaps, condition fear along a similar temporal gradient.

Additional support is suggested by the weight data. It has already been observed by Mirsky and Rosvold (1953) that for at least the first 10 days of a series of daily ECS treatments, rats on ad lib. food and water show a marked decrement in weight gain as compared with normals. Conflicts between remaining in the dark compartment, where grid-shock occurred, or escaping to the light compartment, to which fear of ECS had been conditioned, could possibly potentiate these decrements. The actual finding of lesser weight gains associated with the shorter intervals before ECS support this since the conflicts, based upon the more efficaciously conditioned fear at these shorter intervals, would presumably be stronger and, hence, more potentiating.

Thus, the results of Duncan's experiment and our replication of it were probably due to more than just an amnesic effect of ECS. The data on emotionality and weight change strongly suggest that fear also contributed to the performance of the rats given ECS more immediately after their learning trials. Whether this effect was stronger or weaker than any retrograde amnesic effect is a question that Experiment 2 was designed to answer.

EXPERIMENT 2

Method

SUBJECTS

The Ss were 56 naive male albino rats of the Sprague-Dawley strain approximately 90 days old.

APPARATUS

The apparatus was the same as described in Experiment 1 except for a few changes in the two-compartment box. In order to make the distinction between escape and nonescape as clear as possible, a thin vertical metal strip was placed across its doorway, raising its sill $\frac{1}{2}$ in. In addition, a sliding panel was installed which, when operated, blocked the doorway enough to prevent an S from re-entering the dark compartment after making an avoidance but not enough to dismember any anatomy left behind.

PROCEDURE

HABITUATION.   The same as described in Experiment 1.

TRAINING.   Each animal received 24 training trials, 1 per day, at learning an anticipatory escape from the dark to the light compartment to avoid shock after an initial 10.6-sec. "shock-free" period. The conditions of this training attempted to duplicate the "test" conditions of Experiment 1 with the major exception that ECS was not administered. Ear-clamp electrodes, however, were applied 20 sec., 60 sec., or 1 hr. after each trial, every S being rotated through all of these ear-clamp conditions every three days. In addition, there were a few other changes. To create a stronger and more stable avoidance performance, grid-shock intensity was set at 168 instead of 112 v. for the first 18 days. For the remaining six days it was raised to 224 v. By Day 24 all Ss were avoiding well. However, they varied among themselves with respect to the number of days passed since last being shocked and so were presumably at different stages of extinction of fear. In order to have them all equalized in this respect at the beginning of the test period, the initial "free" period was eliminated on the final day of training so that each S was shocked immediately upon introduction into the dark compartment.

ASSIGNMENT TO GROUPS. A record of the number of anticipatory escapes, of weight changes, and of log-latency to escape was kept on each S during training. On the basis of this record the animals at the end of training were evenly distributed through three groups, which were then randomly assigned to receive ECS at the following intervals after each test trial: 20 sec., 60 sec., and 1 hr. Since the 1-hr. group had not shown any effect in the previous experiment, it was used as a control and the pseudo-ECS group was omitted. These groups initially contained Ns of 18, 19, and 19, respectively, but were reduced by ECS-induced death, paraplegia, and debilitation to 12, 12, and 10, respectively. To equate Ns across groups for the purpose of performing analysis-of-variance trend tests requiring equal Ns, two Ss each were randomly eliminated from both the 20-sec-ECS and the 60-sec-ECS groups. The results to be reported are based on the 30 Ss that remained.

TESTING. Testing covered 12 days. One trial was given each S per day. In this phase the side of the apparatus in which the grid-shock was delivered was reversed, occurring now in the light compartment whenever an avoidance response occurred in contrast to having been previously delivered in the dark compartment for a failure to avoid. Whenever S placed at least three legs in the light compartment, E closed the door behind it and pressed a switch, which delivered a 0.4-sec. shock which began at 112 v. on the first day and increased 56 v. each day to a limit of 560 v. on Day 9. Thereafter, duration of shock doubled each day till 3.2 sec. on Day 12. Each animal performing an avoidance remained in the light compartment 10 sec. after shock before being removed. Unless it was a member of the 20-sec-ECS group, it waited out the remaining time before ECS in its home cage. If S failed to avoid within 120 sec. the time limit of a trial, it was removed from the dark compartment to its home cage and did not receive ECS that day.

During this test phase the number of escapes made within a 120-sec. criterion and the log-latency of these were recorded. A daily urination-defecation count was kept on all animals as in Experiment 1. Weight changes were also recorded daily.

Results

As in Experiment 1, the sooner a group received ECS following its learning trial, the fewer avoidance responses it made. In this case, however, fewer avoidances meant better learning. Over Days 2 through 12 the mean number of avoidances by the 20-sec-, 60-sec, and Hr-ECS groups were 3.0, 4.0, and 6.1, respectively. An analysis of variance, employing arc-sine transformations of the individual scores, found the over-all difference among the above means to be significant at $p < .025$. An F test employing the same set of weights used in Experiment 1 demonstrated that a linear trend effect of treatments accounted for most of this difference and was reliable at $p < .01$. The variance existing between the 20-sec- and the Hr-ECS groups contributed most to this linear effect, for its F ratio was significant while the F ratios of all other comparisons were not.

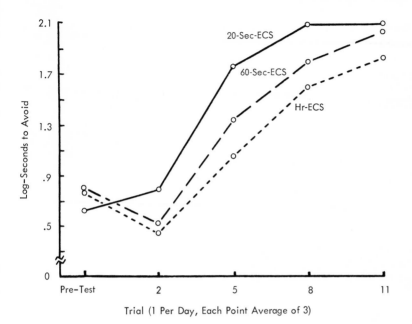

Fig. 3. When the effects of conflict would help and amnesia would hinder learning to stop the avoidance response, learning is better (as indicated by longer avoidance times) the shorter the interval between each training trial and the ECS.

Log-latency to avoid was a more appropriate index of learning in this experiment than in Experiment 1, for each *S* always had a 2-min. opportunity unforced by grid-shock in which to avoid or not. Since the response to be learned was to suppress a previously learned avoidance response, the longer the avoidance latencies, the better this learning. Learning curves for the three groups are presented in Figure 3. It can be seen that learning was best in the 20-sec-ECS group, poorer in the 60-sec-ECS group, and poorest in the Hr-ECS group. The linear component of this between-groups trend accounted for virtually all of the between-group variance and proved to be highly significant ($F = 37.30$ at 1, 27 df; $p < .001$). Furthermore, specific comparisons showed that not only was the difference between the 60-sec- and the Hr-ECS groups significant, but also the difference between the 20-sec- and 60-sec-ECS groups.

Although the direction of urination-defecation differences between groups replicated those established in Experiment 1, the frequency of defecation and urination was much lower, averaging daily for the 20-sec-, 60-sec-, and Hr-ECS groups only .22, .10, and .02, respectively. These reduced scores can be explained at least partially in terms of the smaller number of trials given and by the procedural fact that, as the *S*s ceased avoiding, they also ceased receiving grid-shock and ECS and so presumably began recovering from their emotionality. For this reason a test of significance was conducted only upon the scores obtained in the first five days, a period by the end of which all the 20-sec-ECS Ss had just ceased avoiding. The test, a Mann-Whitney U, detected a difference significant at the .05 level between only the 20-sec- and Hr-ECS groups.

Over the course of this experiment, not just the 20-sec-ECS group but all groups suffered weight losses. Moreover, the direction of the differences between groups was exactly opposite to that obtained in Experiment 1. The Hr-ECS group lost more weight than the 60-sec-ECS group, which in turn lost more weight than the 20-sec-ECS group. However, not only was this trend not significant, but it was very possibly explained by the fact that the longer after each trial a group received its ECS, the longer it continued responding, and so the more grid-shock and ECS it received. To check for this, the mean weights of groups were compared, with all Ss omitted which had avoided more than four times, leaving Ns of 10, 8, and 3 in the 20-sec-, 60-sec-, and Hr-ECS groups, respectively. The respective adjusted mean weight losses were then 25.6, 26.5, and 28.5 gm. as compared with unadjusted means of 25.6, 30.6, and 35.4 gm.

Discussion

According to the amnesia hypothesis, the rats receiving the ECS sooner after running out of the starting compartment should have less tendency to remember the shock introduced into the goal compartment and, hence, should require more trials to adjust to the changed conditions by ceasing to run. But if the ECS produced fear, it should summate with the shock introduced into the goal compartment so that the rats receiving the ECS sooner should learn to stop running in fewer trials. Since the scores for both log-latency and frequency of avoidance showed more rapid learning to stop running the sooner the ECS, the results clearly confirm the fear hypothesis.

A fear induced by the ECS, similar to that demonstrated in this experiment, could explain Duncan's results as well an those of the other previous experiments, since they were all designed so that such an effect would produce a difference in the obtained direction. Even the fascinating results mentioned by Gerard (1955) as supporting the "amnesia" interpretation can be given an alternative interpretation. He reports that when hamsters are chilled to 5° C. during the interval between learning and the ECS, the ECS can be delayed much longer and still be effective. This he interprets as a slowing down of the processes of memory fixation with lowered temperature. However, in terms of our results, it might be that the lowered temperature slowed down not the memory processes but the processes responsible for a temporal gradient of reinforcement and, hence, for a decrement in conditioned fear when the reinforcement (in this case, ECS) was delayed. Thus, it is not clear that this or Duncan's experiment has supplied conclusive proof of retrograde amnesia.

Our experiments have not proven, however, that no retrograde amnesia occurred. All they have shown is that the effects of retrograde amnesia, if any, are weaker than those of the fear induced by the ECS.

SUMMARY

Previous experiments have reported poorer learned performance the more immediately an ECS (electroconvulsive shock) followed each learning trial. These results have been interpreted as demonstrating retrograde amnesia of the type that would be expected if a period of consolidation were required to fixate the memory engram so that it became progressively more resistant to disruption during the rest interval after the trial. But the results could be explained also by assuming that the more immediate administrations of ECS induced more fear of the goal, and hence conflict, which interfered with performance. A previous control for the fear hypothesis is inadequate.

Our first experiment showed that we were replicating the procedures of one of these previous experiments (Duncan's) well enough to replicate the results. It also provided evidence for increased fear, as measured by urination and defecation, in the rats receiving the ECS sooner after each learning trial.

The second experiment was as similar to the first as possible, but designed so that, instead of summating with each other, any aversive and amnesic effects of the ECS would oppose each other. The rat's task was to learn to stop performing an avoidance response when the electric shock in the starting box was turned off and a shock was introduced into the goal box. Under these conditions, learning was faster the sooner the ECS followed each trial. Any amnesia which the ECS may have produced for the immediately preceding shock in the goal box, was overridden by increased fear induced by the ECS. While these results do not disprove the occurrence of retrograde amnesia, they cast serious doubts on the conclusions of previous studies purporting to prove its occurrence.

REFERENCES

DOLLARD, J., & MILLER, N. E. *Personality and psycho-therapy.* New York: McGraw-Hill, 1950.

DUNCAN, C. P. The retroactive effect of electroshock on learning. *J. comp. physiol. Psychol.*, 1949, **42**, 32–44.

GALLINEK, A. Fear and anxiety in the course of electroshock therapy. *Amer. J. Psychiat.*, 1956, **113**, 428–434.

GERARD, R. W. Biological roots of psychiatry. *Science*, 1955, **122**, 225–230.

HAYES, K. J. Cognitive and emotional effects of electroconvulsive shock in rats. *J. comp. physiol. Psychol.*, 1948, **41**, 40–61.

HEBB, D. O. *The organization of behavior.* New York: Wiley, 1949.

JANIS, I. L. Psychological effects of electric convulsive treatments. *J. nerv. ment. Dis.* 1950, **111**, 359–397; 469–489.

LEUKEL, F. A. A comparison of the effects of ECS and anesthesia on acquisition of the maze habit. *J. comp. physiol. Psychol.*, 1957, **50**, 300–306.

MILLER, N. E. & COONS, E. E. Conflict versus consolidation of memory to explain "retrograde amnesia" produced by ECS. *Amer. Psychologist*, 1955, **10**, 394. (Abstract)

MIRSKY, A. F., & ROSVOLD, H. E. The effect of electro-convulsive shock on food intake and hunger drive in the rat. *J. comp. physiol. Psychol.*, 1953, **46**, 153–157.

RUSSELL, W. R. & NATHAN, P. W. Traumatic amnesia. *Brain*, 1946, **69**, 280–300.

THOMPSON, R., & DEAN, W. A further study of the retroactive effect of ECS. *J. comp. physiol. Psychol*, 1955, **48**, 488–491.

Short-Term Retrograde Amnesia in Rats

Stephan L. Chorover
and Peter H. Schiller

ABSTRACT. Retroactive effects of electroconvulsive shock (ECS) were studied in 477 male hooded rats which received ECS 0.5–60.0 sec. after single passive avoidance training trials. As in previous studies, impairment in retention was inversely related to duration of ECS-delay interval. However, unlike earlier studies, impairment was observed only at relatively short (0.5–10.0 sec.) ECS-delays. Impairment is attributed to brief RA and not to aversive effects of ECS which were shown to develop only after repeated ECS treatments. The results are discussed in terms of both the consolidation hypothesis and alternative "conflict" and "competing-response" hypotheses of ECS effects.

Electroconvulsive shock (ECS) tends to impair performance of learned responses in rats. The magnitude of the impairment is generally found to vary inversely with the time interval between learning and the ECS treatment.

From *Journal of Comparative and Physiological Psychology*, 1965, **59**, 73–78. Reprinted with permission of the publisher and authors. Supported in part by the Rockefeller Foundation and by the National Institute of Mental Health Grants No. M-5673 and MG-07923-01. The authors are indebted to Anne Marie DeLuca for assistance in various phases of this research.

Considerable controversy still surrounds the question of whether such impairments are due to retroactive "memory interference" (retrograde amnesia—RA) (Duncan, 1949; Hudspeth, McGaugh, & Thompson, 1964; Leukel, 1957; Thompson & Dean, 1955) or to other disruptive effects such as conflict (Coons & Miller, 1960) or competing conditioned responses (Lewis & Adams, 1963) produced by ECS.

In general, experiments in which repeated convulsive treatments have been employed tend to support the "conflict" or "competing-response" hypotheses, while the results of "one-trial learning" studies (Chorover, 1964; Hudspeth et al., 1964) suggest that ECS may actually produce RA (perhaps by interfering with some hypothetical "consolidation" processes involved in the permanent encoding of "memory traces").

In the present study we attempted to show: (*a*) That it is possible to clearly identify amnestic effects of ECS in a one-trial passive avoidance learning situation; (*b*) that, under the conditions employed, the duration of ECS-induced RA is considerably briefer than previously reported; and (*c*) that aversive effects of ECS, which can also be identified, are experimentally dissociable from the amnestic ones. Our results provide a possible basis for resolving some of the apparent contradictions between the RA hypothesis on the one hand and the conflict or competing response views on the other.

METHOD

SUBJECTS. Four hundred and seventy-seven male hooded rats of the Long-Evans strain were used in the experiment. They were obtained in several lots from a commercial supplier (Research Animals, Incorporated, Pittsburgh, Pennsylvania) at about 60 days of age. At the time of the experiment *S*s were 75–100 days old. Throughout their time in the laboratory they were housed in pairs in standard wire-mesh cages ($17.5 \times 17.5 \times 24$ cm.) and provided with ad-lib. access to food (Purina laboratory chow) and water.

APPARATUS. The apparatus employed was patterned after one first described by Jarvik and Essman (1960). Our version of the apparatus consists of a 40-cm. square compartment with walls 30 cm. high, made of polyvinyl chloride sheet, and a floor of stainless-steel rods ($\frac{3}{32}$ in. diameter) placed 1.25 cm. apart. The grid floor is connected to a source of dc voltage (a Grass S-4 stimulator) through a grid-scrambler so that foot shocks (10 pulses/sec; 0.75 ma.) may be delivered when *S*'s feet touch two or more of the grid rods. Located in the center of the compartment is a 13-cm. square insulated platform 5.5 cm. high.

PROCEDURE. The normal response of most *S*s when placed upon the raised platform was to step down rather rapidly onto the grid floor and explore the test compartment. The time required to perform this step-down response was our measure of the aversive properties of the test situation. In order to obtain adequate control information and base-line performance levels, each *S* was first allowed a 5-day (one trial per day) period of habituation to the apparatus as follows: At the start of each trial, *S* was placed in the center of the raised platform, and the time taken to step down (more precisely, the time required to place both forepaws on the grid) was recorded. Ten seconds after stepping down S was removed from the compartment and returned to its home cage. On Day 3, several hours after the usual habituation trial, two small snap connectors ("Starlet-Dot fasteners"—manufactured by United-Carr Corporation, Cambridge 39, Massachusetts) were set in Ss' pinnae under brief ether anesthesia. On all subsequent trials, wire for administering ECS were attached to the ear snaps just prior to placing S on the raised platform.

Differential treatments were begun on Day 5 and were repeated on the 2 following days. The last test trial was run on Day 8. Animals were matched on the basis of step-down latencies (SDL) obtained on Days 1–4 and were assigned randomly to three main groups and two additional control groups as shown in Table 1. To test for the aversive properties of the foot shock, the first group (FS, $N = 102$) was divided into four subgroups which, upon stepping from the raised platform, received foot shocks lasting 0.5, 1, 2, or 4 sec. The second group (FS-ECS, $N = 242$) was treated exactly like the first, but in addition to the FS these Ss received ECS in the apparatus. The ECS was produced by passing 35–50 ma. ac between the ear snaps for 0.2 sec. Different subgroups of the FS-ECS group received the convulsive treatment 0.5, 2, 5, 10, or 30 sec. after termination of the foot shock. The purpose of the third group was to assay the effects of ECS itself upon the step-down performance. This group (ECS; $N = 111$) did not receive foot shock, but did receive ECS in the apparatus. Different subgroups received the convulsive treatments at delay intervals equal to those of comparable Ss in the FS-ECS group (i.e., 0.5–30 sec.). One additional ECS subgroup ($N = 10$) received the convulsive treatment after a delay of 60 sec. Two additional groups were foot-shock controls patterned after a treatment devised by Duncan (1945). The first group (D_1, $N = 6$) received no FS; these Ss were removed from the apparatus 10 sec. after stepping down; 20 sec. later, after being placed in a large white plastic basin, they were given a 35–50 ma. shock to the hindlegs. The second group (D_2, $N = 6$) received a 2-sec. foot shock followed in 30 sec. by the hindleg shock.

On Days 6, 7, and 8 the same procedure was followed: wires were attached to the ear snaps, S was placed on the platform, and the step-down latency was recorded. After stepping down, FS and/or ECS were given as described above. The maximum latency score was 30; Ss which avoided (i.e., remained on the platform) beyond 30 sec. were gently pushed off in order to equalize the total number of foot shocks and ECS treatments given to all Ss.

Skewness in the distribution of latency scores dictated use of nonparametric statistical analysis. Therefore, within each group, central tendency was calculated in terms of median step-down latency (mdn. SDL) and performance of individual Ss was compared by means of a series of Mann-Whitney U tests (intergroup comparisons) and sign tests (intragroup, day-by-day comparisons).

RESULTS

On the trial prior to implantation of the ear snaps (Day 3), the overall median step-down latency was 1.5 sec; on the following trial (Day 4) it was 1.51 sec.

This indicates that neither the brief operation performed on Day 3, nor attachment of wires to the ear snaps on Day 4 affected *S*s' performance during the habituation phase of the experiment.

The posttreatment results are expressed in terms of the mdn. SCL for each subgroup and the percentage of *S*s avoiding for at least 20 sec. The effects of single treatments (data for Day 6 only) are presented first (Table 1 and Figure 1), followed by results after three repeated treatments (data for Days 6, 7, and 8 combined).

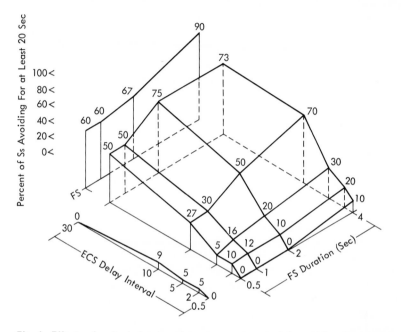

Fig. 1. Effects of a single treatment upon percentage of *S*s avoiding for at least 20 sec. on first posttreatment day (Day 6). (Isometric orthographic projection in center depicts passive avoidance performance of FS-ECS groups as a joint function of FS duration—0.5–4 sec.—and ECS-delay interval—0.5–30 sec. Values on curve in left foreground are for *S*s which received ECS only. Values on curve in left background are for *S*s which received FS only. Numerals on the curves indicate actual percentage values at each data point.)

Effects of Single Treatments

1. *Effects of a single foot shock* (FS). On Day 5 all *S*s dismounted from the raised platform within 4 sec. (mdn. SDL = 1.6 sec.). Animals which received FS upon stepping down on Day 5 showed an increased tendency to remain on the platform on Day 6. The overall mdn. SDL for *S*s in the FS groups rose to 30 sec. ($p < .001$). Avoidance of the grid floor varied slightly as a direct function of FS duration (Figure 1).

2. *Effects of a single ECS treatment.* After receiving a single convulsive treatment on Day 5, most *S*s in the ECS groups showed no increased tendency to remain on the platform on the following day (Table 1).

3. *Effects of a single FS-ECS treatment.* The interactions between FS duration and ECS-delay interval are summarized in Table 1 and in the central portion of Figure 1. After a single FS-ECS treatment, avoidance of the grid increased as a function of duration of the ECS-delay interval. As FS duration was increased, the tendency to avoid the grid also increased. Footshock duration was, however, a weaker determinant of the increased avoidance. With ECS-delay intervals of 5 sec. or more, the FS-ECS groups began to show significantly increased avoidance of the grid. Step-down latencies approaching control (FS) levels were obtained when the ECS-delay interval was increased to 10 sec. Finally, at the 30-sec. delay interval, performance of the FS-ECS groups was indistinguishable from that of FS controls.

Effects of Three Repeated Treatments

1. *Effects of repeated foot shocks* (FS). Figure 2 shows that repetition of the FS treatments produced relatively little overall change in the level of avoidance performance. The mdn. SDL of 30 sec., attained after a single FS, was maintained throughout the subsequent trials.

2. *Effects of repeated ECS treatments.* Although avoidance did not increase following a single ECS treatment (Figure 2), daily repetition of the convulsions for 3 successive days produced a progressive increase in *S*s'

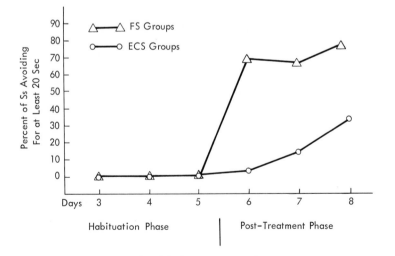

Fig. 2. Development of avoidance performance on Days 6, 7, and 8 by *S*s which received FS or ECS on treatment Days 5, 6, and 7. (Numbers in parentheses indicate number of *S*s at each data point.)

Table 1 Median Step-down Latency on First Posttreatment Trial (Day 6) as a Function of Foot-shock Duration and ECS-Delay Interval

| ECS DELAY (SEC.) | FOOT-SHOCK DURATION (IN SEC) | | | | | | | | ECS ONLY | | N^a |
| | 0.5 | | 1 | | 2 | | 4 | | | | |
	N	MDN. SDL	N	MDN. SDL	N	MDN. SDL	N	MDN. SDL	N	MDN. SDL	
0.5	10	2.25	10	2.75	10	4.55	10	6.50	30	1.55	70
2	10	3.25	17	1.50	10	5.50	10	5.75	20	1.00	67
5	10	3.00	19	2.00	10	9.75	10	15.00	20	1.50	69
10	11	9.50	20	9.00	10	18.00	11	26.80	22	1.25	73
30	10	18.50	10	20.00	24	30.00	10	30.00	19	4.00	74
FS only	10	27.50	20	29.75	62	30.00	10	30.00	—		102^b
N	61		96		126		61		111	1.50	455

a Three subgroups which do not appear in the table make the total $N = 477$: Group D_1 ($N = 6$) received hindleg shock only (mdn. SDL = 17.00); Group D_2 ($N = 6$) received 2-sec. FS plus hindleg shock (mdn. SDL = 30.00); 10 Ss received ECS at 60-sec. delay (mdn. SDL = 1.50).

b Mdn. SDL = 30.00.

tendency to remain on the platform. The mdn. SDL for all ECS groups on Days 6, 7, and 8 was 1.5, 3.5, and 10.3, respectively. Thus, by the end of the 3-day test period, overall avoidance performance of the ECS groups was approaching (but did not yet equal) that of the FS groups. It must be emphasized that all of the ECS-delay subgroups did not contribute equally to this result. On the contrary, marked differences in SDL were observed as a function of the duration of the ECS-delay interval. Thus, it can be seen from Figure 3 that avoidance was least at the shortest (0.5 sec.) delay interval, increased significantly ($p < 0.001$) up to 10 sec. and then declined ; Ss which received the ECS treatments at 30- and 60-sec. delay intervals avoided the grid significantly less than those in the 10-sec. delay subgroup ($p < 0.001$).

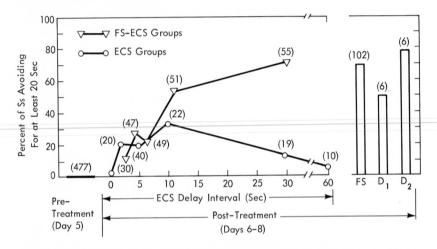

Fig. 3. Overall avoidance performance of FS-ECS, ECS, and control groups. (Central portion of the figure compares performance of FS-ECS and ECS groups as a function of the delay of posttrial ECS administration. Numbers in parentheses indicate the number of Ss in each group. Each point is based upon overall step-down latencies on Days 6, 7, and 8. Vertical bars at the left indicate performance of groups which received FS only—FS, hindleg shock only—D₁—or, FS plus hindleg shock—D₂.)

3. *Effects of repeated FS-ECS treatments.* Duration of FS initially exerted a considerable influence upon the degree of avoidance by the FS-ECS groups (Figure 1). However, when the overall data for each FS-ECS subgroup were combined for 3 successive days (Figure 4) the latency differences originally observed as a function of FS duration tended to disappear. By contrast, after three trials (Figure 4), as after a single trial (Figure 1), avoidance continued to be a negatively accelerated, increasing function of the ECS-delay interval. As shown in Figure 3, the percentage of trials on which FS-ECS Ss avoided for at least 20 sec. was markedly increased when the ECS-delay interval was 10 sec. or longer. Another important result shown in Figure 3 is that the avoidance performance of FS-ECS and ECS groups was equivalent at ECS-delay intervals less than 10 sec.

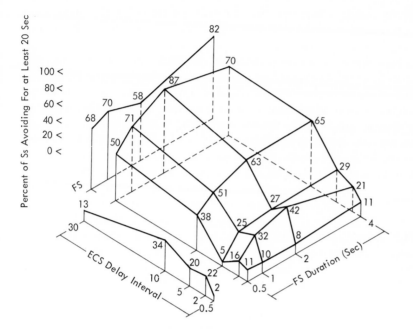

Fig. 4. Effects of three repeated treatments upon percentage of *S*s avoiding for at least 20 sec. (Each data point reflects overall performance on Days 6, 7, and 8. Details of the figure are otherwise the same as for Figure 1.)

DISCUSSION

The results are in agreement with the general observations that (*a*) retention test performance may be impaired by one or more ECS treatments given shortly after avoidance training trials and (*b*) the degree of ECS-induced interference varies inversely with the duration of time elapsed between training and ECS. However, we have found no evidence to support the idea that ECS produces RA for events preceding the convulsion by several hours or even minutes. On the contrary, *S*s in the present situation clearly retained a previously acquired passive avoidance response when ECS was administered as little as 10 sec. after training.

Aversive effects of ECS (without accompanying FS) did not seem to develop after a single convulsion but did become increasingly prominent with repeated ECS treatments (Figure 2). Two specific lines of evidence indicate that the aversive effects were dissociable from the amnestic ones and could not (in the present case at least) be invoked to account for the latter:

1. In the experimental situation, aversive stimuli which evoke fear or competing response should cause the animal to abandon its normal step-down response and to "freeze" on the raised platform. This is precisely the effect produced by the noxious foot shock and by the hindleg shock (Figure 3). It is

clear from Figure 2, however, that this was not the effect of a single ECS although repetition of the ECS treatments increased the probability that a "freezing" response would occur.

2. According to generally accepted principles of conditioning, the influence of a reinforcer (including punishment) may be expected to decline as the delay of reinforcement increases (Kamin, 1959; Kimble, 1961). Therefore, if ECS has aversive properties, its maximum effect upon step-down performance should appear at the shortest ECS-delay intervals and its disruptive influence should decline as the ECS-delay interval is lengthened. This was not the case in the present experiment. On the contrary (see Figure 3) the aversive effects of ECS, which were least at very short-delay intervals, increased up to about 10 sec. and then declined again. The decline in avoidance observed when ECS was administered at relatively long ECS-delay intervals (i.e., 10–6 sec.) may be adequately accounted for in terms of a temporal-delay-of-punishment gradient (Kamin, 1959), but this notion does not explain why ECS groups showed a gradual increase in avoidance up to 10 sec. In order to account for this increase, we must compare performance of the ECS and FS-ECS groups during ECS-delay intervals up to 10 sec. and consider the relationship of our data to the memory interference hypothesis.

The FS-ECS curve in Figure 3 clearly shows that, although Ss were able to retain the avoidance response when the ECS-delay interval exceeded 10 sec., retention declined as the delay of ECS administration was reduced below 10 sec. If we assume (a) that ECS produces RA lasting up to 10 sec. and (b) that ECS has aversive effects which may become associated with antecedent stimuli in accordance with principles of classical conditioning, it becomes possible to account for the increased avoidance of ECS subgroups as the ECS-delay interval is increased up to 10 sec.: Since successful conditioning presumably requires that S "remember" the CS, it is only when delay interval is increased up to 10 sec. (i.e., to the apparent "limits" of the RA) that it becomes possible for the aversive consequences of the ECS to be conditioned to antecedent stimuli in the test situation.

In summary, by proposing that ECS induces a brief RA, we are able to account for (a) the failure of ECS, in the present study, to interfere with retention of a passive avoidance response learned 10–30 sec. prior to ECS and (b) the comparable effects of ECS and FS-ECS at very short ECS-delay intervals (i.e., the apparent failure of the aversive effects of both FS and ECS to produce avoidance of the grid when ECS is given within the first few seconds after a trial).

Although our results appear to support a "brief RA" hypothesis of ECS effects, two important questions remain unanswered. First, how can we account for the apparent contradictions between our results and those of other workers who have reported that impaired retention of different passive avoidance tasks may be produced at much greater ECS-delay intervals (Bureš and Buresová, 1963; Heriot and Coleman, 1962; Weissman, 1963)?

Second, assuming that ECS produces RA which, irrespective of whether it is "brief" or "prolonged," appears to be a true *amnesia* (i.e., loss or absence of memory), is it valid to attribute this effect to interference with "memory trace consolidation?"

REFERENCES

BUREŠ, J. & BUREŠOVÁ, O. Cortical spreading depression as a memory disturbing factor. *J. comp. physiol. Psychol.*, 1963, **56**, 268–272.

CHOROVER, S. L. Rapid memory consolidation: Effects of electroconvulsive shock upon retention in the rat. In D. P. Kimble (Ed.), *Learning, remembering and forgetting*. Vol. 1. *The anatomy of learning*. Washington, D.C.: American Institute Biological Sciences, 1964.

COONS, E. E. & MILLER, N. E. Conflict versus consolidation of memory traces to explain "retrograde amnesia" produced by ECS. *J. comp. physiol. Psychol.*, 1960, **53**, 524–531.

DUNCAN, C. P. The effect of electroshock convulsions on the maze habit in the white rat. *J. exp. Psychol.*, 1945, **35**, 267–278.

DUNCAN, C. P. The retroactive effect of electroshock on learning. *J. comp. physiol. Psychol.*, 1949, **42**, 32–44.

HERIOT, J. T., & COLEMAN, P. D. The effect of electroconvulsive shock on retention of a modified "one-trial" conditioned avoidance. *J. comp. physiol. Psychol.*, 1962, **55**, 1082–1084.

HUDSPETH, W. J., MCGAUGH, J. I., & THOMSON, C. W. Aversive and amnesic effects of electroconvulsive shock. *J. comp. physiol. Psychol.*, 1964, **57**, 61–64.

JARVIK, M. E., & ESSMAN, W. B. A simple one-trial learning situation for mice. *Psychol. Rep.*, 1960, **6**, 290.

KAMIN, L. J. The delay of punishment gradient. *J. comp. physiol. Psychol.*, 1959, **52**, 434–437.

KIMBLE, G. A. *Hilgard and Marquis' conditioning and learning*. (2nd ed.) New York: Appleton-Century-Crofts, 1961.

LEUKEL, F. A comparison of the effects of ECS and anesthesia on acquisition of the maze habit. *J. comp. physiol. Psychol.*, 1957, **50**, 300–306.

LEWIS, D. J. & ADAMS, H. E. Retrograde amnesia from conditioned competing responses. *Science*, 1963, **141**, 516–517.

THOMPSON, R., & DEAN, W. A further study of the retroactive effect of ECS. *J. comp. physiol. Psychol.*, 1955, **48**, 488–491.

WEISSMAN, A. Effect of electroconvulsive shock intensity and seizure pattern on retrograde amnesia in rats. *J. comp. physiol. Psychol.*, 1963, **56**, 806–810.

Effects of Subcortical Electrical Stimulation on Learning in the Rat

Helen Mahut

There is now clear evidence that normal cerebral function is critically related to that of the reticular activating system described by Magoun and others (1958). It is also known that this system, among its other connections, projects diffusely over the whole cortical surface. Changes in the pattern and level of activity in the reticular system have profound effects on the firing of cortical units as well as on the EEG.

It is reasonable to assume that the neural activity of this system is related in an important way to the physiological processes underlying learning and that an intervention with its normal function would have detrimental effects. Chronic electrodes were, therefore, implanted in the reticular formation and related structures of the rat's tegmentum and diencephalon to find out whether electrical stimulation would affect the learning process. Since the formation of memory traces and their temporal characteristics were of primary interest, stimulation was delivered following each response, at a time when, presumably, memory traces were organized.

GENERAL METHOD

SUBJECTS

Subjects were 139 adult, male hooded rats obtained from the Royal Victoria Hospital in Montreal; 117 were operated on, and 22 were unoperated control rats. Bipolar nichrome wire electrodes, described in detail by Olds and Milner (1954), were chronically implanted in all the rats. The electrodes consisted of a Lucite plug with two strands of wire protruding at right angles to the base of the plug. The wires were insulated except at the tips, which were separated by approximately 0.5 mm. Their length varied from 5.5 mm. to 6.5 mm. depending on the intended placements. All operations were performed under Nembutal anaesthesia. A Johnson-Krieg stereotaxic instrument was used to lower the electrodes to a desired depth.

From *Journal of Comparative and Physiological Psychology*, 1962, **55**, 472–477. Reprinted with permission of the publisher and author. The study was supported by funds from the Foundations' Fund for Research in Psychiatry (Grant 275 –64) by D. O. Hebb.

APPARATUS AND GENERAL PROCEDURE

Approximately 1 week after the operations, testing was carried out in a modified open-field Hebb-Williams apparatus in four experiments, and on an elevated T maze in two others. A wooden Skinner box, 12 in. by 12 in. by 4 in., with a protruding metal lever at one end, was used to compare the rate of bar pressing for self-stimulation in some experimental animals and in 22 normal controls.

Electrical stimulation was delivered from an ordinary transformer (110 v., 60-cycle ac power) by means of a flexible lead of sufficient length to allow free movement. Voltage could be varied by means of a potentiometer between zero and 2.5 v.

Since the purpose of the investigation was to study the possible disruptive effects of stimulation on the learning process, it was important not to complicate the interpretation of the results by other effects which are known to accompany electrical stimulation of the brain. Therefore, during the pretraining phase of the first experiment, 13 rats were subjected for 3 days to brief periods of intermittent stimulation while running the maze and, following each run, while eating in the food box. Generally, motor effects similar to those described by Forman and Ward (1957) in cats, were obtained at .75 or 1.0 v. in rats with electrodes aimed at the thalamic reticular system. They frequently consisted of slow lifting of one paw and head followed by rotation to one side. It should be noted that no decrease in speed of running or avoidance of the food box could be observed on the trials following such stimulation.

However, with higher intensities, at between 1.0 and 2.5 v., frequent freezing and interruption of on-going activity was produced at both thalamic and the more posterior tegmental placements. In such cases, in some rats, varying degrees of avoidance of the food box or a reluctance to enter the maze were noted on subsequent trials.

Arbitrarily, .50 and .75 v. were adopted for stimulation of all experimental animals. Depending on the resistance of individual electrodes, current intensities were estimated at between 11 and 20 μa. Such current was below threshold for any overt motor response, it did not influence the rate of running the maze, and it did not have any observable effect on eating behavior during the few seconds the rat was allowed to remain in the food box following each run.

At the conclusion of the experiments, rats were sacrificed and perfused with normal saline and 10% formalin solution. The brains were removed and frozen sections, cut at 40μ, were stained with cresyl violet to determine the location of the electrode tips.

EXPERIMENT 1 : EFFECTS OF STIMULATION

METHOD

Thirteen rats were first trained in the Hebb-Williams apparatus until a running-speed criterion (10 runs under 50 sec.) was reached. Three simple pretraining problems were used and approximately 10 days of familiarization with the training procedure minimized individual motivational differences.

Following this, eight experimental rats had electrodes implanted at the thalamic level and five rats to be used as nonstimulated controls, at the tegmental level of the reticular system.

After recovery the animals were again run on pretraining problems until they reached the running-speed criterion, and then received, for 3 days, brief electrical stimulation described in the General Procedure. After 2 more days of pretraining without stimulation, the rats were given a series of 12 problems, one a day, 10 runs on each problem. Stimulation was delivered for 15 sec., seven to eight 1-sec. bursts, as soon as the front paws of the rats entered the food box.

Results

The mean number of errors made by the experimental group was 176.7 as compared with 105.6 made by the control group. This difference was significant at the .05 level of confidence (Mann-Whitney one-tailed test).

The experimental animals also made fewer errorless runs than the control group: 42% vs. 61%, a difference significant at the .001 level of confidence. Further analysis showed no difference between the two groups on the first run in the block of 10 runs; the difference appeared on the second run following the first stimulation period and continued throughout the rest of the eight runs (Fig. 1).

In order to see whether the effects of stimulation were reversible, the rats were then run again on the same series of 12 problems, but without stimulation. The differences obtained in the mean number of errors made by the two groups were not significant (63.7 for the experimental group and 51.8 for the control group). The decrease in the number of errors from the first series of

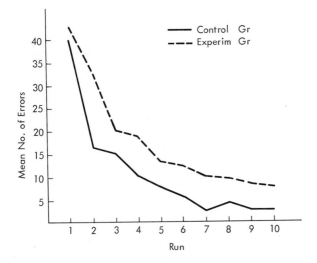

Fig. 1. Mean number of errors for experimental and control rats in blocks of 10 runs (for 12 problems).

problems to the second was 51% for the control group and 64% for the experimental group.

Histological examination revealed that the tips of the electrodes were in the thalamic intralaminar and midline structures (Fig. 2).

Lack of visible motor disturbance at the current intensity used does not preclude the possibility of subtle motivational effects which could be attributed to stimulation. In the light of self-stimulation studies by Olds (1954, 1956) it was important to establish whether there were not any "rewarding" or "punishing" effects to be elicited by stimulating the subcortical structures involved in this study. After the learning experiment was finished, the 13 rats with implanted electrodes and 22 normal control rats were tested for 2 consecutive days, in 20-min. periods, for comparison of bar pressing rates. As can be seen from Table 1, there were no significant differences in rate between rats receiving low current intensity stimulation and non-stimulated rats.

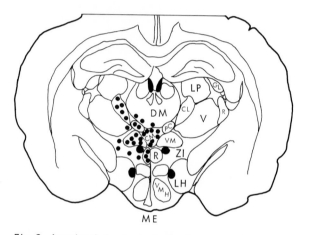

Fig. 2. Anterior thalamic electrode placements. (Intralaminar system : CL = *n. centralis lateralis;* PC = *n. paracentralis;* CM = *n. centralis medialis;* VM = *n. ventralis medialis;* R = *n. reuniens;* ZI = *Zona incerta;* V = *n. ventralis*—Krieg 54.1.)

Table 1 Response Rates for the Experimental and Control Animals in the Skinner Box

		CONDITIONS					
		5 MIN. NO CURRENT		15 MIN. CURRENT ON		5 MIN. NO CURRENT	
GROUP	N	DAY 1	DAY 2	DAY 1	DAY 2	DAY 1	DAY 2
Thalamic	8	5.7[a]	2.5	1.5	0.8	0.6	1.1
Tegmental	5	3.8	2.8	1.4	0.8	1.2	0.7
Control	22	7.6	3.1	2.2	1.7	0.7	0.6

[a] All figures represent mean number of bar presses, per rat, per minute.

EXPERIMENT 2: EFFECTS OF A DELAY BETWEEN THE RESPONSE AND ONSET OF STIMULATION

The interpretation of the results obtained in the first experiment was complicated by the fact that though stimulation was introduced immediately following a run, it also preceded the next run by a few seconds. Instead of disturbing the consolidation period following learning, therefore, the effect of stimulation might have been a proactive disturbance on the learning process itself. In order to examine this possibility, the next experiment varied the time of stimulation following the run.

METHOD

Three groups of rats with implanted electrodes were tested on the Hebb-Williams apparatus. One group of nine rats was stimulated immediately after each run, and a group of eight rats, 2 min. and 45 sec. after each run. Eight operated rats, with electrodes but no stimulation, served as controls. All animals spent 3 min. in the food box after each run, and three runs 6 hr. apart instead of the usual 10 consecutive runs were given daily. In the first part of the study, Problems 1 to 6 were used, and in the second, Problems 7 to 12.

Results

As can be seen in Table 2, the mean error scores for the three groups differed significantly, the delayed-stimulation group showing no detrimental effects.

Contrary to the results of the first experiment, significant differences in the mean number of errors were found even on the first run of each new problem. This suggests that three runs were presumably not enough for any group to acquire a sufficient learning set which could be reflected on the first nonstimulated run of a new problem. There were no differences between the three groups in the number of errorless runs.

*Table 2   Differences in Mean Errors Between the Three Groups
of Rats with and Without Delay of Stimulation*

GROUP	N	STIMULATION (PROB. 1–6)	NO STIMULATION (PROB. 7–12)
No delay, A	9	47.33	42.12
Delay, B	8	32.87	49.50
Control, C	8	30.00	42.12

$F = 9.17; p < .01$
Groups A and B: $t = 3.3, p < .01$
Groups A and C: $t = 3.9, p < .001$

Stimulation was discontinued after the first six problems, and, on the remaining six problems of the series, significant differences between the three groups disappeared (Table 2). It is interesting to note that for the first three problems after stimulation was discontinued for the delay group, the number of errors for that group was consistently higher than that for the nondelay group. This difference, however, was no longer present during the last three problems.

Histological examination revealed that the electrodes were approximately 1 mm. posterior to the placements of the preceding experiment. The structures involved, apart from the thalamic intralaminar system, were the posterior hypothalamus and the parafascicular nucleus (grouped functionally with the thalamic nonspecific system). Two electrodes may have been stimulating the *habenulo-peduncular* tract (Fig. 3).

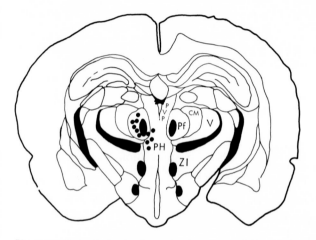

Fig. 3. Posterior thalamic electrode placements. (Pf = *n. parafascicularis;* PH = *posterior hypothalamus*—Krieg 53.6.)

EXPERIMENT 3: CONDITIONAL RESPONSE AND BRIGHTNESS DISCRIMINATION

METHOD

Since it was important to determine whether the deficit produced by stimulation was a general one rather than specific to the type of task used, the following experiment was performed with eight experimental and four control rats. The task consisted of a type of conditional response on a T maze: The rats were first trained to go to one side of the maze with food at both sides. When an incorrect response was made the rat was picked up and brought back to the starting point. As soon as a criterion of 18 correct choices in 20 trials was reached, the opposite arm of the maze had to be chosen. Ten trials a day were given without stimulation. After two such pretraining reversals, the actual learning situation consisted of choosing the right arm to food if a white card appeared when the rat reached the choice point, the left arm if it did not. Stimulation was given after the correct choice while the rat was eating, and after the incorrect choice while the rat was being brought back to the starting point. The intertrial interval was approximately 10 to 15 sec.

Results

Here again the differences were highly significant. Since the experimental animals were still responding at chance level 4 days, or 40 trials, after the slowest of the control animals had reached criterion, stimulation was discontinued (mean number of trials for control and experimental rats was 11.0 and 80 plus, respectively). The previously stimulated rats then reached criterion in about the same number of trials as the control rats took to learn the problem originally (13.14 trials).

Histological examination revealed the same placements as those in the first experiment: the intralaminar and midline nuclei of the thalamus.

As an additional check on possible long lasting effects of stimulation, the two groups were taught a brightness discrimination on the same T maze, but without stimulation. One side was correct when a white card appeared at the choice point, but the opposite side became correct when a black card appeared. There were no significant differences in the number of trials to criterion between the two groups when no stimulation was used for the experimental group (6.7 and 7.4 trials, respectively).

EXPERIMENT 4: EFFECTS OF TEGMENTAL AND CORTICAL STIMULATION

In order to establish whether the detrimental effects obtained by electrical stimulation were specific to the thalamic portion of the reticular formation, anatomical control was needed. Accordingly, the performance of six experimental rats was compared with that of eight operated control rats on the first 12 problems of the Hebb-Williams series. The electrodes in all rats were aimed at the tegmentum. There were no significant differences between the two groups (mean number of errors was 158.83 and 153.85, respectively).

In addition, the performance of nine more experimental rats with electrodes in the tegmentum was compared with that of 10 sham-operated controls on the six first problems of the Hebb-Williams series. No significant differences were found between the two groups of rats (mean number of errors for tegmental rats 48.55 and for controls 46.20).

It will be noted that in these two experiments, the mean number of errors made by the control animals (153.8 and 46.2, respectively) is much higher than that made by the control animals in the first two experiments (105.6 and 32.8, respectively). This difference is most likely due to important differences in procedure. In the first experiment of the series, all rats received extensive pretraining. Running-speed criterion was obtained before and after surgery. Also, several days of overtraining were allowed when thresholds of stimulation were being established. In the second experiment, though there were only three runs given on any one problem instead of the usual 10, intertrial intervals were 6 hr. rather than approximately 15 sec., as in the present experiment. The differences in scores may, therefore, be due to massed rather than distributed practice.

Histological examination revealed that the tips of the stimulating electrodes were in the brainstem reticular formation, at the tegmental level (Fig. 4).

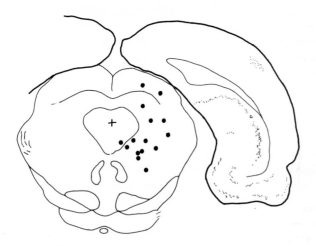

Fig. 4. Tegmental electrode placements (Krieg 51.3.)

The effects of cortical stimulation were then studied in eight experimental and seven operated control rats, in the conditional T maze situation. Here, again, no significant differences between the two groups were found in the number of trials to criterion (43.7 and 49.1 trials, respectively). The greater number of trials needed to learn the problem in this experiment was due to the fact that the rats were made to learn the conditional response without the benefit of two pretraining reversals which were given to the rats in the first T maze experiment.

Histological examination revealed that the tips of the electrodes were in the frontal region, Krieg's areas 6 and 10 (Krieg, 1946), in both experimental and control rats.

DISCUSSION

In interpreting the results obtained in the present studies at least two questions can be raised. The first is, Could not the detrimental effect of stimulation be attributed to a performance rather than to a learning deficit? It will be remembered that in the first experiment rats which received stimulation were significantly worse than control rats, but when stimulation was discontinued on the second series of problems, significant differences in the mean number of errors between the two groups disappeared. This result could be interpreted as lending support to the hypothesis of a performance deficit. However, as can be seen in Figure 1, experimental rats in the first part of the experiment showed consistent improvement during each block of 10 runs in spite of stimulation. This could well account for the acquisition of a sufficient "learning set" during the first series of problems, so that when stimulation was discontinued, the previously stimulated rats were able to do as well as the control rats on the second series.

Furthermore, a separate experiment was performed to compare the effects of stimulation on new vs. old learning, and the results strongly support the learning deficit hypothesis: 9 experimental rats with electrodes in the thalamic portion of the reticular formation and 10 sham-operated control rats (Lucite plug but no electrodes) were first given a learning set on the first 10 problems of the Hebb-Williams series, without stimulation. Then, they were given the same 10 problems, with stimulation for experimental rats, and it was found that there were no significant differences between the two groups in the mean number of errors (38.8 for experimental rats, 34.5 for control rats). These results, together with the absence of detrimental effects when stimulation was administered after a delay of 2 min. and 45 sec., would make a performance deficit highly unlikely.

The second question must be raised in the light of self-stimulation studies (Olds, 1956; Olds & Milner, 1954): Can the deficit obtained in the present experiments be interpreted as a pure learning deficit? Though the Skinner box data showed no differences between normal and experimental rats in the rate of bar pressing for self-stimulation, at the low current intensities used, it might still be possible, though unlikely, that some subtle motivational effect influenced performance in a learning situation.

The interpretation of the deficit found in the present studies in terms of pure learning deficit, however, received support from recent experiments conducted at McGill (Cooper, 1961). Cooper was able to show that "rewarding" effects of thalamic stimulation could, in some cases, be changed into "punishing" effects, with longer stimulus durations. However, when learning deficits were obtained, they were obtained in all experimental animals with stimulus intensities and durations below threshold for eliciting either rewarding or punishing effects of stimulation.

There still remains the possibility that since rats were stimulated following each run when they were eating in the Hebb-Williams apparatus, and approximately on half such runs in the T maze, they had difficulty in remembering that a run was reinforced by food. No detectable differences in latency and speed of running were observed, but, unfortunately, they were not measured. This possibility is now being specifically investigated.

The final question is, What is the nature of the learning deficit? One way of thinking about it might be by extending some of the concepts proposed by Hebb (1949) concerning the establishment of cell-assemblies, the neural substrate of early learning. If the memory trace be conceived of as a new pattern of connections established between the already existing assemblies, the following interpretation of the results can be given:

1. The physiological effects of stimulation will be thought of as analogous to interference; cortical cells, as well as cells in related structures, fired by reticular stimulation become unavailable to the memory traces which are in the process of being organized. This could well account for the deficit found in the first three experiments.

2. However, once organized and given sufficient time to undergo relatively stable changes, the neural systems become less vulnerable to disruption by the same pattern of bombardment from the reticular formation. Hence, no deficit was obtained when the onset of stimulation was delayed by 2 min. and 45 sec.

3. Such a consolidation process is, however, a relative matter and one of statistical probabilities. It may very well be that there are marked differences in the rate at which permanent changes occur over the different pathways of the memory trace as imagined here, so that a weak stimulus, as the one used in the present study, may affect some systems of neurons, leaving others intact. And there is enough evidence from the literature on electroconvulsive shocks (Duncan, 1949; Thompson, 1955) to suggest that a more powerful storm induced by convulsions would have been quite effective in erasing a memory trace of only 3-min. duration.

A final comment should be made about the lack of functional equipotentiality between the rostral and caudal portions of the reticular formation emphasized by the present results. It may well be that the current intensity used in the present experiments was too weak to obtain a detrimental effect from stimulation of the tegmentum, and there is evidence from Glickman's study (1958) that higher voltages did produce a deficit in an avoidance situation. However, it is also possible that the relative integrity of the two components of the reticular formation may be important at different stages of the learning process. This hypothesis, as well as the effects of stimulation *during* the response, are being at present investigated.

SUMMARY

The effects of low-intensity electrical stimulation on learning were studied in the rat, using a Hebb-Williams maze and a conditional situation on a T maze.

Stimulation was shown to have detrimental effects; these effects, however, appeared only when the animals were stimulated immediately after they had made a response, but not when there was a delay between the response and the onset of stimulation. Also, stimulation affected new rather than old learning and appeared to have detrimental effects in both types of task used.

The results also emphasized functional differences between the rostral and caudal portions of the reticular formation.

REFERENCES

COOPER, R. Nonspecific thalamic functions in learning. Unpublished doctoral dissertation, McGill University, 1961.

DUNCAN, C. P. The retroactive effect of electroshock on learning. *J. comp. physiol. Psychol.*, 1949, **42**, 32–44.

FORMAN, D., & WARD, J. W. Responses to electrical stimulation of caudate nucleus in cats in chronic experiments. *J. Neurophysiol.*, 1957, **20**, 230–244.

GLICKMAN, S. Deficits in avoidance learning produced by stimulation of the ascending reticular formation. *J. Canad. Psychol.*, 1958, **12**, 97–102.

HEBB, D. O. *Organization of behavior*. New York: Wiley, 1949.

KRIEG, W. J. S. Accurate placement of minute lesions in the brain of the albino rat. *Quart. Bull. Northwestern U. Med. School, Chicago*, 1946, **20**, 199–209.

MAGOUN, H. W. *The waking brain*. Springfield, Ill.: Charles C Thomas, 1958.

OLDS, J. Runway and maze behavior controlled by basomedial forebrain stimulation in the rat. *J. comp. physiol. Psychol.*, 1956, **49**, 507–512.

OLDS, J., & MILNER, P. M. Positive reinforcement produced by electrical stimulation of septal area and other regions of rat brain. *J. comp. physiol. Psychol.*, 1954, **47**, 419–427.

THOMPSON, R., & DEAN, W. A further study on the retroactive effect of ECS. *J. comp. physiol. Psychol.*, 1955, **48**, 488–491.

Retrograde Amnesia Produced by Anesthetic and Convulsant Agents

Chester A. Pearlman, Jr.,
Seth K. Sharpless,
and Murray E. Jarvik

The striking ability of electroconvulsive shock and other agents to impair retention of an acquired response has been the subject of numerous investigations. In general, it has been shown that the memory deficit is most extensive if the treatment is administered within a short time after the learning trial. The effective agents include concussion (Russell, 1959), convulsions (Zubin & Barrera, 1941), anoxia (Thompson, 1957), and direct electrical stimulation of specific brain structures (Glickman, 1958; Thompson, 1958). It is agreed that the interval during which such agents can exert significant retrograde effects is relatively short, a few hours at most. The concept of a consolidation process has been proposed to account for this period during which a memory is vulnerable, implying the perseveration of some form of neural activity after the learning trial which results in an increased stability of the memory trace.

The effects of anesthesia on recent memory are controversial. Although Leukel (1957) showed some impairment of learning in a water maze when thiopental was administered 1 min. after each daily trial, at least one author has expressed the opinion that rapidly induced anesthesia does not affect recent memory (Burns, 1958). According to this view, the process of consolidation can take place even when central synaptic transmission is severely depressed by anesthetic agents.

In studying the consolidation process, it is desirable to have precise control over the interval between the learning experience and the memory-disrupting event. This control is difficult to achieve in experiments involving

From *Journal of Comparative and Physiological Psychology*, 1961, **54**, 109–112. Reprinted with permission of the publisher and authors. This work was supported by Interdisciplinary Grant 2M-6418, National Institute of Mental Health; U.S. Public Health Service Grant M-1225; and National Science Foundation Grant G-4459.

practice and repetition of learning trials. Glickman (1958) adapted the one-trial avoidance learning procedure of Hudson (1950) to study the effects of brain stimulation on consolidation. In the present experiment, a similar design was used to compare the effects of convulsant and anesthetic drugs on consolidation. Additional control of the interval between learning experience and drug treatment was achieved by administering the drugs, where appropriate, through permanently indwelling, intravenous catheters.

METHOD

SUBJECTS

Eighty-five naive male rats of the Sprague-Dawley strain were used. They were received in four separate samples; animals in each sample were 90 to 120 days old at the beginning of the experiment.

PROCEDURE

TRAINING. The procedure involved the suppression of a previously learned bar-pressing response as the result of a single electric shock administered through the bar. The animals were trained to press a bar for water on a continuous reinforcement schedule. They were maintained on a $23\frac{1}{2}$-hr. water-deprivation schedule and trained for 10 min. a day until a stable rate of pressing was attained. The criterion of stability was that the number of presses on the final day of training should not deviate by more than 10% from the mean of the previous three days. On the day after achievement of the criterion, an avoidance response was established by electrifying the bar and reward nozzle with 750 v. through 750,000 ohms after the animal had been in the apparatus for 5 min.

TREATMENT. In some animals, chronically indwelling catheters were inserted in the external jugular vein and then run subcutaneously to an incision just below the base of the skull. A more detailed description of the procedure appears elsewhere (Sharpless, 1959). Since the catheters remained patent for about two weeks, the animals were allowed two days of rest after the operation and then tested for retention of the stability criterion before being subjected to the avoidance training.

The Ss were divided into groups of five animals for treatment. Three groups were anesthetized with ether at approximately 10 sec., 5 min., and 10 min. after the shock, respectively. Anesthesia was induced by placing the rat under an inverted beaker containing cotton saturated with ether. Surgical anesthesia was produced in about 35 sec., and the animals recovered to their normal state of arousal within 10 min.

Sodium pentobarbital (30 mg/kg) was administered through the intravenous catheters to four groups, at approximately 20 sec., 5 min., 10 min., and 20 min. after the shock. Surgical anesthesia was produced within 10 sec. after the injection and persisted for about an hour. An attempt was made to produce roughly equivalent depths of anesthesia in all groups, as indicated by superficial (conjunctival and pinna) reflexes.

In five groups, pentylenetetrazol (Metrazol, 20 mg/kg) was injected through the catheters about 20 sec. after the shock or intraperitoneally 2 hr., 4 hr., 8 hr., and 4 days after the shock. All injections of pentylenetetrazol produced a clonic-tonic-clonic seizure in which the clonic activity persisted for about 4 min.

Table 1 Rate of Bar-Pressing During Test for Retention of Avoidance Response After Drug Treatment Expressed as Percentage of Initial Rate of Pressing (Mean Values for Groups of 5; SD in parentheses)

TIME INTERVAL BETWEEN SHOCK AND DRUG TREATMENT	ETHER	PENTO-BARBITAL	PENTYLENE-TETRAZOL	CONTROL (NO DRUG)
Control (no shock)	100% (3)	98% (5)	99% (3)	—
10 sec.	36% (4)[b]	76% (5)[b]	100% (6)[b]	2% (2)
5 min.	17% (6)[b]	48% (4)[b]	—	—
10 min.	4% (2)	23% (4)[b]	—	—
20 min.	—	˙1% (1)	—	—
2 hr.	—	—	94% (8)[b]	—
4 hr.	—	—	98% (5)[b]	—
8 hr.	—	—	92% (7)[b]	—
4 days	—	—	70% (19)[a,b]	1% (1)[a]

[a] These two groups were tested for retention five days after the shock. Other groups were tested 24 hr. after the shock.
[b] Significantly different from untreated control group ($p < .01$).

RETENTION.   The experimental groups were tested for retention of the avoidance response 24 hr. after the shock, with the exception of the group receiving pentylenetetrazol four days after the shock. These animals were tested for retention one day after being convulsed (i.e., five days after the original avoidance learning). Loss of the avoidance response was measured by expressing each animal's performance as a percentage of its normal rate of pressing. The latter value was calculated by averaging the results of the last four days of training before the shock.

CONTROLS.   As shown in Table 1, five groups served as controls. The animals in three of these groups received no shock but were given the various drugs and tested 24 hr. later to determine whether there were any delayed effects of the drugs on the bar-pressing response which might obscure the results. The remaining two groups were given the shock but no drug. They were tested either one day or five days later in order to measure the retention of the avoidance response in the absence of pharmacological interference.

The statistical significance of the data was evaluated by the Mann-Whitney U test.

RESULTS

The mean value for each group is shown in Table 1. Failure to avoid (i.e., loss of memory due to drug treatment) is indicated by a high rate of pressing and a high percentage score.

Animals given ether within 5 min. and those given pentobarbital within 10 min. after the shock show significantly less avoidance than the unanesthetized controls, and each pentobarbital group shows significantly less avoidance than the corresponding ether group ($p < .01$).

Pentylenetetrazol given up to 8 hr. after the shock completely suppressed the avoidance response. Animals convulsed as long as four days after the shock still showed significantly less avoidance than untreated controls tested after the same interval ($p < .01$).

DISCUSSION

Anesthesia induced within a few minutes after a learning trial impaired retention of an avoidance response acquired during that trial. Moreover, the effect was graded, dependent upon the time elapsing between the learning experience and the induction of anesthesia. Pentobarbital was more effective than ether in impairing retention and was effective for a longer time after the learning trial.

The greater potency of pentobarbital anesthesia in interfering with recent memory may be due to the longer sleeping time induced by this agent— about an hour as compared with 10 min. for ether. Russell (1959) observed that the extent of retrograde amnesia following head injury was roughly correlated with the duration of posttraumatic amnesia, which may be a measure of the duration of abnormal cerebral function. It is difficult to judge depth of anesthesia by superficial reflexes, however, and it is possible that the initial level of anesthesia was deeper with pentobarbital than with ether.

Previous evidence concerning the effects of anesthetic agents on memory is ambiguous. Artusio (1955) has shown that there is a stage of anesthesia with ether at which patients are unable to form new memories although their mental function is intact as measured by response to spoken voice, problem solving, old memory, etc. Orkin, Bergman, and Nathanson (1956) reported similar results with thiopental. In the experiment of Leukel (1957), referred to previously, intraperitoneal injection of thiopental 1 min. after each daily trial produced impairment, whereas thiopental given 30 min. after the trial had no such effect.

On the other hand, Summerfield and Steinberg (1959) report that the anesthetic gas, nitrous oxide, actually improves memory for nonsense syllables when it is given after learning and continued until just before recall. Ether (Hunt, Jernberg, & Lawlor, 1953) and pentobarbital (Siegel, McGinnies, & Box, 1949) have been reported to protect against some of the amnesic effects of electroconvulsive shock.

It is probable that a general anesthetic can have two effects on memory. When given after consolidation is more or less complete, the anesthetic may reduce interference and retroactive inhibition and thus conserve the memory trace ; when given within a few minutes after the learning experience, it may block the consolidation process before the memory has attained stability and permanence. In addition, the observations of Artusio (1955) suggest that the consolidation process may be selectively impaired in the absence of generalized depression of cerebral function.

In the present study, very marked impairment of retention was produced by a single pentylenetetrazol convulsion 8 hr. and even *four days* after the learning trial. This is in contrast with the results with anesthesia, where the maximum interference time was approximately 15 min. It is difficult to avoid the conclusion that the mode of interference is different when the disturbing event occurs within a few minutes of the learning trial and when it occurs days later. In the first case, the disturbing event disrupts a consolidation process, which requires only a few hours at most to bring the memory to a stable, permanent condition. In the case of impairment of memory by a single convulsion or multiple convulsions days after the initial learning, it is likely that a different process is involved. It would be in accord with both clinical experience and previous experimental studies to expect that in the latter case, the memory impairment would be temporary and concomitant with the confusional state that comes as the aftermath to convulsant therapy (Brady, 1952; Kalinowsky & Hoch, 1946).

In previous studies, if convulsive treatment was not begun until a day or more after the acquisition of an emotional response, many convulsions were required to produce significant impairment of retention. Why a single convulsion was so effective in the present experiment is an interesting question. Perhaps the emotional response acquired in this situation was relatively weak since it was established in a single trial by an easily escaped shock from the bar of the Skinner box rather than the customary inescapable grid shock repeated several times. The fact that the convulsion was induced by pentylenetetrazol rather than electric shock may also be relevant, but clinical experience suggests that there is no difference in the degree of memory impairment produced by the various convulsant agents (Kalinowsky & Hoch, 1946).

SUMMARY AND CONCLUSIONS

Rats were trained to press a bar for water. They were then taught to avoid the bar in a single trial during which they received a shock through the bar when they touched it. At various intervals after learning the animals were subjected to ether or pentobarbital anesthesia or a pentylenetetrazol convulsion. A day later, they were tested for retention of the avoidance response with the following results:

1. Surgical anesthesia severely impaired retention of the avoidance response if the anesthesia were induced within 10 to 15 min. after the learning trial.

2. Intravenous pentobarbital was more effective than ether in producing this retrograde amnesia.

3. A single pentylenetetrazol convulsion abolished the avoidance response when as much as 8 hr. intervened between learning and treatment and markedly depressed the response even when the interval between learning and convulsion was increased to four days.

4. It was concluded that the consolidation process, at least in its initial stages, is incompatible with a state of surgical anesthesia.

5. Interference with memory by convulsions occurring hours or days after the learning trial probably depends upon a different mechanism, related to the clinically observed sequelae of convulsive treatment, which are characterized by various transient derangements including confusion and memory lacunae.

REFERENCES

ARTUSIO, J. F. Ether analgesia during major surgery. *J. Amer. Med. Ass.*, 1955, **157**, 33–36.

BRADY, J. V. The effect of electroconvulsive shock on a conditioned emotional response: The significance of the interval between the emotional conditioning and the electroconvulsive shock. *J. comp. physiol. Psychol.*, 1952, **45**, 9–13.

BURNS, B. C. *The mammalian cerebral cortex.* London: Arnold, 1958.

GLICKMAN, S. E. Deficits in avoidance learning produced by stimulation of the ascending reticular formation. *Canad. J. Psychol.*, 1958, **12**, 97–102.

HUDSON, B. B. One-trial learning in the domestic rat. *Genet. psychol. Monogr.*, 1950, **41**, 99–143.

HUNT, H. F., JERNBERG, P., & LAWLOR, W. G. The effect of electroconvulsive shock on a conditioned emotional response: The effect of electroconvulsive shock under ether anesthesia. *J. comp. physiol. Psychol.*, 1953, **46**, 64–68.

KALINOWSKY, L. B., & HOCH, P. H. *Shock treatments and other somatic procedures in psychiatry.* New York: Grune & Stratton, 1946.

LEUKEL, F. A comparison of the effects of ECS and anesthesia on acquisition of the maze habit. *J. comp. physiol. Psychol.*, 1957, **50**, 300–306.

ORKIN, L., BERGMAN, P. S., & NATHANSON, M. Effect of atropine, scopolamine, and meperidine on man. *Anesthesiology*, 1956, **17**, 30–37.

RUSSELL, W. R. *Brain: Memory and learning.* London: Oxford Univer. Press, 1959.

SHARPLESS, S. K. The effect of intravenous epinephrine and norepinephrine on a conditioned response in the cat. *Psychopharmacologia*, 1959, **1**, 140–149.

SIEGEL, P. S., MCGINNIES, E. M., & BOX, J. C. Runway performance of rats subjected to electro-convulsive shock following nembutal anesthesia. *J. comp. physiol. Psychol.*, 1949, **42**, 417–422.

SUMMERFIELD, A., & STEINBERG, H. Using drugs to alter memory experimentally in man. In P. B. Bradley, P. Deniker & C. Radouco-Thomas (Eds.), *Neuropsychopharmacology.* Amsterdam: Elsevier, 1959. Pp. 481–483.

THOMPSON, R. The comparative effects of ECS and anoxia on memory. *J. comp. physiol. Psychol.*, 1957, **50**, 397–400.

THOMPSON, R. The effect of intracranial stimulation on memory in cats. *J. comp. physiol. Psychol.*, 1958, **51**, 421–426.

ZUBIN, J., & BARRERA, S. E. Effect of electroconvulsive therapy on memory. *Proc. Soc. Exp. Biol., N Y*, 1941, **48**, 596–597.

II

THE PROBLEM OF WHAT: THE NATURE OF THE STRUCTURAL CHANGE IN LEARNING

The neural basis of permanent, long-term memory can hardly be electrical, since memory can survive cessation or violent disturbance of electrical activity produced by hibernation, cooling, ECS, and deep anesthesia. It therefore must involve a structural change. Structural theories of learning have been divided into interneuronal, intraneuronal, and extraneuronal. Interneuronal theories postulate growth or movement at the synapse (for example, Hebb, 1949) or changes in synaptic resistance (for example, Eccles, 1959) to be the basis of learning. The more recent intraneuronal (neurochemical) theories of learning suggest that proteins, RNA or DNA, are involved in memory storage (for example, Hyden, 1963). Most extraneuronal theories (for example, Galambos, 1961) involve glia, those ubiquitous denizens of the central nervous system (there are about ten for every neuron). These theories are not really alternatives. Any intraneuronal or extraneuronal change must act through interneuronal mechanisms; any interneuronal change must involve intraneuronal events and perhaps extraneuronal ones as well.

Although the search for structural changes in learning is not a new one, it is only in the last few years that *any* anatomical changes have been found to occur in the nervous system of adult mammals. For example, Liu and Chambers (1958) showed considerable sprouting of axon collaterals after spinal-cord injury; and Rose, Malis, and Baker (1961) destroyed a single cortical layer and showed that new fibers subsequently invaded the zone of destruction from adjacent layers. Although both situations were "abnormal" and very different from learning, they do demonstrate that neuron growth can occur in adult mammals.

Experience alone produced changes in brain chemistry and histology in the series of experiments by Rosenzweig and his collaborators (1966) described in the first article of this part (see page 66). These investigators showed that rats kept in complex environments had thicker and heavier cerebral cortex than rats kept under standard laboratory conditions. The cortex of the rich-environment rats had more glial cells but a similar number of neurons. Since glia (but not neurons) multiply in adult rats and glia seem to be intimately involved in neuron function, the greater number of glia might reflect neuron growth. As Rosenzweig acknowledges, his studies may also be open to accusations of pathology. The differences between his groups may have reflected pathological changes in the "standard" rats, whose environment was very unnatural, rather than enhancement by the relatively normal "rich" environment of his "enriched" group. That is, the thicker cortex may have been normal and the "normal" cortex pathologic.

In the past five years, there has been a rapid growth of interest in the neurochemistry of learning. In the 1950's a number of scientists such as Linus Pauling, Ralph Gerard, and Warren Halstead began to publish speculations that protein molecules were likely candidates for the substrate of learning and memory. This molecular approach to memory gained widespread interest only after the dramatic discoveries in molecular biology that followed Watson and Crick's paper in 1953 suggesting the structure of DNA and its fundamental role. Not only did DNA contain the genetic material, but through RNA it controlled protein synthesis in the cell and thus all life processes. If DNA and RNA were involved in genetic memory and in immunological memory, then why not behavioral memory as well? In their critical review "Molecular Theories of Memory," Dingman and Sporn (see page 87) consider the current evidence for a specific role of macromolecules in memory and find it rather feeble. As they point out, RNA is of course involved in behavior; it is crucial for all cellular mechanisms. However, whether it or any other giant molecule plays a unique role in the encoding of experience is still unknown.

Although a specific coding role for RNA or any other macromolecule has not been unequivocally demonstrated, certain drugs which are known to affect protein synthesis do have behavioral effects. One of these is the antibiotic puromycin. In the final paper of this section, Flexner (see page 95) describes his studies on the effects of puromycin on retention of a Y-maze habit by mice. Flexner and his colleagues found that injections of puromycin into the temporal regions of the brain the day after learning wiped out memory for the task, whereas after a week it was necessary to inject several brain areas to impair memory, as if the engram had spread. They suggest that puromycin may have specific effects on memory through inhibition of protein synthesis. However, a problem with this interpretation is raised by the recent report by Cohen and Barondes (1967) that puromycin produces seizure activity which may be the basis of its amnesic effect rather than any direct interference with protein synthesis.

C.G.G.

REFERENCES

COHEN, H. D., & BARONDES, S. H. Puromycin effect on memory may be due to occult seizures. *Science*, 1967, **157**, 333–334.

ECCLES, J. C. *The neurophysiological basis of mind.* Oxford: Oxford University Press, 1953.

GALAMBOS, R. A glia-neural theory of brain function. *Proc. Nat. Acad. Sci.*, 1961, **57**, 129–136.

HEBB, D. O. *The organization of behavior: A neuropsychological theory.* New York: Wiley, 1949.

HYDEN, H., & EGYHAZ, E. Nuclear RNA changes of nerve cells during a learning experiment in rats. *Proc. Nat. Acad. Sci.*, 1963, **49**, 618–624.

LIU, C. N., & CHAMBERS, W. W. Intraspinal sprouting of dorsal root axons. *Arch. Neurol. Psychiat.*, 1958, **79**, 49–61.

ROSE, J. E., MALIS, L. I., & BAKER, C. P. Neural growth in the cerebral cortex after lesions produced by monoenergetic deuterons. In W. A. Rosenblith (Ed.), *Sensory communication.* Cambridge, Mass.: M.I.T. Press, 1961. Pp. 279–301.

WATSON, J. D., & CRICK, F. H. C. Molecular structure of nucleic acids. *Nature*, 1953, **171**, 737–738.

Environmental Complexity, Cerebral Change, and Behavior

Mark R. Rosenzweig

Relating brain processes to behavior in animals is the subject of this paper. Addressing an audience not from my own special field reminds me of the animal psychologist who presented a paper at a psychoanalytic meeting. At the end of the paper, one of the psychoanalysts grumbled, "We knew all this already." "Yes," a colleague placated him, "but we didn't know that it was true of *rats*!" In my own case, I hope that you will neither reject this research as irrelevant to your own nor, on the other hand, apply it uncritically to work in human behavior and development. Therefore, after presenting the main findings, I will want to discuss with you the possible significance of such work for the study of human behavior.

The research has been done by a team in which Edward L. Bennett, a biochemist, David Krech, a psychologist, and I have collaborated for a dozen years. More recently we have been joined by Marian C. Diamond, a neuroanatomist. The overall scope of our program concerns both hereditary and environmental factors that have been demonstrated to affect learning ability. We have been attempting to determine whether they do so by affecting the anatomy and chemistry of the brain. Today I will concentrate on these questions: Can differential experience modify the brain in measurable anatomical and chemical terms? If so, can these cerebral changes be related to the effects of experience on learning ability?

The suggestion that thinking might induce growth of the brain is an old one, dating back at least to the late eighteenth century (Sömmering, 1791). In

From *American Psychologist*, 1966, **21**, 321–332. Reprinted with permission of the publisher and author. Abbreviated version of an address given to the Division of Developmental Psychology at American Psychological Association, Chicago, September 1965. This research has been supported by grants or contracts from the National Institute of Mental Health, U.S. Public Health Service; the Surgeon General's Office; and the National Aeronautics and Space Agency. It has also received support from the U.S. Atomic Energy Commission.

the early nineteenth century, the phrenologist Spurzheim (1815) held it highly probable that "the organs [of the brain] increase by exercise." Showing more caution than usual, Spurzheim added, "In order, however, to be able to answer this question positively, we ought to observe the same persons when exercised and when not exercised; or at least observe many persons who are, and many others who are not, exercised during all periods of life [pp. 554–555]." This idea has recurred from time to time; essentially the same research proposal was made a century and a half later by the anatomist J. Z. Young (1964, p. 272).

EXPERIMENTAL PROGRAM

Procedures

In our research on this question starting in 1958, we followed essentially the design suggested by Spurzheim. However, we benefited from many intervening investigations demonstrating that the brain is relatively stable and not likely to show large changes—a fact of which Sömmering (1785) was already aware. Because the cerebral effects that we hoped to induce might be small at best, we employed procedures that we hoped would *maximize* these effects of experience and that would *minimize* variability from extraneous sources.

In an attempt to maximize the effects of differential experience on the brain, we decided to set up two markedly different experimental situations, to put the rats in one or the other at an early age when their brains might be most plastic, and to maintain the animals in these situations for a prolonged period. Animals are therefore assigned at weaning (about 25 days of age) and kept for 80 days in either an enriched environment—environmental complexity and training (ECT)—or in an impoverished condition (IC). These conditions have been described in some detail elsewhere (Krech, Rosenzweig, & Bennett, 1960), so only a summary description will be given here. In the enriched situation the animals are housed in groups of 10 to 12 in a large cage that is provided with "toys" such as ladders, wheels, boxes, platforms, etc. The toys are selected each day from a larger group. To enrich the rats' experience further, we give them a daily half-hour exploratory session in groups of 5 or 6. This takes place in a 3- by 3-foot field with a pattern of barriers that is changed daily. Rat pups are as playful and as amusing to watch as kittens in these situations. After about 30 days in this permissive free play environment, some formal training is given in a series of mazes. In the home cage they have food and water ad lib. Thus these animals are stimulated by their cagemates, by their complex environment, and by trials in several apparatuses.

Each ECT animal has a littermate assigned to the impoverished condition. Here animals live in individual cages with solid side walls, so that an animal cannot see or touch another. These cages are placed in a separate, quiet, dimly lighted room, while the ECT cages are in a large, brightly lighted room with considerable incidental activity. The IC rats have food and water ad lib and, like their ECT brothers, they are weighed about once a week. In some experiments there is also an intermediate group in which animals are kept under standard-colony (SC) conditions, three to a cage and without any special handling or training.

In order to minimize variability from extraneous sources, we have consistently observed the following precautions: In any given experiment, animals of only one strain, age, and sex are used. (In most cases, they are males.) All comparisons are made between littermates. The littermates are assigned randomly between the experimental conditions, so that no initial bias can enter. All brain analyses are carried out under code numbers that do not reveal the experimental treatment, so that no analytical bias can affect the results.

At the end of the behavioral phase of an experiment, the brains are removed and, in most cases, divided by gross dissection into five samples (see Figure 1 in Rosenzweig, Krech, Bennett, & Diamond, 1962). With the aid of a small calibrated plastic T square, a sample of the visual cortex is first circumscribed and then peeled off from the underlying white matter. Next, a sample of the somesthetic cortex is removed. The third sample is the remaining dorsal cortex. (In the rat, cortex can be separated from the white matter much more readily and accurately than is the case in the cat or dog or primate.) The fourth sample includes ventral cortex and associated tissues such as the hippocampus, the amygdaloid nuclei, and the corpus callosum; by weight, it is about two-thirds hippocampus. The fifth and final sample consists of all the rest of the brain after the cortex and associated tissues have been removed. This final sample includes not only the core of the cerebral hemispheres, but also the olfactory bulbs, the midbrain, the cerebellum, and the medulla.

Results

Anatomical Effects. Our first attempts were to measure effects of experience on brain chemistry. Brain anatomy was disregarded, since we had inherited the dogma of absolute stability of brain weight. Fortunately, we had to record the weights of our brain samples in order to measure chemical activity per unit of tissue weight. After about 2 years of contemplating the chemical effects, we finally realized that the weights of the brain samples were also being altered by the environmental manipulations (Rosenzweig et al., 1962). It will be simpler to present the weight effects first.

The results demonstrate that the ECT rats consistently develop greater weight of cerebral cortex than do their impoverished littermates, as Table 1 shows. Here all four cortical samples are pooled into total cortex for simplicity of exposition. This table is based on 130 littermate pairs of male rats of the S_1 strain; they were run in 12 experiments conducted over a 5-year period. Overall, the cortex of the enriched rats weighs 4% more than that of the

Table 1   Effects of Enriched (ECT) and Impoverished (IC) Conditions on Brain
Weights of 130 Littermate Pairs of S₁ Rats Run from 25 to 105 Days of Age

	TOTAL CORTEX		REST OF BRAIN	
	M	*SD*	*M*	*SD*
ECT	698	31	939	39
IC	671	30	952	40
No. pairs				
ECT > IC[a]	101/130		54/130	
ECT/IC[a,b]	1.040		.987	
p[c]	< .001		< .01	

[a] Number of littermate pairs in which the ECT value exceeds the IC value.
[b] The value for each ECT animal was divided by that of its IC littermate, and the mean of these ratios was then calculated.
[c] Determined by analyses of variance.

restricted rats ($p < .001$), and four-fifths of the pairs show a difference in this direction. The standard deviation is small, being only about 4% of the mean. The rest of the brain does not show the gain in weight with experience that is characteristic of the cortex. Several other strains of rats have also been used in such experiments, and they have yielded similar results. It is worth noting that we probably would not have noticed any effect if we had not analyzed separately the cortex and the rest of the brain.

Now, let us look at a distribution of weight differences between littermates (Figure 1). Each square represents the difference in cortical weight between the two members of a littermate pair. It is clear that the mean difference cannot be attributed to some aberrant animals but rather that the entire distribution has been shifted to one side by the experimental treatment.

Although the ECT animals are greater in cortical weight, they are about 7% less in body weight than the IC animals. If we were to express brain weight in terms of body weight or to correct for differences in body weight, this would enlarge the effects that we have reported. As Sömmering (1778) noted long ago, body weight can fluctuate rather widely due to many factors, and he suggested expressing the weight of one part of the brain in terms of another part. If we take the ratio of weight of total cortex to that of the rest of the brain, we obtain the results shown in Figure 2. Here we see that the cortical/subcortical weight ratio is consistently greater for the enriched than for the restricted rats, 90% of the differences being in favor of the ECT member of a pair ($p < .001$).

Not only does the cortex differ from the rest of the brain in its response to differential experience, but the regions of the cortex do not participate equally, as Table 2 demonstrates. With our standard ECT and IC situations, the occipital region shows the largest changes in weight, amounting to 6% ($p < .001$). The nearby somesthetic region shows the smallest differences,

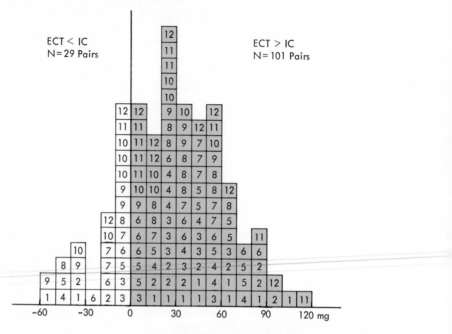

Fig. 1. Differences in cortical weight between the enriched-experience (ECT) and impoverished (IC) members of 130 littermate pairs of S₁ rats. (Each square represents the weight difference, in milligrams, between the members of a pair. The data came from 12 successive experiments, and the number in each square is the number of the experiment. In each of the experiments, most of the cases will be seen to lie on the right-hand side; i.e., the ECT animal has greater weight of total cortex than does its IC brother.)

Table 2   Effects of ECT and IC in Weights (Milligrams) of Four Cortical Tissue Samples of 130 Littermate Pairs of S₁ Rats Run from 25 to 105 Days of Age

	VISUAL		SO-MESTHETIC		REMAINING DORSAL		VENTRAL	
	M	*SD*	*M*	*SD*	*M*	*SD*	*M*	*SD*
ECT	65.0	4.2	51.2	3.1	282.1	17.0	299.3	22.7
IC	61.3	4.6	50.3	3.1	269.2	15.6	290.0	22.7
No. pairs ECT > IC	97/130		78/130		96/130		84/130	
ECT/IC	1.061		1.019		1.048		1.032	
p	< .001		< .05		< .001		< .001	

amounting to 2% ($p < .05$). Further experiments that we have done indicate that it is possible to modify selectively one or another region of the cortex, depending upon the particular program of enrichment used. For example, raising rats in the dark results in measurable shrinkage of the visual cortex. If the environment is complex, the dark-raised rats develop heavier somesthetic areas than light-raised littermates. Thus the effects are opposite in the visual and somesthetic regions. Time will not allow us to consider these specific regional effects further here, although I will later make a suggestion for human research based upon them.

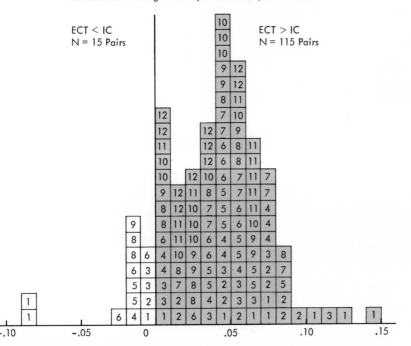

Differences in Weight Ratios, Total Cortex/Rest of Brain

Fig. 2. Differences between ECT and IC littermates in the ratio of weight of total cortex to weight of the rest of the brain. (Each square represents the differences in this ratio between the two members of a pair. The data are based on the same animals as in Figure 1. The numbers inside the squares indicate in which of the 12 replication experiments a pair of animals was run.)

The greater weight of the cortex of the stimulated rats reflects greater thickness of cortex, as we found in independent experiments. In these experiments we made anatomical sections of the brains, rather than consuming the tissue for chemical analyses. Depth has been measured in a standard part of the occipital area. The results of four experiments (Table 3) demonstrate that the cerebral cortex becomes significantly thicker in the ECT rats than in

Table 3 Depths (μ) of Visual Cortex from ECT and IC Rats (Excluding Layer I)

EXPERIMENT	N (PAIRS)	ECT		IC		ECT/IC	p	NO. PAIRS ECT/IC
		M	SD	M	SD			
				FROZEN SECTIONS (25 μ)				
I	11	1332	56	1271	73	1.048	<.01	9/11
II	9	1404	87	1298	81	1.082	<.001	9/9
I & II	20	1364	72	1284	76	1.062	<.001	18/20
				CELLOIDIN SECTIONS (10 μ)				
III	12	813	35	779	38	1.044	<.05	11/12
IV	9	844	35	772	36	1.093	<.001	9/9
III & IV	21	826	38	776	35	1.064	<.001	20/21

their IC littermates. The outermost layer of the cortex shows no change, so it has been excluded from these data. For the remaining layers, the overall effect amounts to 6 % ($p < .001$). Preliminary measures indicate that the hippocampus also becomes thicker as a consequence of enriched experience. So the whole gray bark of the brain grows thicker with enriched experience.

In one experiment (Diamond, Krech, & Rosenzweig, 1964) we measured the diameter of capillaries in the cortex, and we found the average diameter to be greater in the ECT animals than in their IC littermates. Other investigators have found that with acclimatization to high altitude, the cortical capillaries of the rat increase in diameter (Opitz, 1951). Apparently, then, the anatomy of the cerebral vasculature can respond adaptively to increased demand.

Biochemical Effects.   Much of our biochemical work has concerned the enzyme acetylcholinesterase (AChE). This enzyme is important at those central synapses where acetylcholine is the chemical transmitter that conveys messages from one neuron to the next. Enzymes are measured in terms of their activity; one can consider either the total activity in a sample or the activity per unit of weight of the sample. The total activity of AChE is found to increase slightly but consistently in the ECT animals, both in the cortex and in the rest of the brain (Table 4). In the cortex, this increase in enzymatic activity is less than the increase in tissue weight, so the activity per unit weight decreases in the ECT animals.

Table 4   Effects of ECT and IC on Total AChE Activity in 130 Littermate
Pairs of S₁ Rats Run from 25 to 105 Days of Age

	TOTAL CORTEX		REST OF BRAIN	
	M	*SD*	*M*	*SD*
ECT	6,358	392	18,734	938
IC	6,231	323	18,475	977
No. pairs				
ECT > IC	81/128		82/130	
ECT/IC	1.020		1.014	
p	< .001		< .01	

Note.—Activity measured in terms of mμmoles acetylthiocholine hydrolyzed/min.

Now there are other enzymes in the brain that can also act on acetylcholine, although less specifically than does AChE. These other enzymes are known collectively as cholinesterase (ChE). In the rat, there is relatively little ChE activity, but we wanted to be certain that the effects we were measuring could not be attributed to ChE. Therefore, we measured ChE activity independently. These measures confirmed our previously reported AChE effects, since there is too little ChE activity to affect the AChE values. Unexpectedly, these new measures also showed that ChE activity was being modified by differential experience and according to its own pattern (Table 5). Total ChE activity is up by 8 % in the cortex of the ECT rats, while showing no change in the rest of the brain.

Let us summarize these effects by showing results for 88 littermate pairs of S_1 rats for whom we have both enzymatic measures (Figure 3). Note that at the cortex, tissue weight and the total activity of both enzymes increase significantly,

Table 5   Effects of ECT and IC on Total ChE Activity in 89
Littermate Pairs of S₁ Rats Run from 25 to 105 Days of Age

	TOTAL CORTEX		REST OF BRAIN	
	M	SD	M	SD
ECT	231	13	551	27
IC	214	14	552	25
No. pairs				
ECT > IC		80/88		41/88
ECT/IC		1.078		0.998
p		< .001		NS

Note.—Activity measured in terms of mμmoles butyrylthiocholine hydrolyzed/min.

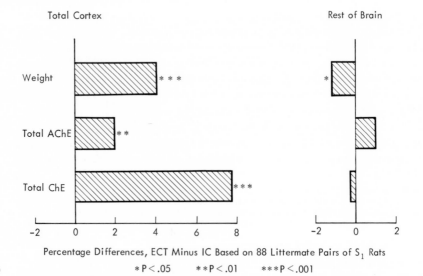

Percentage Differences, ECT Minus IC Based on 88 Littermate Pairs of S_1 Rats

*P < .05   **P < .01   ***P < .001

Fig. 3. Percentage differences between ECT and IC littermates in tissue weight, total activity of AChE and of ChE. (The data were obtained from 88 littermate pairs of S₁ rats. Results are shown separately for total cortex and for the rest of the brain. In the cortex, total activity of AChE is seen to increase significantly but by a lesser percentage than does tissue weight; total activity of ChE increases by a greater percentage than does weight.)

but with the percentage change in AChE lagging beyond that in tissue weight, while the percentage change in ChE surpasses the change in weight. Note also that, on these measures at least, the cortex is clearly more responsive to the environmental influences than is the rest of the brain.

In other experiments we have taken further chemical measures. These have included total protein, the enzyme hexokinase, and RNA. In all these further regards, the chemical measures per unit of tissue weight are unchanged. That is to say, the cortex added as a consequence of enriched experience is normal in these respects and is unusual only in the relative activities of AChE and ChE.

In seeking to understand what these enzymatic changes might mean, it occurred to us that neurons contain chiefly AChE, while the glial cells contain chiefly the less specific enzyme ChE. The glia had long been regarded simply as structural members, supporting the neurons, but there have been many recent indications that glia may play an active role in the brain. It has also been known that the number of nerve cells, like the number of muscle cells, is fixed at birth or soon thereafter, but glia may multiply. We therefore sought to determine whether the increased bulk of cortex as a consequence of experience might be due, in part at least, to proliferation of glia. This sent us back to anatomy, now at a cellular level.

Histological Results. To test this possibility, we made counts of neurons and of glia in a specified region of the occipital cortex. In order to obtain a satisfactory degree of reliability in such counts, we devised a procedure in which photographic enlargements were made of the anatomical slides, and two anatomists made independent counts. The results of these cell counts in two experiments are given in Table 6. The number of neurons within the region measured shows a slight decrease for the ECT rats. Presumably this decrease in packing density occurs because the number of neurons is fixed, and they are forced somewhat further apart as the cortex expands. The glia, on the contrary, increase significantly in number, and the ratio of glia to neurons then also increases. Both our chemical and anatomical findings therefore

Table 6   *Effects of ECT and IC on Neural and Glial Counts in 17 Littermate Pairs of S₁ Rats Run from 25 to 105 Days of Age (Visual Cortex)*

	M NO. NEURONS	*M* NO. GLIA	*M* GLIA/NEURON RATIO
ECT	485.8	185.4	.385
IC	500.6	162.8	.332
No. pairs			
ECT > IC	6/17	13/17	12/17
ECT/IC	.970	1.139	1.160
p	NS	< .01	< .02 W

demonstrate that one response of the brain to heightened environmental demands is a proliferation of glia. This conclusion has recently been supported by Altman and Das (1964), using a different measure of glial proliferation.

What the increase in the number of glia cells means in the functioning of the brain is not clear, since the role of the glia is a subject of active research and controversy. Here are two possibilities, among many that could be advanced: If the glia help to nourish the neurons, as has been suggested, then increasing the functional load on the neurons may raise their metabolic turnover and thus require more glial support. Again, it is possible that the branches of the neurons ramify more completely during learning. (We are attempting to test this in some experiments in progress.) Since the glia form the sheaths around neural processes, more branching may require more glia.

Control Experiments. Granting that the brain adapts anatomically and chemically to the differential environments, we still need to determine to what extent various features of the environments are responsible for the effects. Is it possible, for example, that unintended features have played an important role? And if the effects *are* due to complexity of experience, what relative weights should be attached to the social grouping, to the varied cage environment, and to the formal training?

We have done some experiments to test possible effects of differential amounts of locomotion and of handling.[1] The ECT animals are handled every day and they engage in more locomotor activity than do their IC brothers. The results indicate that neither handling nor differential locomotion nor a combination of the two is responsible for the effects we have reported.

The possibility that our effects are due to isolation stress rather than to enrichment of experience must also be considered. The difference in cortical weight, for example, might be caused either by an *increase* in the ECT group, or by a *decrease* in the IC group, or by a combination of both effects. There are reports in the literature that isolated rats become aggressive and less healthy than animals kept in groups. Rats of our strains do not become aggressive in isolation; you can still pick them up easily with bare hands after they have endured months of isolation. Nor do they show poor health; they actually gain somewhat more weight than their ECT littermates. Nevertheless, the cerebral effects might be due principally to isolation. To test this, we employed a colony comparison group in some experiments. The brain values of these SC rats were found to be intermediate between those of their ECT and IC littermates, just as their environment was intermediate. But the SC values were generally closer to those of the isolated rats, indicating that isolation is less important than enviromental complexity in producing the differences we have seen between ECT and IC groups.

---

[1] For indications that handling can affect certain physiological variables and physical development, see chapters by Levine, Schaeffer, Casler, and Maier in Newton and Levine (1966).

In further experiments we have intensified the environmental impoverishment and have produced still greater cerebral differences from the ECT animals. These experiments with more stringent impoverishment were carried out in the Space Sciences Laboratory of the University of California. Each isolation cage was suspended in an individual box lined with fibreglass, and the boxes were placed in a sound-insulated room. Figure 4 gives values of weight and of AChE activity per unit of weight for visual cortex and for total cortex. It demonstrates that the animals isolated in extreme impoverishment (IEI) differ more from ECT littermates than do the animals in our usual IC condition; the animals in the SC condition differ least of all from their ECT littermates. Thus, the greater the difference in environments, the greater the resultant differences in brain anatomy and chemistry.

One of our graduate students, Robert Slagle, is now trying to unravel some of the complexities of the ECT program to decide what the various features contribute to the overall results. It is too early to give definitive results, but here are some preliminary indications: Simply putting the animals in groups of 12 in a large cage accounts for part of the cerebral effects, and equipping the cage with toys adds more. The inclusion of two training trials a day in various mazes adds relatively little. Whether intensified formal training without group living will produce brain growth is the subject of further experiments, both in progress and projected.

Effects in Adult Animals.   One of the procedures in all the experiments that I have described so far was to put the animals into the differential situations rather young—at weaning—when their brains might be most plastic. More recently we have tested to see whether or not similar results could be obtained with adult rats. For this purpose we kept rats under SC conditions until 105 days of age—the age of sacrifice in most of our experiments. At 105 days the rat has been sexually mature for over a month, and brain growth, which never completely ceases in the rat, has leveled off. Figure 5 shows brain weights of rats sacrificed at three ages—25 days, at weaning; 105 days, after spending 80 days in one of the three environments; 185 days, after spending their last 80 days in one of the three environments. These anatomical results, and the chemical results as well, indicate that the cortex of the adult rat brain is as capable of adaptive growth as is the cortex of the young animal. If these cerebral changes reflect learning and storage of memory, these results may be encouraging to those of us who are gray around the edges.

Extensions and Confirmatory Findings.   Our first announcements of measurable changes in the brain as consequences of experience met with the expected scientific skepticism. Could the results be replicated? Could they be produced in other laboratories?

By now we have shown that the results are obtained consistently in experiment after experiment during 5 years in our laboratory, and with all the strains of rats that we have tried. I even assigned this as a class laboratory last

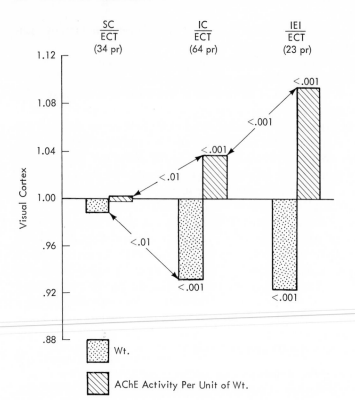

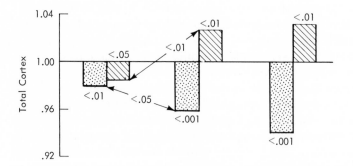

Fig. 4. Cerebral measures from (ECT) rats are compared with those of littermates in three different conditions—standard colony (SC), our usual impoverished condition (IC), and isolation in extreme impoverishment (IEI). (Values in the upper part of the figure are for the visual sample, the part of the cortex that is most responsive to differential experience, while the lower part of the figure gives results for total cortex. As the environmental differences become greater, going from left to right in the figure, the resultant cerebral differences become greater.)

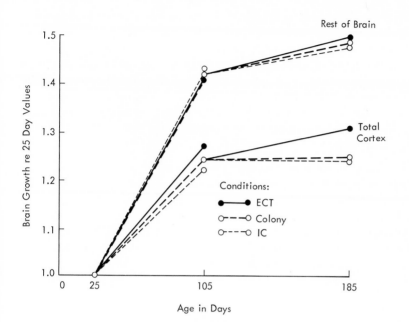

Fig. 5. Growth of total cortex and of the rest of the brain is shown in relation to weight values at 25 days of age. (Keeping rats from 25 to 105 days under three different conditions—ECT, SC, or isolated (IC)—leads to differences in cortical weights but not in weight of the rest of the brain. Taking animals that have been in the SC condition until 105 days and then dividing them among the three conditions also leads to differences in cortical weight—and to some degree in weight of the rest of the brain as well. Thus, the adult rat brain appears capable of adaptive growth.)

spring, using a strain we had not tried previously, Long-Evans rats. The class obtained clear-cut results.

This research has also been extended to mice in recent experiments done by Jean Moller, a graduate student of McGill University working at the University of California under my supervision. Two inbred strains of mice, the A and the C57, were employed. Both showed patterns of effects rather like rats in that they yielded significant results in total cortex and little or no effect in the rest of the brain. Again, there were significant increases in cortical weight and in total AChE and ChE. The increase in total AChE activity with enriched experience fell below the increase in weight; total ChE activity increased significantly, although it did not surpass the increase in weight.

Other laboratories have also begun to report results that confirm or extend our own. I have already mentioned that Altman and Das (1964) reported glial proliferation in the rat as a consequence of ECT; they also found an increase in cortical depth. Workers at the University of California, Los Angeles—Geller, Yuwiler, and Zolman (1965)—have found increased weight of brain and certain chemical changes as a consequence of enriched experience. A doctoral thesis by Bryan (1965) at Utah also reports the increase in cortical weight but no clear change in RNA per unit of weight. Pryor, Otis, and Uyeno (1965) at Stanford Research Institute have found increases in brain weight and some changes in AChE and ChE activities with electrical stimulation of the brain. Other laboratories have informed us of work in progress on cerebral changes with experience, so that this appears to be a growing area of study. We hope to help attract more workers to the field so that it may be cultivated intensively.

Relations Between Cerebral Changes and Learning Ability. One more type of experimental result should be mentioned before we consider the implications of this research for the study of human behavior. This last line of research is concerned with the following problem: Are the cerebral changes actually related to effects of experience on learning ability? We do not yet have a definitive answer, but we do have some evidence indicating that the brain changes run in parallel with changes in problem-solving ability.

In 1962, we reported a study (Krech, Rosenzweig, & Bennett, 1962) in which rats were raised for 1 month in either ECT or IC environments and then were tested on a reversal discrimination problem. The tester had not participated in the earlier treatment of the animals nor was he informed which rats came from which situation. In error scores on the first rather simple light-dark discrimination problem, the groups did not differ. This is important because it has been suggested that isolated animals have an unsatiated exploratory tendency which leads them to make apparent errors when they are only finding out about the world. Perhaps because of our prolonged pretraining, no such effect appeared. But when the rats had to reverse cues and the problems became more difficult, the previously isolated group became relatively worse and worse in its performance. The difference in favor of the ECT animals on all reversal problems was significant at the .01 level. This experiment has since been replicated with rats of both the S_1 and S_3 lines, and the original effect has been confirmed in each experiment.

Other experiments are being done to determine whether the cerebral changes and the changes in ability go together regularly or whether they can be split apart. To date, the results have not forced us to abandon our initial hypothesis that changes in the brain induced by experience underlie the changes in learning ability brought about by experience.

IMPLICATIONS OF ANIMAL RESEARCH FOR HUMAN STUDIES

Now that you have seen that enriched experience leads to anatomical and chemical changes in the brains of rats and mice, what relevance may this or other animal research have for the study of human behavior? I would like to discuss three ways in which animal research may contribute. And I would also like to point out a few limitations that should be kept in mind.

Contributions of Animal Research

Extrapolating from Animal to Man.   First, animal experiments and especially a comparative approach may allow extrapolation to human behavior where direct experiments with humans are not possible. To take an example close at hand, we have seen that the hypothesis of growth of the brain with use was originated in the eighteenth century with regard to the human brain. During the nineteenth century much research was conducted on this problem, but by the end of the century it was recognized that the results were inconclusive. It simply was not possible to secure brains of matched samples of men where everything except the exercise of the brain has been kept constant. Now, suppose (as we hope) that we can extend our experiments on rodents to carnivores and to primates, and that cerebral differences as a consequence of experience are found throughout the series. (A conceivable finding is that the difference will increase in magnitude as we examine animals capable of more and more complex behavior.) It should then be possible to extrapolate from this animal series to the human brain.

As another example, Harold Jones (1954) stated in the *Handbook of Child Psychology* in both 1946 and 1954 that studies to test whether early training increases the IQ remained inconclusive. Jones pointed out a number of design requirements for adequate research in this area. The first of his several points was this: "The experimental and the control group should consist of matched pairs from the same population, one member of each pair being assigned at random to the experimental procedure [p. 679]." He showed why attempting to match pairs after the fact is unlikely to be successful.

Well-designed animal experiments on effects of early training are feasible, and in fact they are being performed in increasing numbers. (See chapters and references in Newton & Levine, 1966.) Donald Hebb foresaw this in 1954 (just when Harold Jones was pointing out the deficiencies of the human studies). Hebb (1954) wrote,

> Failing the possibility of radical rearing experiments with human children, it seems that comparative study offers a solid line of advance in this field. Studies of . . . a number of species will provide some basis for tentative extrapolation of the curves of phylogenetic development through chimpanzee to man, where the ideas thus arrived at can be tested for their value in clarifying clinical and naturalistic observations [p. 534].

Providing Perspectives for Study of Human Behavior.   The second value of animal studies is that they may provide new or broader perspectives in which to place and understand human behavior. Thus Ford and Beach (1951) in their book, *Patterns of Sexual Behavior*, set up a threefold frame of reference to assist in understanding human sexual behavior. One perspective is cross-cultural; the second is evolutionary or zoological, involving comparisons between human beings and lower animals; the third perspective is physiological, and this of course also draws upon animal studies. In the perspective of comparative psychology, Ford and Beach consider many aspects of man's sexual behavior to be part of a common mammalian pattern. On the other hand, they relate his unique degree of dependence upon learning and experience to the evolution of his large and complex cerebral cortex.

In considering effects of early experience on human development, both cross-cultural and animal studies may provide clues to understanding. For example, Jones (1954) reviewed several studies indicating that the firstborn is more likely to be gifted or eminent than are his siblings. Jones felt that there was no satisfactory interpretation for these findings. Subsequent studies have yielded these further findings (Hunt, 1961, p. 341 ff.): Twins on the average have IQs several points lower than singletons. Pairs of siblings spaced further apart in age do better on intelligence tests than those born closer together. One way of interpreting all of these findings is to hypothesize with Hunt that siblings born close together do not get all the adult attention and stimulation they need for full development. Support for this hypothesis comes from cross-cultural studies on African children who receive a great deal of attention and stimulation until weaning and whose intellectual and motor development to that point is well in advance of European children (Geber, 1958).

Geber describes the Ugandan mother's care of the child in this way:

> Before the child is weaned, the mother's whole interest is centred on him. She never leaves him, carries him on her back—often in skin-to-skin contact—wherever she goes, sleeps with him, feeds him on demand at all hours of the day and night, forbids him nothing, and never chides him. . . . He is, moreover, continually being stimulated by seeing her at her various occupations and hearing her interminable conversations, and because he is always with her, his world is relatively extensive. He is also the centre of interest for neighbours and visitors . . . [p. 194].

Weaning in Uganda is usually abrupt and severe, and most children tested after weaning no longer show the earlier precocity. "On the other hand, children for whom weaning had not caused a sudden break in the way of life retained their liveliness after weaning, and developed without interruption [p. 195]."

One further point from Geber's paper strengthens the interpretation that early stimulation is the main cause of the precocious development of Ugandan children: "A few children . . . were being brought up in the European way, passing most of their lives in their cots and fed at regular intervals. . . . They did not show similar precocity after the first month, and later were inclined to be quiet or subdued [pp. 194–5]."

Further support comes from animal studies of the last 15 years showing that the greater the richness and variety of experience the subject receives, the more does its learning ability increase. You saw some examples of this from our own research reported above.

Now let us speculate somewhat broadly. Suppose it could be demonstrated that for full development of their potential our children need more adult care than they now receive. Does anyone suppose that American mothers could be persuaded to adopt the early Ugandan pattern and to sustain this degree of care and attention throughout childhood? Is this degree of adult tutelage possible when over half our population is under 20 years of age? Or are we on our way to a society where the child graduates from aircrib to neighborhood play group to teen-age society, almost untouched by adult hands? Challenging most current prophets, the biophysicist John R. Platt (1965) argues that in population and in many other characteristics of society we are already "past the middle of the S-curve" of expansion. He pictures a future steady-state population with "just as many people at age 40 or at age 60 as at age 10. And if they all live to about 80, as it now seems they might, then half of them will be over 40 and only one-fifth of them will be children under 15 [p. 611]." Platt suggests that such a society could use its " great excess of adult-power, prosperous and leisured, to make the richest education for children that the world has ever known [p. 611]." Coming back to the present, there would seem to be a great deal of research necessary with both human and animal subjects, to provide a comprehensive picture of how capacity develops with training and of how available instructional time can be spent most effectively.

Suggesting New Hypotheses About Human Behavior. Since human learning is distinctively verbal, there is great potential in research on the effects of encouraging early verbal development. Specifically, I would like to suggest using the Human Relations Area Files to compare intellectual development in those cultures where adults speak a great deal to infants and expect children to speak early and in those cultures where adults neither speak much to infants nor expect them to speak before the age of 3 or 4.

This brings me to the last value of animal research that I would like to discuss: It may prompt investigators to make new observations or to formulate hypotheses about human behavior that would not otherwise have occurred to them. Let me give two examples, one potential and the other actual.

For the potential example let us refer back to two points mentioned earlier: First is the difficulty of studying brain growth as a consequence of experience in human beings. Second are the animal studies indicating that differential growth of cortical regions can be induced by specific programs of experience. The reason for giving up human studies was that it was not possible to obtain adequate controls. To meet this requirement, it may be possible, following the animal model, to use the individual as his own control by measuring differential development of various regions of the brain as a function of differential experience. In one of the first numbers of the *American Journal of Psychology*, Donaldson (1892) did in fact consider in this way the brain of the blind deaf-mute, Laura Bridgman. He reported from postmortem examination a somewhat deficient development of the cortical areas representing the lacking senses, coupled with essentially normal development of the area representing the skin senses. To my knowledge, there has not been a systematic compilation of human data concerning relative development of cortical areas in relation to sensory impairment or to heightened experience. Our recent animal studies suggest that this might be a valuable line of research to pursue.

Now for an actual example in which animal research has prompted investigators to make new observations and to formulate a novel hypothesis about human development. This example is found in the recent paper "Infantile Stimulation and Adult Stature of Human Males" by Landauer and Whiting (1964). Here is part of their summary:

> We have reviewed some recent studies that have shown that rats and mice stimulated during an early period of life attain greater size in adulthood. We have indicated that there are plausible explanations for this effect involving changes in functioning of the adrenal-pituitary system. In exploring whether these results could be generalized to humans, we found that for two independent cross-cultural samples, in societies where the heads or limbs of infants were repeatedly molded or stretched, or where their ears, noses, or lips were pierced, where they were circumsized, vaccinated, inoculated, or had tribal marks cut or burned in their skin, the mean adult male stature was over two inches greater than in societies where these customs were not practiced. The effects of these practices appear to be independent of several other factors known to be associated with increased stature [p. 1018].

Landauer and Whiting do not claim that their data give conclusive evidence that infantile stress enhances growth. Nevertheless, they point out that their hypothesis is given strong support by the fact that the correlation they found

> for humans corresponds to an experimentally demonstrated effect in laboratory mammals, and the type of phenomenon—endocrine control of growth—is one in which interspecies generality is common. Therefore, [they conclude] it seems to us that the inference from our data of a causal relation between infant experience and human growth is sufficiently plausible to warrant serious consideration [p. 1018].

Some Limitations

This last example can be used to make a transition to some of the limitations of extrapolating from animals to human beings. It should be clear that each species of animal starts at its own level of development and displays its own rate and sequence of development. The rat, for example, is born in a very immature state compared to the human. Rapid changes in its brain chemistry occur during the first 2 weeks after birth, and these are analogous to changes that occur before birth in the human baby. In the rat the first 10 days seems to be the "critical period" for inducing alterations in the pituitary-adrenal axis and in growth. The human baby at an analogous period of its cerebral development is still safely in the womb. Thus it is not clear that the first 2 years of human life—chosen by Landauer and Whiting to be the equivalent of the preweaning period in rats and mice—is physiologically equivalent to the critical period for inducing growth in the rat. It is quite possible that this discrepancy, if it is real, may point the way to some factor other than the pituitary-adrenal system as being responsible for the growth effect in humans. To take another example, the fact that in the rat we can induce brain growth in the adult as readily as in the young animal by giving enriched experience, does not necessarily indicate that this will be true of people. A series of comparative studies will be necessary before we can tell whether higher mammals show a critical period for brain development as a function of experience.

Now for a final word of optimism about this long-range enterprise of animal and human studies of growth and behavior. Long ago men were reminded of their limitations in these words: "Which of you by taking thought can add one cubit unto his stature?" This admonition retains its force, and it appears that rather drastic action is required to add even two inches to human stature. Yet I hope that the research that we have been considering may eventually add, not cubits to stature, but cubic centimeters to human brains.

REFERENCES

ALTMAN, J., & DAS, G. D. Autoradiographic examination of the effects of enriched environment on the rate of glial multiplication in the adult rat brain. *Nature*, 1964, **204**, 1161–1163.

BRYAN, R. N. Brain RNA metabolism in differential experience. Unpublished doctoral dissertation, University of Utah, 1965.

DIAMOND, M. C., KRECH, D., & ROSENZWEIG, M. R. The effects of an enriched environment on the histology of the rat cerebral cortex. *Journal of Comparative Neurology*, 1964, **123**, 111–119.

DONALDSON, H. H. Anatomical observations of the brain and several sense-organs of the blind deaf-mute: Laura Dewey Bridgman. *American Journal of Psychology*, 1892, **4**, 247–294.

FORD, C. S., & BEACH, F. A. *Patterns of sexual behavior*. New York: Harper, 1951.

GEBER, M. The psychomotor development of African children in the first year, and the influence of maternal behavior. *Journal of Social Psychology*, 1958, **47**, 185–195.

GELLER, E., YUWILER, A., & ZOLMAN, J. Effects of environmental complexity and training on constituents of brain and liver. Paper read at International Neurochemical Conference, Oxford, 1965.

HEBB, D. O., & THOMPSON, W. R. The social significance of animal studies. In G. Lindzey (Ed.), *Handbook of social psychology*. Cambridge, Mass.: Addison-Wesley, 1954. Pp. 532–561.

HUNT, J. MCV. *Intelligence and experience*. New York: Ronald Press, 1961.

JONES, H. E. The environment and mental development. In L. Carmichael (Ed.), *Handbook of child psychology*. New York: Wiley, 1954. Ch. 10.

KRECH, D., ROSENZWEIG, M. R., & BENNETT, E. L. Effects of environmental complexity and training on brain chemistry. *Journal of Comparative and Physiological Psychology*, 1960, **53**, 509–519.

KRECH, D., ROSENZWEIG, M. R., & BENNETT, E. L. Relations between brain chemistry and problem-solving among rats raised in enriched and impoverished environments. *Journal of Comparative and Physiological Psychology*, 1962, **55**, 801–807.

LANDAUER, T. K., & WHITING, J. W. M. Infantile stimulation and adult stature of human males. *American Anthropologist*, 1964, **66**, 1007–1028.

NEWTON, G., & LEVINE, S. (Eds.) *Early experience.* Springfield, Ill.: Charles C Thomas, in press.

OPITZ, E. Increased vascularization of the tissue due to acclimatization to higher altitudes and its significance for oxygen transport. *Experimental Medicine and Surgery*, 1951, **9**, 389–403.

PLATT, J. R. The step to man. *Science*, 1965, **149**, 607–613.

PRYOR, G. T., OTIS, L. S., & UYENO, E. Effects of nonspecific stimulation on behavior, brain chemistry, and brain weight. Paper read at Western Psychological Association, Honolulu, 1965.

ROSENZWEIG, M. R., KRECH, D., BENNETT, E. L. & DIAMOND, M. C. Effects of environmental complexity and training on brain chemistry and anatomy: A replication and extension. *Journal of Comparative and Physiological Psychology*, 1962, **55**, 429–437.

SÖMMERING, S. T. *De basis encephali.* Gottingen, 1778.

SÖMMERING, S. T. *Ueber die Korperliche Verschiedenheit des Negers von Europaer.* Frankfurt am Mainz, 1785. (Extracts given as an appendix in C. White, *An account of the regular gradation in man and in different animals and vegetables.* London, 1799.)

SÖMMERING, S. T. *Von Baue des menschlichen Koerpers*, Vol. 5, Part 1. Frankfurt am Mainz: Barrentropp & Wenner, 1791.

SPURZHEIM, J. G. *The physiognomical system of Drs. Gall and Spurzheim.* London: Baldwin, Cradock, & Joy, 1815.

YOUNG, J. Z. *A model of the brain.* Oxford: Clarendon Press, 1964.

Molecular Theories of Memory

Wesley Dingman
and Michael B. Sporn

Recently there has been a surge of interest, both theoretical and experimental, in what might be called "the molecular basis of memory." The spectacular success of recent investigations of the molecular basis of transmission of genetic information has suggested that there may be an analogous molecular mechanism for storing and utilizing experiential information during the life of the individual—that is, that the memory of an experiential event is stored in the nervous system by the formation or alteration of a particular molecule or set of molecules, which may be regarded as a molecular engram or memory trace. Various types of molecules, including DNA, RNA, proteins, and lipids, have been suggested as the actual engram. This article is an attempt to provide a critique, rather than a comprehensive review, of certain theoretical and experimental approaches to this general hypothesis (*1*). Since the particular hypothesis that specific changes in neuronal RNA represent the molecular engram of memory has received special attention of late, we consider it in some detail here. Our aim is to use this particular molecular theory to illustrate the problems that are fundamental to all purely molecular theories which fail to consider the cellular environment within which molecules exist.

RNA AND MEMORY

A large number of experiments have now been performed which support the view that RNA metabolism may be intimately connected with memory storage and learning. Although there is still definite controversy about some of the methods and techniques that have been used in these investigations, we limit this discussion to interpretations of experimental data and do not discuss experimental methods. The most direct suggestion that RNA metabolism is involved in memory storage is the report (*2*) that a significant change in the

From *Science*, 1964, **144**, 26–29. Reprinted with permission of the publisher and author. ~vright 1967 by the American Association for the Advancement of Science.

base composition of nuclear RNA of Deiters' nerve cells occurs when a rat learns a balancing task (the adenine-to-uracil ratio of the nuclear RNA of these cells was reported to be increased significantly) and that this change persists for at least 48 hours after the end of the learning experiment. Changes in the base composition of RNA in associated glial cells were also reported in these studies (3).

The formation of an epileptogenic mirror focus, a neurophysiological model of memory, has been shown to be correlated with an increase in the total amount of neuronal RNA in the cells involved (4). Furthermore, studies on planarians have indicated that ribonuclease blocks the retention of a conditioned response in regenerating planarian tails (5), and it has been claimed that learning is transferable from one planarian to another by way of cannibalistic ingestion (6). However, the interpretation of the cannibalism data is by no means straightforward, since it appears that in these experiments it was transfer of the general capacity to learn, rather than transfer of the specific learning of a particular task, that was being measured. 8-Azaguanine, a purine analog which can cause formation of nonfunctional RNA (7), has been found to depress a rat's ability to learn a new maze without impairing its ability to traverse and recall a previously well-learned maze (8). This same antimetabolite was also shown to prolong the interval required for "fixation of experience" in an assay in which the spinal cord of rats was used (9); moreover, in the latter report (9) it was noted that 1, 1, 3-tricyano-2-amino-1-propene, a drug believed to increase the RNA concentration of neurons (10), shortens the interval required for "fixation of experience." Finally, long-term administration of yeast RNA has been reported to improve memory function in human subjects with cerebral arteriosclerotic and presenile dementia (11), and, in animal experiments, long-term treatment with yeast RNA increased the rate at which the animal acquired a behavioral response motivated by shock (12).

CRITERIA FOR A PERMANENT MEMORY TRACE

None of the experiments just described directly test the proposition that an RNA molecule, or set of molecules, represents the molecular engram which is the permanent memory trace; they merely stress the fact that RNA metabolism is an important parameter of neuronal function. In order to prove that a given molecule or set of molecules may be regarded as a permanent memory trace, a more rigorous set of criteria should be met.

We suggest that the following criteria must be satisfied in order to demonstrate that a given molecule, set of molecules, structure, or set of structures is indeed a permanent memory trace: (i) It must undergo a change of state in response to the experience to be remembered. (ii) The altered state must persist as long as the memory can be demonstrated. (iii) Specific destruction of the altered state must result in permanent loss of the memory.

If these criteria are applied to the experimental data relating RNA and memory, it is apparent that the evidence that RNA molecules are specific memory traces is highly circumstantial at present. In particular, a change in the base composition of nuclear RNA in cells involved in a learning task does not necessarily signify that these RNA molecules are permanent memory traces; it might signify that they are transient intermediates in the formation of permanent memory traces, or merely that changes in RNA occur concomitantly with learning. The effects of ribonuclease on learning in planarians may also be regarded in this fashion, since this enzyme was applied during the time the "trained" tail was regenerating a head, and presumably, then, the process of formation of permanent memory traces in the regenerating head. Likewise, in the experiments in which drugs were used to affect RNA metabolism during the fixation of experience, the drugs were active at the time the proper functioning of transient intermediates in the formation of memory traces would be expected to be important.

In summary, not all the experiments cited have yet satisfied criteria ii and iii for establishing a set of molecules as a permanent memory trace. Indeed, any attempt to show that *specific* destruction of a *particular* set of molecules results in the permanent loss of an already established memory trace would appear to be beset with great experimental difficulties. Thus, in experimental work on the RNA hypothesis it has not yet been possible to distinguish between the following alternatives.

1) RNA molecules, like many other types of molecules, are important constituents of the nervous system whose structural and functional state may change dramatically during a learning experience, but they do not function as permanent memory traces; or

2) RNA molecules do have a unique role in the nervous system, that of serving as the final engram of experiential memory, the permanent memory trace.

A RESTATEMENT OF THE PROBLEM

It should be apparent that there is now an abundance of data which suggests some relationship between RNA metabolism in brain and the process of memory storage. What, however, is known about the specificity of this relationship? The major function of all known types of RNA is participation in protein synthesis (*13*); no other function has thus far been demonstrated for RNA in brain. Since protein synthesis is one of the most fundamental of all cellular processes, and since the proteins of a cell are largely responsible for its behavior, one would expect that the process of memory storage in a neuron might well involve some participation of the protein-synthesizing mechanism (*14*). It is not surprising to find that this mechanism may undergo some change of state during cellular activity, or that interference with this mechanism may cause changes in the overall behavior of a cell. Indeed, it would be more surprising if it could be unequivocally demonstrated that RNA function is in no way involved in memory storage. The important point is that proponents of the RNA hypothesis have yet to demonstrate that a unique set of RNA molecules functions as specific permanent memory traces. Criticisms of the RNA hypothesis similar to this one have also been made by Briggs and Kitto (15).

At this point one might raise the question: Is there perhaps an inherent difficulty in *any* hypothesis which attempts to explain the encoding of memory solely in terms of *one* set of molecules? Cellular metabolism is not merely a rigid hierarchy whereby DNA controls the synthesis of RNA, RNA controls the synthesis of proteins, and proteins control the synthesis of other metabolites in the cell. Rather, the cell has many regulatory mechanisms, whereby proteins, hormones, and metabolites of low molecular weight may regulate the synthesis of RNA by DNA, as well as many feedback mechanisms for the regulation of functional activity of enzymes (16). Thus one cannot logically specify one set of molecules as totally controlling the activities of another set. Furthermore, in the neuron, in which certain functional activities (for example, RNA synthesis) are localized in the cell body and other functional activities (for example, synaptic transmission) are localized in peripheral processes of the cell, the cell body and peripheral synaptic structures exert mutual regulatory effects. Consequently, proper functioning of the nucleic-acid- and protein-synthesizing mechanisms of the cell body is necessary for the proper maintenance of synaptic structure (17), and the phenomenon of axoplasmic flow would appear to provide the necessary communication channel whereby centrally synthesized metabolities reach the peripheral synaptic regions (18). Moreover, proper synaptic function is necessary for the proper performance of the nucleic-acid- and protein-synthesizing structures of the cell body. A great deal of experimental work indicates that pronounced changes in the state of RNA and proteins occur in the cell body of a neuron that is actively stimulated (19), and conversely, that removal of afferent stimulation of a neuron can also cause marked changes in its cell body (20). The latter phenomenon is dramatically illustrated by the extreme degeneration of cell bodies of retinal ganglion cells of rabbits that were born and raised in darkness and never received visual stimulation (21). Moreover, there is much evidence, from the neuroembryological literature, which indicates that the nature of efferent connections of neurons may influence the structure and function of the cell body (22). Whereas we now understand the details of some aspects of the synthetic mechanisms (for example, RNA and protein synthesis) whereby the metabolism of the cell body may control synaptic function, we have almost no understanding of the mechanisms whereby synaptic function may control the metabolism of the cell body.

Thus we may perhaps more adequately investigate the structural basis of the permanent memory trace if we seek to answer the following questions: What permanent changes in neuronal structure and function result from stimulation of the neuron, and what is the mechanism of production of these changes? In such an approach an attempt is made to bridge the gap between current investigations, which emphasize the importance of particular molecules in memory storage, and the more cytologically and physiologically oriented theories of Ramon y Cajal (23), Hebb (24), and Sholl (25), in which emphasis is on the importance of synaptic interrelationships between neurons. These older theories stressed the role of growth of new axonal and dendritic connections as a fundamental process in memory storage and learning. At the time they were formulated little was known of the molecular biochemistry of nucleic acid and protein synthesis, and thus there is an incompleteness in these formulations. It is now apparent that the molecular and the cytological approaches to the problem of memory are by no means mutually exclusive, especially if one postulates that a major function of the synthetic mechanisms of the cell body is to provide molecules necessary for the growth and maintenance of axonal and dendritic connections. Weiss (26) has stressed that the adult neuron, as well as the immature neuron, appears to be in a perpetual state of growth or regeneration, or both, and he has emphasized the importance of axoplasmic flow for this process. The axonal termination of a synapse is essentially devoid of ribosomes (27), which are necessary for protein synthesis; hence any new proteins required for new axonal growth would, presumably, have to be synthesized in the cell body and reach new synapses by the process of axoplasmic flow. The major advantage of including synaptic structure and function in *any* hypothesis of memory storage is that one thereby takes into consideration a unique cytological feature of the neuron—namely, the fact that such a vast amount of its surface area (25) and functional mass (28) is located a great distance from the central cell body. As Sholl (25) has noted, "The activity of a single cortical neuron may well affect that of 4000 other neurons, [while] a single neuron may have more than 50 dendritic branches." No other type of cell in the body has thus become specialized for direct intercellular communication. Moreover, consideration of possible changes in synaptic structure during memory storage may provide an experimental approach to test for satisfaction of criteria ii and iii; hypotheses which consider memory storage solely at the molecular level have been weakest at this point. Therefore, we may be able to achieve a more comprehensive understanding of the phenomenon of memory if we regard this process as a property of a neuron or set of neurons rather than solely as a property of individual molecules. The molecular approach to the problem has already elucidated certain crucial biochemical processes which might underlie this phenomenon, but the picture is by no means complete at present.

SOME FUTURE PROBLEMS

In biochemical studies of memory, little attention has been paid, so far, to the lipids of the nervous system, in spite of the fact that lipids are such an important constituent of synaptic membranes. Little is known about the turnover of phospholipids and sphingolipids in such cell membranes. Are such lipids synthesized peripherally, or must they, too, reach the synapse by axoplasmic flow after being synthesized in the cell body? Are new membranes formed as part of the establishment of the memory trace? The recent description of specific inhibitors of fatty acid synthesis (*30*) should make possible an experimental approach to some of these problems.

The kinetics of the behavioral effects of drugs which have been used to produce a specific inhibition or acceleration of synthesis of essential metabolites is another problem which has so far received scant attention. If synthesis of certain necessary metabolites for synaptic growth occurs in the cell body, inhibition or acceleration of such synthetic activities may not be immediately reflected at the synapse. The rate of axoplasmic flow has been estimated to be of the order of 1 to several millimeters per day (*31*); thus, in neurons with long processes there may be a considerable delay between the time a molecule is synthesized and the time it reaches peripheral regions of the neuron. It is thus suggested that, in studies of the kinetics of memory-trace formation, both the initial learning and the later retention trials should be carried out at varying intervals after administration of drugs whose principal mechanism of action is upon synthetic activities in the cell body, since such drugs may fail to produce an immediate behavorial effect but may have a pronounced delayed effect. Some of these problems have been approached in the recent and intriguing investigations of Flexner *et al.* (32) on the effects of puromycin (an inhibitor of protein synthesis) on learning and memory in mice. These workers investigated the effect of injecting the drug at various sites and the effect of varying the interval between the initial learning experience and the subsequent administration of puromycin and they found that under certain conditions puromycin caused loss of memory. Further experiments, on the effect of varying the interval between an initial injection of puromycin and a subsequent learning experience, would be of interest in evaluating the hypothesis that axoplasmic transport of newly synthesized proteins to synaptic terminals is necessary for the fixation of new experiences by means of synaptic growth.

The mechanism of synaptic influence on the metabolism of the cell body is yet another major problem to be solved. It has been suggested (*33*) that the phenomenon of enzyme induction brought about by synaptic stimulation may be important in establishing memory traces, but experimental evidence is scanty. The finding of changes in base ratios of RNA in response to learning situations does not prove that there has been induction of a new type of RNA; since there are many types of RNA in the cell, a change in the relative proportions of the different types being synthesized could produce the same result as induction of a new type. Further studies on the specificity of any such evoked changes in the metabolism of the cell body are critically needed.

SUMMARY

If one establishes a rigorous set of criteria for defining a given type of molecule as a memory trace in the nervous system, then no one type of molecule may at present be regarded as the sole engram of a permanent memory trace. Much evidence already exists that RNA and protein metabolism are intimately involved in the process of memory storage, but the role of other molecules, such as lipids, must also be considered. Sophisticated techniques of molecular biology and enzymology will undoubtedly provide valuable data on biochemical processes involved in memory storage. However, a comprehensive theory of the structural basis of memory must also consider the function of the entire neuron, with consequent emphasis on the reciprocal relationships between the cell body and the synapse, as well as the complex functional interrelationships between neurons (34).

REFERENCES AND NOTES

1. Several recent reviews and symposia provide a more comprehensive summary : for example, H. HYDÉN, in *The Cell*, J. Brachet and A. E. Mirsky, Eds. (Academic Press, New York, 1960), vol. 4, p. 215; F. O. SCHMITT, Ed., *Macromolecular Specificity and Biological Memory* (Massachusetts Institute of Technology Press, Cambridge, 1962); W. S. FIELDS and W. ABBOTT, Eds., *Information Storage and Neural Control* (Thomas, Springfield, Ill., 1963); J. GAITO, *Psychol. Rev.* **70**, 471 (1963).
2. H. HYDEN & E. EGYHÁZI, *Proc. Natl. Acad. Sci. U.S.* **48**, 1366 (1962).
3. H. HYDEN & E. EGYHÁZI, *ibid.* **49**, 618 (1963).
4. F. MORRELL, *Physiol. Rev.* **41**, 443 (1961).
5. W. C. CORNING & E. R. JOHN, *Science* **134**, 1363 (1961).
6. J. V. MCCONNELL, *J. Neuropsychiat.* 3, suppl. 1, S42 (1962).
7. E. H. CREASER, *Biochem. J.* **64**, 539 (1956).
8. W. DINGMAN & M. B. SPORN, *J. Psychiat. Res.* **1**, 1 (1961).
9. T. J. CHAMBERLAIN, G. H. ROTHSCHILD, R. W. GERARD, *Proc. Natl. Acad. Sci. U.S.* **49**, 918 (1963).
10. E. EGYHAZI & H. HYDEN, *J. Biophys. Biochem. Cytol.* **10**, 403 (1961).
11. D. E. CAMERON & L. SOLYOM, *Geriatrics* **16**, 74 (1961); V. A. Kral and S. Sved, paper presented at the 35th annual meeting of the Midwestern Psychological Association, Chicago, 1963.
12. L. COOK, A. B. DAVIDSON, D. J. DAVIS, H. GREEN, E. J. FELLOWS, *Science* **141**, 268 (1963).
13. J. D. WATSON, *ibid.* **140**, 17 (1963).
14. Some time ago cytologic and electron-microscope studies led to the suggestion that the neuron is a cell specialized for protein synthesis; see, for example, H. HYDÉN, *Acta Physiol. Scand. Suppl.* **17**, (1943), and S. L. PALAY and G. E. PALADE, *J. Biophys. Biochem. Cytol.* **1**, 69 (1955). More recent investigations have provided further support for this view; see H. WAELSCH and A. LAJTHA, *Physiol. Rev.* **41**, 709 (1961), for a review.
15. M. H. BRIGGS & G. B. KITTO, *Psychol. Rev.* **69**, 537 (1962).
16. "Cellular regulatory mechanisms," *Cold Spring Harbor Symp. Quant. Biol.* **26**, (1961); P. KARLSON, *Perspectives Biol. Med.* **6**, 203 (1963).

17. H. WAELSCH & A. LAJTHA, *Physiol. Rev.* **41**, 709 (1961).
18. P. WEISS and H. B. HISCOE, *J. Exptl. Zool.* **107**, 315 (1948).
19. For numerous references, see H. HYDÉN, in *The Cell*, J. Brachet and A. E. Mirsky, Eds. (Academic Press, New York, 1960), vol. 4, p. 215.
20. For a recent review, see J. H. MENDELSON and F. R. ERVIN, in *Progress in Neurobiology*, R. G. Grenell, Ed. (Hoeber, New York, 1962), vol. 5, p. 178.
21. S. BRATTGARD, *Acta Radiol. Suppl.* **96** (1952).
22. P. WEISS in *Analysis of Development*, B. H. Willier, P. Weiss, V. Hamburger, Eds. (Saunders, Philadelphia, 1955), p. 346.
23. S. RAMÓN Y CAJAL, *Histologie du Système Nerveux* (Paris, 1910).
24. D. O. HEBB, *The Organization of Behavior* (Wiley, New York, 1949).
25. D. A. SHOLL, *The Organization of the Cerebral Cortex* (Methuen, London, 1956).
26. P. WEISS, in *Regional Neurochemistry*, S. S. Kety and J. Elkes, Eds. (Pergamon, New York, 1961), p. 220.
27. S. L. PALAY, *J. Biophys. Biochem, Cytol,* **2**, suppl., 193 (1956).
28. O. H. LOWRY, N. R. ROBERTS, K. Y. LEINER, M. WU, L. FARR, R. W. ALBERS, *J. Biol. Chem.* **207**, 39 (1954); R. L. FRIEDE, in *Regional Neurochemistry*, S. S. Kety and J. Elkes, Eds. (Pergamon, New York, 1961), p. 151.
30. J. D. ROBINSON, R. O. BRADY, R. M. BRADLEY, *J. Lipid Res.* **4**, 144 (1963); R. O. BRADY, *Biochim. Biophys. Acta* **70**, 467 (1963).
31. P. WEISS & H. B. HISCOE, *J. Exptl. Zool.* **107**, 315 (1948); B. DROZ and C. P. LEBLOND, *Science* **137**, 1047 (1962); S. OCHS, D. DALRYMPLE, G. RICHARDS, *Exptl. Neurol.* **5**, 349 (1962).
32. J. B. FLEXNER, L. B. FLEXNER, E. STELLAR, G. DE LA HABA, R. B. ROBERTS, *J. Neurochem.* **9**, 595 (1962); J. B. FLEXNER, L. B. FLEXNER, E. STELLAR, *Science* **141**, 57 (1963).
33. D. KRECH, M. R. ROSENZWEIG, E. L. BENNETT, *J. Comp. Physiol. Psychol.* **53**, 509 (1960); M. R. ROSENZWEIG, D. KRECH, E. L. BENNETT, M. C. DIAMOND, *ibid.* **55**, 429 (1962); M. H. BRIGGS and G. B. KITTO, *Psychol. Rev.* **69**, 537 (1962); C. E. SMITH, *Science* **138**, 889 (1962).
34. We thank DRS. DONALD B. TOWER, SEYMOUR S. KETY, and ROBERT MICHELS for their helpful criticisms of the manuscript.

Memory in Mice Analyzed with Antibiotics

Louis B. Flexner,
Josefa B. Flexner,
and Richard B. Roberts

Memory is thought to consist of overlapping stages. In the first stage the essential process is believed to be the electrical activity of those nerve cells which participate in a learning procedure. In this stage memory can be destroyed by electroconvulsive shock which disrupts this selective electrical activity. The period when memory is vulnerable to electroconvulsive shock in the mammal varies greatly, with a minimal value of less than 1 minute (*1*).

The learning process also leads to changes of a permanent kind so that in man, for example, memory of an event in childhood may persist for life. Thus long-term memory appears to be a relatively stable condition reached as the outcome of events occurring in a period of consolidation. In this period electrical activity is transformed into a more permanent record. Halstead (*1*) in 1951 suggested that the durability of memory may depend upon changes in neuronal nucleoprotein. The past several years have seen a surge of interest in this area and numerous efforts are being made to evaluate the roles of RNA and protein in the function of the brain.

Further clues to the nature of the learning process and memory can be obtained by considering instinctive or inherited behavior. Such behavior must be attributed to certain stable patterns of gene expression which become established during the development of the individual. These patterns of gene expression are dictated by the sequence of nucleotides in the DNA and are manifested during the complicated and mysterious process known as differentiation.

Behavioral patterns acquired by learning or training are so similar to instinctive ones that they are often difficult to distinguish. Accordingly it is

From *Science*, 1967, **155**, 1377–1383. Reprinted with the permission of the publisher and author. Copyright 1967 by the American Association for the Advancement of Science.

95

reasonable to assume that well-consolidated, long-term memory has the same fundamental basis as instinctive behavior, that is, it is the manifestation of a stable pattern of gene expression. Nature frequently uses the same mechanism for a variety of purposes. According to this view, the difference between the two situations is that the instinctive pattern develops from precursor patterns in response to some of the multitude of interactions which comprise differentiation, but the learned pattern is derived from an earlier quasi-stable pattern in response to the chemical events which are initiated by the learning experience.

Although the detailed mechanisms of differentiation remain obscure, there is little doubt that they involve repression and derepression of genes, as differences in the RNA components have been demonstrated in different organs and in different stages of development. Control of the rate of protein synthesis and of the final behavior of the proteins themselves is also likely to play an important role. Interactions within the cell, between one cell and its neighbors, and with distant organs are all parts of the process. Furthermore, the stability of the patterns which persist in the adult organism depends on the stability of a dynamic state. Individual molecules, cellular substructures, or complete cells can be degraded and replaced if synthesis and degradation remain in balance.

In accord with these principles it seems reasonable that the changes in the patterns of gene expression which result from learning will be accompanied by changes in the kinds and quantities of RNA and proteins (as well as small molecules) which are produced by the brain cells. Furthermore, interference with these synthetic processes by inhibitors might prevent the establishment of new patterns of expression or might upset patterns which were partially (or even completely) established.

Whether or not these broad speculations are valid, it is desirable to identify what, if any, macromolecular events are essential for the maintenance of memory. We hoped to approach this goal by injecting into the brain antibiotics which inhibit the synthesis of a specific macromolecule and then testing the effect of this inhibition on established memory. An antibiotic may also provide a way of differentiating different stages in the formation of memory and of indicating molecular events necessary for learning and for its fixation. This article will be concerned with these several aspects of memory and learning in mice.

PROCEDURE

We use a simple behavioral situation. Mice are trained in a Y-maze with a grid floor through which shock can be applied. The mouse is placed in the stem of the Y. If it fails to move out of the stem within 5 seconds (error of avoidance) it is shocked. If it fails to enter the selected arm of the Y (error of discrimination) it receives shock until it moves to the correct arm. Training is continued in one session (usually lasting 15 to 20 minutes) until the mouse has achieved nine correct responses out of ten attempts (the criterion). The same procedure is used to test for memory of the training experience (retention testing); shock is given for errors of performance. Memory is evaluated in the retention tests in terms of the percentage savings of trials and errors. These percentages are calculated by subtracting the number of trials or errors to criterion in the retention tests from the number to criterion in training, dividing by the number in training, and multiplying by 100. Savings of 100 percent indicate perfect memory; zero savings, complete loss of memory.

In our biochemical studies we have so far been concerned only with changes in the rate of cerebral protein synthesis after injection of antibiotics. At various times after treatment, a constant amount of radiovaline is injected subcutaneously. The mouse is killed 40 minutes later, since the rate of incorporation of labeled essential amino acids into cerebral proteins is practically constant during this interval. Protein precipitates are prepared from the following parts of the brain which are separated by dissection: the hippocampus, amygdala, thalamus, corpus striatum, temporal cortex (including entorhinal cortex), and the parietal and frontal portions of the neocortex (Fig. 1). The rate of synthesis of protein is calculated from the amount of radiovaline incorporated into protein and from the specific radioactivity of the valine pool.

Intracerebral injections are placed so as to expose the hippocampus, the entorhinal, and the neocortex to relatively high concentrations of the antibiotics. In our early efforts the spread of injected material was estimated from intracerebral injections of fluorescein, which is easily identified with ultraviolet light. These injections, each of 12 microliters, were made through small holes in the skull and at a depth of 2 mm from the surface of the skull. From one to three injections were made in each hemisphere. Bilateral injections, designated frontal injections, were made near the midline in the forward part of the skull. Ventricular injections were made near the midline well behind the frontal injections. Temporal injections were made below and behind the ventricular injections (2). Frontal injections of fluorescein heavily stained the forward third of the neocortex; ventricular injections stained all of the hippocampus and the caudal half of most of the neocortex, but importantly, spared the entorhinal cortex; and temporal injections stained all of the hippocampus and the caudal third of the cortex including the entorhinal cortex (Fig. 1). The staining obtained from combinations of these three types of injections was essentially additive.

EFFECTS OF PUROMYCIN

Our initial choice of an antibiotic was determined by the possibility that maintenance of memory might depend upon protein sustained above a critical level by continuing synthesis. We proposed to drastically reduce the rate of synthesis of cerebral protein for several hours and then to test the ability of mice to remember their training in the Y-maze. At that time

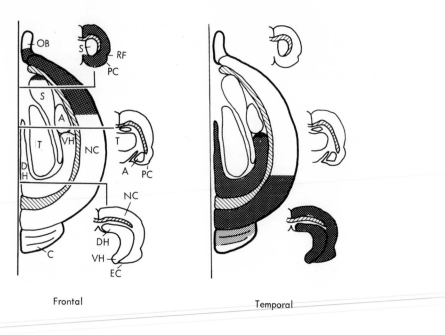

Frontal   Temporal

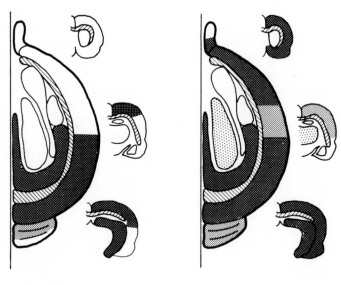

Ventricular   F + T + V

Fig. 1. Spread of fluorescein after it is injected intracerebrally. The diagrams at the left indicate structures viewed from the top after removal of a horizontal section of the hemisphere; at the right, cross (frontal) sections of the hemisphere at the level indicated in the diagram for frontal injections. Relative intensity of staining is indicated by relative density of stippling. *A*, Amygdaloid nucleus; *DH*, dorsal

Yarmolinsky and de la Haba (3) had found that puromycin is a powerful inhibitor of protein synthesis. Intracerebral injections of puromycin were made with the same procedure used with fluorescein.

Puromycin is used with caution. Its intracerebral injection in our albino mice causes toxic symptoms. There are often lethargy and loss of alertness followed by hyperexcitability, as well as loss of weight due to failure to eat and drink normally. If sufficient time is not given for recovery, there is the possibility that apparent loss of memory may be due to illness with an attendant impairment of motivation and performance. We delay tests for memory until weight is recovered and behavior is normal, usually 3 to 4 days after treatment. In addition, there is the possibility that an antibiotic may interfere with several cellular functions and so give a misleading answer to the question for which it was chosen. It may consequently be important to use several antibiotics before making firm interpretations of the effects of any one of them. This has proved to be the case with puromycin.

The effects on memory produced by puromycin 1 day or 11 to 60 days after training are given in Table 1. The table shows, after various types of intracerebral injections, the number of mice in which memory was lost, impaired, or retained. The first series of experiments were made with mice trained to criterion and injected 1 day later with puromycin. After six injections (bilateral temporal, ventricular, and frontal), each of 30 to 60 micrograms of puromycin, retention tests showed that memory of the training experience had been lost completely and permanently (memory was absent when tested 3 months after puromycin). An effort was then made to localize this effect. Memory was also consistently lost with bitemporal injections of 90 micrograms of puromycin. By contrast bilateral frontal or ventricular or combined frontal plus ventricular injections were essentially without effect. The next series of experiments was made with mice injected with puromycin 11 to 60 days after training to criterion. In these mice only bilateral temporal plus ventricular plus frontal injections quite consistently destroyed memory. Bitemporal injections, which destroyed 1-day memory, were ineffective.

What do these results indicate about the parts of the brain concerned with recent (1-day-old) and longer-term (11- to 60-day-old) memory? Recent memory was lost when puromycin was given by temporal injections, involving, on the basis of the distribution of fluorescein, the hippocampal area (hippocampus plus entorhinal cortex), while loss of longer-term memory required puromycin additionally in a substantial part of the neocortex. The conclusion from these observations that the hippocampal area is concerned with recent memory and an enlarged area of the neocortex with older memory

---

hippocampus; *EC*, entorhinal cortex; *FC*, frontal cortex; *NC*, neocortex; *PC*, parietal cortex; *S*, corpus striatum; *T*, thalamus; *TC*, temporal cortex; *VH*, ventral hippocampus; *OB*, olfactory bulb; *RF*, rhinal fissure; *C*, cerebellum; *F + T + V*, frontal + temporal + ventricular injections. From Flexner, Flexner, and Stellar (2).

Table 1   Effects of Different Sites of Injection of Puromycin on Short- and Longer-Term Memory[a]

	PUROMYCIN INJECTIONS		NO. OF MICE IN WHICH MEMORY WAS		
SITE	DAYS	DOSE (MG)	L	I	R
Short-term memory					
T +V +F	1	0.03–.06	7	0	0
T	1	.09	10	0	0
V	1	.09	0	0	5
F	1	.09	0	0	5
V +F	1	.09	0	1	2
Longer-term memory					
T +V +F	11–60	0.03	17	2	0
T	11–35	0.06–.09	0	0	7
V	12–38	.06–.09	0	0	3
F	16–27	.06–.09	0	0	3
V +F	28	.06–.09	0	2	2
V +T	28–43	0.09	1	1	2
T +F	28	.09	0	0	3

[a] L, lost; I, impaired; R, retained; Days, days after learning. T, V, and F refer, respectively to temporal, ventricular, and frontal injections, all given bilaterally. For the mice with loss of memory, the means and standard deviations for percentages of savings of trials and of errors were respectively 1 ± 3 and 2 ± 6; for those with impaired memory, 26 ± 29 and 39 ± 12; for those with retention of memory, 90 ± 14 and 90 ± 9. From Flexner, Flexner, and Stellar (2, 5).

is supported by the evidence that has come from neurosurgical and autopsy findings on man and from ablation experiments on animals (4).

As indicated by our method, how long does it require after learning for an enlarged area of the neocortex to participate in the effective memory trace? Bitemporal injections consistently destroyed memory 2 days after training (Table 2), but they were consistently without effect 6 days after training. Results were variable at 3, 4, and 5 days. Thus it appears that the enlarged locus of longer-term memory in the type of training experience we have used with mice becomes effective in from 3 to 6 days, depending upon the individual.

We have put these observations on recent and longer-term memory to an additional test by means of reversal training. A mouse was first trained, for example, to move from the stem of the Y into its left arm; then 3 weeks later it was retrained to move into the right arm. Puromycin was injected bitemporally 24 hours later. Would recent memory be destroyed by this treatment and longer-term memory be preserved? Shock was omitted in the retention trials

Table 2 Effect of Bilateral Temporal Injections of
Puromycin on Memory of Increasing Age[a]

INJECTIONS: DAYS AFTER LEARNING	NO. OF MICE IN WHICH MEMORY WAS		
	LOST	IMPAIRED	RETAINED
2	3	0	0
3	4	0	1
4	0	1	1
5	0	1	2
6	0	0	3

[a] Each injection contained 0.09 milligram of puromycin. For the seven mice with loss of memory, the means and standard deviations for percentages of savings of trials and of errors were respectively 1 ± 4 and 0 ± 0; for the seven mice with retention of memory, 85 ± 19 and 93 ± 7. In one mouse with impaired memory the percentages of savings for trials and errors were respectively 38 and 20; for the other, 39 and 55. From Flexner, Flexner, and Stellar (2).

3 days after injection of puromycin since there was, within the design of the test, no right or wrong response. As shown in Table 3, when they were tested for memory, the first choice of all mice was consistent with the first learning experience, as were the large majority of subsequent choices. Untreated mice, in contrast to the experimental group, made choices consistent with their recent or reversal training. The results fit our evidence for the difference in the parts of the brain concerned with recent and longer-term memory.

We had chosen to use puromycin to test the possibility that continuing protein synthesis is essential for the maintenance of memory. We were encouraged in this view by the destructive effects of puromycin on memory. As has been mentioned, however, our results might have been due to some side effect not related to protein synthesis and it was consequently essential to test our tentative interpretation in other ways. We have done this by correlating the effects on memory and cerebral protein synthesis of consistently destructive and of smaller intracerebral doses of puromycin, of puromycin subcutaneously injected, of several substances related to puromycin, and of other antibiotics which are known to be inhibitors of protein synthesis (5).

Figure 2 gives the percentage of inhibition of protein synthesis in six areas of the brain as a function of time after bitemporal injections of 90 micrograms of puromycin, a treatment which uniformly leads to loss of recent memory. The figure shows that puromycin, unlike fluorescein, spreads widely from the site of the injection to other parts of the brain, but inhibition is most drastic in the hippocampus and temporal cortex (including entorhinal cortex). Inhibition in both of these areas with one exception was maintained at a level in excess of about 80 percent from the first to the tenth hour after the injection. On the supposition that destruction of memory by puromcyin is related to its effect on protein synthesis, we tentatively concluded that to

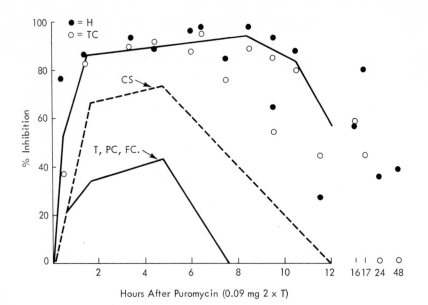

Hours After Puromycin (0.09 mg 2 × T)

Fig. 2. Changes with time in the inhibition of incorporation of radiovaline into protein of the hippocampus (*H*), temporal cortex (*TC*), corpus striatum (*CS*), thalamus (*T*), parietal cortex (*PC*), and frontal cortex (*FC*) after bitemporal injections each with 90 micrograms of puromycin in 12 microliters. From Flexner, Flexner, Roberts, and de la Haba (5).

Table 3   Differential Effect of Bilateral Temporal Injections of Puromycin on Recent and Longer-Term Memory[a]

MOUSE	INITIAL LEARNING (NO. TRIALS)	REVERSAL LEARNING (NO. TRIALS)	CHOICE OF ARM OF Y-MAZE
			Experimental animals
26A	13	22	1, 1, 1, 1, 1, 1, 1, 1, 1, 1, 1, 1, 1, 1, 1, 1, 1
24A	7	10	1, 1, 2, 1, 1, 1, 1, 2, 1, 1, 1, 1, 1, 1, 1, 1, 1, 1, 1, 1, 1, 2, 1, 1, 1
25A	8	10	1, 1, 1, 1, 2, 1, 1, 1, 1, 2, 1, 2, 2, 1, 2
22A	9	8	1, 2, 2, 1, 1, 2, 1, 2, 1, 2, 1, 1, 1, 1, 1, 1, 1, 1, 1, 1, 1, 1
23A	13	4	1, 1, 1, 1, 1, 1, 1, 1, 1, 1, 1, 1, 1
49	22	9	1, 1, 2, 2, 1, 1, 1, 2, 1, 1, 1, 1, 2, 1, 1, 1, 1, 1, 1, 1, 1, 1, 1
27A	12	5	1, 1, 1, 1, 1, 1, 1, 1, 1, 2, 1
			Control animals
58A	10	14	2, 2, 2, 2, 2, 2, 2, 2, 2, 2, 2, 2, 2, 2, 2
60A	10	12	2, 2, 2, 2, 2, 2, 2, 2, 2, 2, 2

Each injection had a volume of 0.012 milliliter and contained 0.06 or 0.09 milligram (mouse 49) of puromycin. Choices of the arm of the Y-maze by an animal after injection were scored as 1 if consistent with initial learning, and as 2 if consistent with reversal learning. Trials were continued irregularly beyond the ten originally planned. From Flexner, Flexner and Stellar (2). Learning was always to criterion, and reversal learning occurred 3 weeks after initial learning.

produce consistent loss of recent memory in our experimental situation, protein synthesis must be inhibited in the hippocampus and temporal cortex for about 9 hours at a level exceeding 80 percent.

Inhibition of protein synthesis in six areas of the brain was also measured after six injections (bilateral, temporal, ventricular, and frontal) each of 30 micrograms of puromycin. This dose leads to loss of longer-term (greater than 5-day-old) memory. The inhibitory effects of these combined injections on protein synthesis is most pronounced in the hippocampus and temporal cortex. In these two areas inhibition exceeded 80 percent from at the most 1.7 hours to more than 11 hours after the injection. Inhibition in the frontal cortex was somewhat less over this period with a minimum of about 70 percent. The parietal cortex, thalamus, and corpus striatum showed with time a greater decrement, reaching 35 to 50 percent inhibition 11.7 hours after the injection. Again on the supposition that destruction of memory by puromycin is related to its effect on protein synthesis, we tentatively concluded that longer-term memory is destroyed by injections which inhibit protein synthesis in the hippocampus and temporal cortex by at least 80 percent for 10 hours, and in a substantial part of the remaining neocortex to a minimum of 70 percent for the same period of time.

The relationship between puromycin's effect on memory and on protein synthesis was studied further by injecting graded amounts of the antibiotic into the mouse brain. The amounts were smaller than required to consistently destroy memory. As the amount of puromycin was reduced it became progressively less effective in destroying memory; there was a similar trend in its effect on the degree and duration of inhibition of protein synthesis.

In studying the effects of subcutaneous injections of puromycin we used the highest amount of the antibiotic which could be tolerated. We could not detect any interference with memory in these experiments. Again, biochemical measurements showed that protein synthesis was inhibited at a substantially lower level and for a shorter time with the subcutaneous than with the effective intracerebral injections.

A series of substances of interest because of their chemical relationship to puromycin or because they were known inhibitors of protein synthesis were also tested. These substances, injected intracerebrally, were puromycin hydrolyzed at the glycosidic bond, the aminonucleoside of puromycin, the D- and L-isomers of phenylalanyl puromycin, and chloramphenicol. All were without effect on memory. The biochemical studies showed that all failed to produce the severe, sustained inhibition of protein synthesis obtained with puromycin. At this time there was consequently nothing in our experience to contradict the view that memory depends upon protein maintained above a critical level by continuing synthesis.

Before proceeding to experiments with acetoxycycloheximide, designed further to test this oversimplified working hypothesis, several unpublished observations will be briefly mentioned to give a more complete picture of the effects of intracerebral injections of puromycin. (i) To obtain consistent destruction of memory, the volume of puromycin which is injected intracerebrally must be increased with increased skull size. Our routine procedure is designed for mice that weigh 28 to 32 grams. In addition, injections must promptly follow one another. With bitemporal injections, for example, irregularities of response occur if the injections are made more than 5 minutes apart. (ii) In mice trained to criterion, both recent and longer-term memory are maintained for 10 to 20 hours after injection of puromycin, then they disappear permanently (the longest time at which memory has been tested after injection of puromycin is 3 months; at this time, memory was absent). (iii) If mice are run through the maze a sufficient number of times after reaching criterion (that is, over-trained), puromycin, as we inject it, has no effect on memory. About 60 trials beyond criterion on the average are needed to give this protection against puromycin. (iv) Dorsal hippocampal lesions and ventricular dilatation, varying from slight to moderately severe, may be found after injections of puromycin. Damage to other parts of the brain, including the entorhinal cortex, has not been seen except in areas of the neocortex surrounding the needle tracks. Under our conditions the effects of puromycin on memory are unrelated to the degree of severity of the hippocampal lesions. Indeed, ventricular injections cause damage to the hippocampus in the same way as temporal injections, but they have no effect on memory. (v) After treatment with puromycin, all mice are capable of relearning the maze, are capable of reversal learning, and retain memory of their last training indefinitely. Some reach criterion on second learning in practically the same number of trials with the same number of errors as on first learning; in others, second learning is substantially more difficult than first learning. No correlation has been found between this difference on second learning and the degree of hippocampal damage. (vi) Mice which had their memory destroyed by puromycin were retrained. In most instances the standard treatment with puromycin then failed to destroy memory and in addition had relatively little effect on protein synthesis. We have shown with tritiated puromycin that the antibiotic is lost more rapidly from the brain after the second injections, probably because of vascular changes which persist after the first injections. A similar resistance to puromycin often develops after any procedure in which the skull is entered.

EFFECTS OF ACETOXYCYCLOHEXIMIDE

The antibiotic acetoxycycloheximide became available to us at about the time we had completed these experiments with puromycin. It is a powerful inhibitor of protein synthesis and, importantly for us, suppresses protein synthesis by a mechanism different from that of puromycin. Puromycin produces its effect by being incorporated into the carboxyl ends of growing polypeptide chains and causing their premature release from ribosomes (6).

Acetoxycycloheximide, by contrast, inhibits the transfer of amino acids from s-RNA to polypeptide (6). Thus, unlike puromycin, the heximide suppresses the formation of peptide bonds. Could we destroy memory with the heximide and, as with puromycin, correlate this effect with severe inhibition of protein synthesis? If this proved to be the case, our tentative view that memory depends upon the continuing synthesis of protein would receive strong support.

Figure 3 shows the drastic and sustained effect of bitemporal injections of the heximide, up to 10 hours after treatment, on rate of protein synthesis in the hippocampus, an effect at least equal to that produced by puromycin (Fig. 2). Unlike puromycin, however, the most severe inhibitory effect of bitemporal injections of the heximide is not limited to the hippocampus and temporal cortex. Suppression of protein synthesis in the other six areas of the brain which were studied over the first 10 hours after the injections was as severe as in the hippocampus. Acetoxycycloheximide provided just the agent which we needed to test our working hypothesis.

Table 4 gives the results of the behavioral studies with acetoxycycloheximide. They, like the biochemical results, were unequivocal. Memory was not affected by the heximide in spite of its profound suppression of protein synthesis. Thus it was clear that the simplified version of our working hypothesis was inadequate to explain the destruction of memory by puromycin.

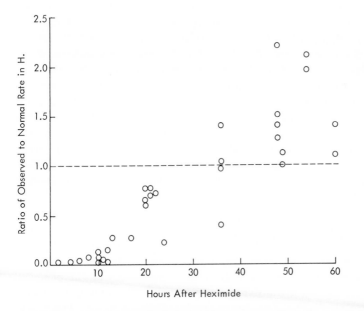

Fig. 3. Rate of protein synthesis in the hippocampus after bitemporal injections of 60 micrograms of acetoxycycloheximide. Values below the dotted line show inhibition; values above, increase of rate over normal level. From Flexner and Flexner (7), and Flexner, Flexner, and Roberts (8).

Table 4   Lack of Effect of Acetoxycycloheximide (A)
and of a Mixture of It and Puromycin (P) on Recent
(1 Day) and Longer-Term (12 to 35 Days) Memory[a]

SUBSTANCE	INJECTION SITE	DOSE (μg)	DAYS AFTER LEARNING	NO. OF MICE IN WHICH MEMORY WAS		
				LOST	IMPAIRED	RETAINED
A	T	60	1	0	1	8
A	T	120	1	0	1	3
A	T +V +F	15–30	1	0	0	2
A	T +V +F	15–30	12–35	0	0	5
A+P	T	120 A +120 P	1	0	1	6
A+P	T +V +F	8 or 15 A +30 P	14	0	0	6

[a] T, V, and F refer, respectively, to temporal, ventricular, and frontal injections, all given bilaterally. For the 30 mice with retention of memory, the means and standard deviations for percentages of savings of trials and errors were, respectively, 90 ± 15 and 92 ± 10; for the three mice with impaired memory, the corresponding means were 45 and 68. From Flexner and Flexner (7).

What explanation might be given for the differences between puromycin and acetoxycycloheximide in their effects on memory? One possibility is that the heximide also inhibits the degradation of protein; as a result continued synthesis would not be required to maintain the quantity above a critical level necessary for the expression of memory. That peptide bond formation occurs at a normal rate with puromycin but is suppressed by the heximide suggests two other possibilities. With puromycin it was possible that small, abnormal peptides are synthesized which are toxic and which somehow destroy memory. The second possibility rests upon the assumption, to be stated fully later, that memory depends in part upon the preservation of certain species of messenger RNA (mRNA) which are produced by a learning experience. It is also assumed that puromycin destroys memory because this essential mRNA decays without replacement, while with heximide memory is maintained because essential mRNA is preserved. In support of this possibility it has been found that mRNA is degraded at a normal rate in the presence of puromycin and that puromycin inhibits the synthesis of RNA (9). By contrast, the rate of decay of mRNA is decreased with suppression of peptide bond formation as occurs with acetoxycycloheximide (9).

If either of these latter explanations were valid, it could be predicted that puromycin would have no effect on memory in the presence of an agent which adequately suppresses the formation of peptide bonds. This prediction was tested (7) by using intracerebral injections of puromycin in mixture with acetoxycycloheximide, as well as with cycloheximide or chloramphenicol, which also interfere with transfer of amino acids to protein. All of these antibiotics protected memory against puromycin (Table 4).

Our attempts to demonstrate the presence of small, abnormal poly-peptides was based on identification of the puromycin which they would be expected to contain in terminal position. Tritiated puromycin was injected intracerebrally. We were unable to demonstrate radioactivity in protein precipitates prepared from appropriate areas of the brain (5). Chromatographs of the supernatant fluid had significant radioactivity only in the spot occupied by free puromycin. However, marked effects on memory have been reported after the injection of small quantities of peptide (10). Accordingly, we do not consider that our failure to find an accumulation of abnormal peptides is conclusive evidence that they are not involved in the loss of memory. This possibility remains open.

SELF-INDUCING SYSTEM

Understanding of an experimental test which we have made of the alternate possibility involving mRNA depends upon a more complete presentation of our working hypothesis than has thus far been given. We assume that an established memory of long duration depends, not on the continued presence of any protein or nucleic acid molecules, but on the establishment of a self-sustaining system for their synthesis. Such a system can occur whenever some of the products of a gene's expression act as inducers (or derepressors) of that gene. If the gene is repressed, inducers are not synthesized and the gene stays repressed. On the other hand, if the gene is induced for a sufficient time, inducers will accumulate above a critical level and the gene will stay induced. If, however, the synthetic processes are inhibited for a sufficient time, the level of inducers will fall below the critical level and the gene will revert to its repressed state. (A more quantitative description of the self-inducing system is given in 11.)

The processes involved in the establishment of a long-term memory can be described in terms of the self-inducing system. We assume that the initial learning experience triggers the synthesis of one or more species of mRNA. This mRNA alters the synthetic rate of one or more proteins which are essential for the expression of memory. These proteins are thought to modify the characteristics of synapses concerned in a learning process so that the passage of impulses between nerve cells is facilitated. In turn, the proteins or their products act as inducers of their related mRNA; in this way the concentration of the inducer proteins is maintained. In this view, expression of memory depends upon changes in proteins, changes which are initiated and sustained by qualitative and quantitative changes in mRNA produced by a learning experience. Loss of this mRNA would lead to loss of essential protein with consequent permanent loss of memory. In the presence of an inhibitor of protein synthesis, the concentration of essential protein could fall to levels too low for expression of memory, but loss of memory would be temporary if mRNA were conserved to direct the synthesis of protein when the inhibitor had disappeared (7).

Such a loss and recovery of memory has been observed in the behavior of mice at various times after training conducted (i) during or (ii) immediately before the severe suppression of protein synthesis which follows treatment with acetoxycycloheximide. Both sets of experiments showed an initial period in which memory was retained, an intermediate period in which memory was temporarily lost, and a final period during which expression of memory returned (*8*).

The duration of the initial period during which memory is retained in spite of severe inhibition of protein synthesis seems to vary with the conditions of learning and the inhibiting agent. Barondes and Cohen (*12*) observed that when mice are trained to a Y-maze in the presence of puromycin, they retain their memory of the maze at a high level for less than 45 minutes. In our mice trained immediately before treatment with acetoxycycloheximide, the initial period lasted for more than 14 hours. Memory of training in the presence of the heximide appeared to persist for between 3 to 5 hours, though the reliability of the upper limit is questionable because of the relatively poor condition of the mice at this time. In any event, there is a period in which memory is retained in spite of drastic inhibition of protein synthesis throughout the brain. Similar observations have been made on goldfish by Davis and Agranoff (*12*). Memory during the initial period may be based on changes in concentrations of ions or small molecules or in the configuration or location of preexisting macromolecules.

The intermediate period is characterized by failure of the mice to perform the training procedure. Our observations seem to indicate that the temporary loss of memory is not due to a general, nonspecific failure of performance or recall. Memory of training immediately before injection of heximide was expressed during a period when memory of training after injection of heximide could not be demonstrated. Furthermore, relearning occurred in both groups at the time when mice with loss of memory were given retention tests; this relearning indicated again an adequate capacity for performance. During the intermediate period memory appears to reside in a form which cannot be expressed until protein synthesis has been restored.

The final period is characterized by the return of memory to a condition where it can control performance. In essentially all mice in both experimental situations memory returned at a high level 58 to 96 hours after training. This period is at least 20 hours after protein synthesis was found to have returned to normal or higher than normal rates (Fig. 3).

Clearly only a beginning has been made in testing the hypothesis based on a self-sustaining system. The hypothesis is consistent with the results of Hydén and collaborators (*12*) who demonstrated an increase in nuclear RNA following training. It is also consistent with the recent finding by Zemp *et al.* (*12*) that rate of synthesis of nuclear RNA is increased in a learning situation. There is, however, as yet no completely convincing demonstration that changes in RNA and protein are fundamental to memory.

CONCLUSION

It is apparent that antibiotics are useful in differentiating different stages in the formation of memory. Puromycin gave the first indication that very early memory can be established and survive, for a short period at least, in spite of inhibition of protein synthesis (*12*). Injection of actinomycin D indicates that RNA synthesis is not essential during this early stage (*13*). The duration of this early period seems to vary with the inhibiting agent; with puromycin memory was notably degraded in less than an hour, but with actinomycin D or with acetoxycycloheximide it persisted for several hours or more.

The fixation or consolidation of memory involves whatever processes give permanence to memory. These processes are disrupted when electroconvulsive shock is administered shortly after a learning experience, presumably because of the interference with organized patterns of neuronal electrical activity. Memory acquired in the presence of antibiotics appears to proceed to a stage beyond that based purely on electrical activity because the memory persists beyond the period usually reported as sensitive to electroconvulsive shock. Further work should show whether this stage is truly insensitive to electroconvulsive shock. Memory acquired in the presence of puromycin does not seem to achieve any durable consolidation. In contrast, memory acquired in the presence of or immediately before injection of acetoxycycloheximide does appear to initiate the later stages of consolidation, as permanent memory reappears some days after the initial stages have become ineffective in controlling performance.

Finally, puromycin has provided evidence of the enlarged area of the neocortex which participates as memory matures. Puromycin also indicates the time required for this maturation process.

Since antibiotics have also been useful in studying learning and memory in goldfish (*14*), this approach seems to have general applicability in defining various stages in the process of memory formation.

The initial purpose of these investigations was to determine the molecular basis of the "memory trace." This goal still remains distant, although there are some indications that protein synthesizing systems are involved. This objective, though of enormous interest, is to be regarded as only a necessary first step. Whether new proteins or some other molecules cause the changes in synapses thought to underlie memory, this knowledge of itself will contribute only a beginning to our understanding of the events which account for the functioning of the brain. A determination of the composition of computer components would provide very little information towards unraveling their function.

As the experiments proceeded, however, information of a more general nature was being obtained. The identification of different stages of consolidation show how injections of antibiotics can supplement electroconvulsive shock as a way of disrupting the establishment of memory and how it can supplement ablation in destroying memory already laid down in a permanent mode. Applied to larger animals the localization of various regions sensitive or insensitive to the action of the drugs should become more definitive. We hope that such experiments will contribute increasingly to the general problem of brain function.

REFERENCES AND NOTES

1. J. L. MCGAUGH, *Science* **153**, 1351 (1966); W. HALSTEAD, in *Cerebral Mechanisms in Behavior*, L. A. Jeffress, Ed. (Wiley, New York, 1951), p. 244.
2. J. B. FLEXNER, L. B. FLEXNER, E. STELLAR, *Science* **141**, 57 (1963).
3. M. B. YARMOLINSKY & G. DE LA HABA, *Proc. Nat. Acad. Sci. U.S.* **45**, 1721 (1959).
4. B. MILNER & W. PENFIELD, *Trans. Amer. Neurol. Ass.* **80**, 42 (1955); W. B. SCOVILLE and B. MILNER, *J. Neurol. Neurosurg. Psychiat.* **20**, 11 (1957); L. S. STEPIEN, J. P. CORDEAU, T. RASMUSSEN, *Brain* **83**, 470 (1960).
5. J. B. FLEXNER, L. B. FLEXNER, E. STELLAR, G. DE LA HABA, R. B. ROBERTS, *J. Neurochem.* **9**, 595 (1962); L. B. FLEXNER, J. B. FLEXNER, R. B. ROBERTS, G. DE LA HABA, *Proc. Nat. Acad. Sci. U.S.* **52**, 1165 (1964); L. B. FLEXNER *et al.*, *Neurochem.* **12**, 535 (1965); L. B. FLEXNER, J. B. FLEXNER, E. STELLAR, *Exp. Neurol.* **13**, 264 (1965).
6. D. W. ALLEN & P. C. ZAMECNIK, *Biochim. Biophys. Acta* **55**, 865 (1962); D. NATHANS, *Proc. Nat. Acad. Sci. U.S.* **51**, 585 (1964); M. R. SIEGEL and H. D. SISLER, *Nature* **200**, 675 (1963); H. L. ENNIS and M. LUBIN, *Science* **146**, 1474 (1964).
7. L. B. FLEXNER & J. B. FLEXNER, *Proc. Nat. Acad. Sci. U.S.* **55**, 369 (1966).
8. L. B. FLEXNER, J. B. FLEXNER, R. B. ROBERTS, *ibid.* **56**, 730 (1966).
9. S. VILLA-TREVINO, E. FARBER, T. STAEHELIN, F. O. WETTSTEIN, H. NOLL, *J. Biol. Chem.* **239**, 3826 (1964); R. R. WAGNER and A. S. HUANG, *Proc. Nat. Acad. Sci. U.S.* **54**, 1112 (1965); A. R. WILLIAMSON and R. SCHWEET, *J. Mol. Biol.* **11**, 358 (1965).
10. B. BOHUS & D. DE WIED, *Science* **153**, 318 (1966).
11. R. B. ROBERTS & L. B. FLEXNER, *Amer. Sci.* **54**, 174 (1966).
12. S. H. BARONDES & H. D. COHEN, *Science* **151**, 594 (1966); R. E. DAVIS and B. W. AGRANOFF, *Proc. Nat. Acad. Sci. U.S.* **55**, 555 (1966); J. W. ZEMP, J. E. WILSON, K. SCHLESINGER, W. O. BOGGAN, E. GLASSMAN, *ibid.*, p. 1423; H. HYDÉN and E. EGYHÀZI, *ibid.* **52**, 1030 (1964); H. HYDÉN and P. W. LANGE, *ibid.* **53**, 946 (1965).
13. H. D. COHEN & S. H. BARONDES, *J. Neurochem.* **13**, 207 (1966).
14. B. W. AGRANOFF, R. E. DAVIS, J. J. BRINK, *Brain Res.* **1**, 303 (1966).

III

THE PROBLEM OF WHERE: FUNCTIONAL LOCALIZATION

The study of the role of different brain structures in learning and memory is one of the oldest and most active areas of neuropsychological research. Its chief method is the study of effects of brain damage or *lesion*. In animal experiments, lesions are usually made by removing (*ablating*) tissue or cutting (*sectioning*) pathways. More recently, methods have been developed for producing "reversible lesions" by cooling or electrically stimulating a particular area. Like other approaches to brain and behavior the lesion method has its hazards. Although specific lesions often have highly specific behavioral effects, it may be misleading to try to "localize" psychological functions such as learning or memory in particular parts of the brain. In studying the behavioral effects of a brain ablation one is not studying the effect of removing a function. Indeed, the behavioral effect may be due to release from inhibition of another structure whose activity is normally suppressed by the ablated structure. Similarly, a lesion may interfere with two or more independent mechanisms rather than produce a single dysfunction.

The most eminent practitioner of the ablation method was Karl Lashley (1890–1958). Lashley pioneered in the use of objective training methods for studying the effects of ablations on behavior and established the practice of reconstructing lesions from stained sections of the brain. He spent much of his long and distinguished career exploring the relationship between the size of cortical lesion and the severity of its effect on behavior.

The most convincing evidence Lashley obtained for a relationship between size of lesion and severity of deficit came from experiments with rats in a complex maze. He found that the number of errors made in the maze was a function of the amount of cortical damage but was independent of the site of the damage. These results led him to formulate his hypotheses of *equipotentiality* and *mass action*. He defined equipotentiality as the apparent capacity of any part of an area to carry out equally (with or without loss of efficiency) the functions which are lost by destruction of the whole area. Thus, equipotentiality implies no specialization within an area that is involved in a particular behavior. Since only a small area might be equipotential for a given task, Lashley believed that equipotentiality was fully compatible with localization. Furthermore, equipotentiality, according to Lashley, is not absolute but is subject to a law of mass action whereby the degree of deficit produced by a lesion in an equipotential area is a function of the size of the lesion.

Today, reports of specific effects of brain lesions are very common, and mass-action findings (except when limited to a small area) are relatively rare. The only test situation in which Lashley found a mass-action effect involving the entire cortex was a complex maze, a task which involves a number of skills and sensory systems. Thus, in this case, Lashley's mass-action effects may have been due, at least in part, to progressive encroachment on multiple foci critical for different aspects of the maze problem (Hunter, 1930). In one study which supports this view, Gross, Chorover and Cohen (1965) found a critical area in anterior cortex for alternation behavior and another one in posterior cortex for visually guided behavior, both skills being involved in learning Lashley's maze.

Much of the recent lesion work on learning and memory has involved the *association cortex* of monkeys. Association cortex traditionally includes all neocortex other than the primary sensory and motor areas. Frontal association cortex (prefrontal cortex) includes all neocortex anterior to the premotor area. Posterior association cortex includes neocortex in the temporal lobe, the posterior parietal lobe, and the nonstriate regions of the occipital lobe. Among the advantages of using monkeys rather than rats in lesion studies are the clearer anatomical delineation of these cortical areas and the greater ease of training in highly specific behavioral tasks.

The modern study of frontal association cortex began when Jacobsen discovered that frontal lesions make monkeys incapable of performing the *delayed-response* test (Jacobsen, 1936). In this test (a version of the shell game) the monkey sees the experimenter place a bait under one of two cups and, seconds later, is given the opportunity of choosing the baited cup. Subsequent investigations, described by Rosvold and Szwarcbart (see page 116) revealed that a critical focus for the delayed-response deficit lay in the middle of the dorsolateral surface of the frontal lobe. Furthermore, they found subcortical areas whose destruction also impairs delayed response. These areas turn out to be anatomically related to the dorsolateral surface, thereby suggesting at least part of the underlying "circuitry" involved in delayed-response performance.

Weiskrantz, Mihailović, and Gross (see page 132) present a method of producing a reversible frontal lesion. When they electrically stimulated frontal cortex, their monkey could not perform delayed alternation (a variant of the delayed-response test) but was normal in other tasks. However, as soon as the current was turned off, the monkey behaved normally again. By introducing "noise" into the tissue, its normal function was temporarily disrupted. This method of "functional ablation," unlike surgical ablation, makes it possible to compare different lesions in the same animal and to test, in the normal state, memory of a problem learned in the "ablated" state.

In 1939, Klüver and Bucy reported rather bizarre behavior in monkeys after removal of their temporal lobes. The normally fierce animals were now tame, hypersexual, and "psychically blind" (that is, their learning and memory of visual discrimination was severely disturbed). Subsequent work by Chow, Pribram, and their associates revealed that lesions confined to the neocortex on the inferior convexity of the temporal lobe (*inferotemporal cortex*) would produce the visual-discrimination deficit without the other symptoms of temporal lobe removal. By contrast, lesions of the *amygdala*, a large nucleus in the medial and basal portion of the temporal lobe, would produce the tameness and hypersexual effects without the learning deficit. Thus, the *"Klüver-Bucy syndrome"* could be "fractionated" or "dissociated" into components by smaller temporal lobe lesions (Pribram, 1954).

Mishkin's 1966 paper "Visual mechanism beyond the striate cortex" (see page 136) reviews current thinking about inferotemporal cortex and describes his elegant experiments on the relationship between infero-temporal cortex and the classical visual area in the occipital lobe. Mishkin was able to show that in order to function normally in visual discrimination, inferotemporal cortex has to receive information from striate cortex, presumably over a cortico-cortical route from striate to prestriate to inferotemporal cortex. It should be noted, however, that inferotemporal cortex may also need subcortical input for normal function (Pribram *et al.*, 1966). There are other parts of posterior association cortex that also seem to play modality-specific roles in discrimination learning. Their role may be analogous to the role of inferotemporal cortex in visual learning. For example, tactile discrimination learning is impaired by lesions of posterior parietal cortex (Wilson, 1957), olfactory discrimi-nation by anterior temporal lesions (Brown *et al.*, 1963), and auditory discrimination by lesions of superior temporal association cortex (Massopust *et al.*, 1965).

The next group of selections deals with the effects of brain lesions in man. Milner (see page 158) describes the debilitating effects of bilateral hippocampal damage in man—virtually total loss of the ability to remember anything for more than a few moments; the "recording apparatus" appears to have been permanently destroyed. As in the study of retrograde amnesia, the clinical material often presents the problem more clearly than the data from experimental animals.

Although Teuber's (1959) selection, "Some alterations in behavior after cerebral lesions in man" (see page 170), does not deal directly with learning and memory, it makes several general points relevant to ablation studies. One is that the behavioral changes produced by even massive brain damage are often not detectable by observation or routine testing but may require special experimentation for their discovery. Another point, similar to one made by Lashley, is that a given lesion may have both effects specific to a particular locus and more general effects independent of the site of damage. A third is that the dichotomy between "lower sensory or motor functions" and "higher cognitive functions" that is often implicit in lesion studies, particularly of man, may not be a valid or useful one.

The usual approach of clinical neurology has been to study a small number of patients selected for their interesting symptoms. Teuber, on the other hand, gathered a large group of brain-injured patients selected for their injuries rather than their symptoms and then began to examine experimentally various aspects of their behavior. His work is also characterized by more reliance on statistical and experimental techniques than is usual in the study of human brain damage.

The final group of brain-lesion studies utilizes one of the most exciting advances of the decade, the "split-brain preparation." Sperry and his colleagues have shown that it is possible to produce two independent minds within one monkey by cutting the major connections between the cerebral hemispheres. If sensory input is then confined to one hemisphere, that hemisphere can be taught a problem without the other hemisphere learning it. In fact, the two hemispheres can be taught opposite habits. The surgical methods for producing two minds in one head and the behavioral tests that reveal them are described by Sperry in his selection beginning on page 200. He also describes some of the current puzzles in this area, such as the finding that some types of information seem to transfer from one side of the brain to the other even with very deep surgical splits. Finally, Sperry discusses some of the powerful applications of the split-brain procedures to the study of functional localization and of eye-hand coordination.

In all animals except man the two halves of the brain appear to be identical in function. In man, however, there is marked asymmetry of function as revealed by the effects of unilateral brain damage. The most striking functional asymmetry concerns the areas of the brain involved in speech and language. In right-handed people, damage to the left side of the brain may result in language disturbances, but damage to the right side almost never does. Thus, if the two sides of the brain were disconnected in a right-handed man one might expect him to be able to use items in his left hand but not be able to name them. As described by Gazzaniga, Bogen, and Sperry (see page 216) this is exactly what happens in "split-brain people." Even more fascinating is the undeniable demonstration of two independent sets of perceptions, thought, and emotions existing within the heads of these patients.

In the final split-brain selection, Sechzer (see page 233) demonstrates that when shock is used to motivate split-brain cats, at least certain types of information can get from one hemisphere to the other. The information may be traveling down the nervous system, crossing the unsplit brain stem, and coming up the other side. On the other hand, the transmission may be via some peripheral or autonomic mechanism.

C. G. G.

REFERENCES

BEACH, F. A., HEBB, D. O., MORGAN, C. T., & NISSEN H. W., (Eds.) *The Neuropsychology of Lashley.* New York: McGraw-Hill, 1960.

BROWN, T. S., ROSVOLD, H. E., & MISHKIN, M. Olfactory discrimination after temporal lobe lesions in monkeys. *J. Comp. Physiol. Psychol.*, 1963, **56**, 190–195.

GROSS, C. G., CHOROVER, S. L., & COHEN, S. M. Caudate, cortical, hippocampal and dorsal thalamic lesions in rats: Alternation and Hebb-Williams maze performance. *Neuropsychologia*, 1965, **3**, 53–68.

HUNTER, W. S. A consideration of Lashley's theory of the equipotentiality of cerebral action. *J. Gen. Psychol.*, 1930, **3**, 455–468.

JACOBSEN, C. F. Studies of cerebral function in primates. I. The functions of the frontal association areas in monkeys. *Comp. Psychol. Monogr.*, 1936, **13**, 3–60.

KLÜVER, H., & BUCY, P. C. Preliminary analysis of functions of the temporal lobes in monkeys. *Arch. Neurol. Psychiat.*, 1939, **42**, 979–1000.

LASHLEY, K. S. *Brain Mechanisms and Intelligence.* New York: Dover, 1963.

MASSOPUST, L. C., BARNES, H. W., MEDER, J., & MEDER, R. Deficits in auditory frequency discrimination following temporal and frontal lobe lesions in monkeys. *J. Audit. Research.*, 1965, **5**, 85–93.

PRIBRAM, K. H. Toward a science of neuropsychology (method and data). In *Current trends in psychology and the behavioral sciences.* Pittsburgh: University of Pittsburgh Press, 1954. Pp. 115–142.

PRIBRAM, K. H., BLEHERT, S. R., & SPINELLI, D. N. Effects on visual discrimination of crosshatching and undercutting the inferotemporal cortex of monkeys. *J. Comp. Physiol. Psychol.*, 1966, **62**, 358–364.

WILSON, M. Effects of circumscribed cortical lesions upon somesthetic and visual discrimination in the monkey. *J. Comp. Physiol. Psychol.*, 1957, **50**, 630–635.

Neural Structures Involved in Delayed-Response Performance

H. Enger Rosvold
and Maria K. Szwarcbart

The evidence implicating the prefrontal cortex in functions serving delayed-response-type tests does not need to be reviewed in detail for the participants of this symposium. Only rarely since Jacobsen (1935) first demonstrated that disturbance of these functions was severe and permanent following frontal lobe damage has the reliability of his finding been questioned. Even then exceptions could be attributed to the use of special testing procedures (Malmo, 1942; Battig et al., 1960; French & Harlow, 1962). Less widely accepted has been his finding that frontal lobe damage did not disturb visual-discrimination performance although, here too, it has been suggested that the apparent exceptions can be attributed to the presence of special factors in the testing procedures (Rosvold & Mishkin, 1961). No other cortical lesion results in this pattern of severe impairment in delayed-response and intact visual-discrimination performance. As may be seen in Figure 1.1 (Mishkin & Pribram, 1958), lesions in virtually all other association cortex and the amygdala as well have yielded either opposite or negative results. So consistently have studies confirmed this selective deficit in delayed response to be a unique effect of lesions in frontal cortex that it has seemed reasonable to suppose that those subcortical structures in which damage results in the same selective effect must be integrally related to the frontal cortex. Together they may constitute a neural system serving delayed-response-type functions. What, then, are the probable components of this " system," and what is the neurophysiological and neuroanatomical evidence which would lend this functional unit some reality?

From *The Frontal Granular Cortex and Behavior* by J. M. Warren and K. Akert (Eds.) (New York: McGraw-Hill, 1964), pp. 1–15. Reprinted with permission of the publisher and authors.

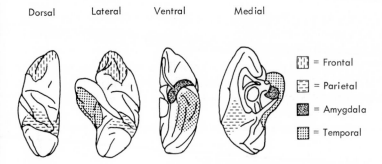

Figure 1.1. Typical cortical lesions which Mishkin and Pribram (unpublished report, 1958) used to establish that only prefrontal lesions resulted in delayed-response deficits.

First, it is generally agreed that the cortical component of this system is located in the dorsolateral frontal cortex. Some dissent arises chiefly from the fact that in an early study by Pribram et al. (1952) half the animals with ventromedial frontal lesions, such as those illustrated in Figure 1.2, did show some impairment in the retention of a delayed-response task. However, the ventromedial animals differed from normal in only one of the two delay tasks presented and then showed only partial impairment. More recently, Pribram et al. (1962) fanned this smolder by reporting that impairment on such tasks may be produced even by lesions limited to the cingulate portion of medial cortex. However, it should be noted that in this more recent study also, performance was affected on only the more difficult delay task (viz., delayed alternation) and then one of the two animals with cingulate lesions ultimately achieved criterion. Similarly, even though lesions limited to the ventral surface of the frontal cortex may have some effect, it is very little indeed. For example, lesions such as those labeled VF in Figure 1.3 (Mishkin, 1957) have no effect at all. Those labeled orbital frontal in Figure 1.4 (Brutkowski, Mishkin & Rosvold, 1960) result in only partial impairment in alternation performance; the animals required approximately twice as many trials to achieve criterion as would be expected of normal animals (Rosvold et al., 1958). In contrast to these partial and transient effects of ventral and medial lesions is the severe and permanent effect of dorsolateral lesions. Here, in fact, maximal deficits may be obtained even from small lesions confined to the midlateral region (Blum, 1952; MF11 and MF87 in Figure 1.3, Mishkin, 1957; Weiskrantz et al., 1962). Clearly, then, the major cortical focus for functions measured by delayed-response tests is located in the dorsolateral prefrontal convexity.

Turning to subcortical structures, the one which most clearly seems to belong to this sytem is the head of the caudate nucleus. Performance on delayed alternation is impaired following either electrical stimulation or damage to this structure (Rosvold & Delgado, 1956). The severity of the deficit increases as the size of the electrolytic lesion is increased (Rosvold et al., 1958), approaching complete loss (defined as sustained performance at chance levels) when large ablations are made (Migler, 1958). The similarity in function of the caudate nucleus and prefrontal cortex is further supported by the finding that damage to either structure results in impairments not only in delayed alternation (Figure 1.5), but in delayed response as well (Figure 1.6; Battig et al., 1960). Other similarities in the effects of these two lesions are

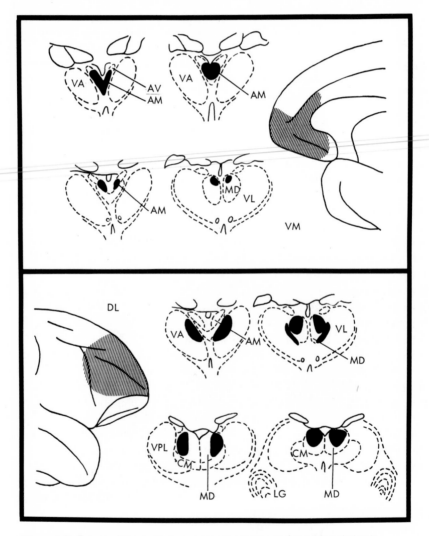

Figure 1.2. Extent of the typical ventromedial lesion and resulting thalamic degeneration. For comparison, the typical dorsolateral lesion and consequent thalamic degeneration are also shown. (Modified from Pribram et al., 1952.)

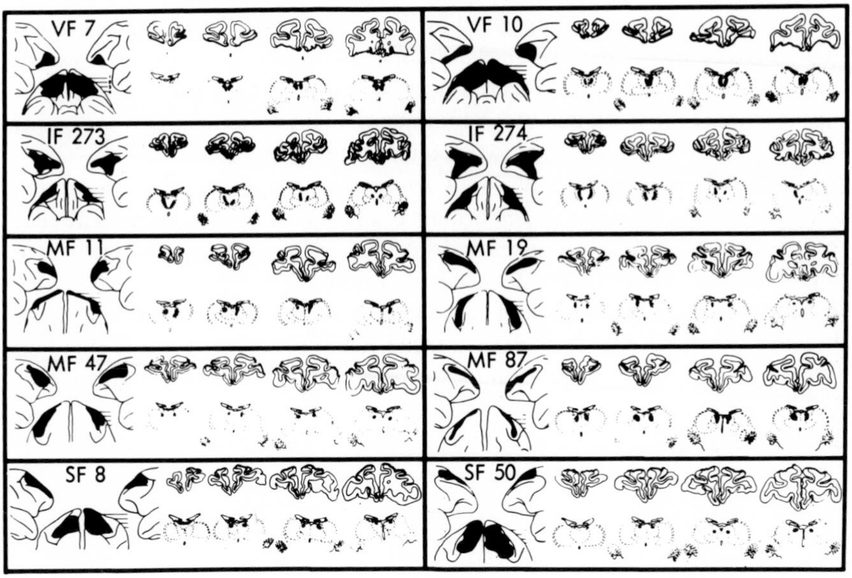

Figure 1.3. Reconstructions of the small frontal lesions and consequent thalamic degeneration which Mishkin (1957) used to establish that a principal focus of delayed-response functions is in the midlateral prefrontal cortex.

illustrated in Figure 1.7 (Battig et al., 1962), where it may be seen that both result in similar impairments on auditory as well as visual differentiation tasks. Thus, without exception, the behavioral effects of frontal and caudate lesions have proved to be qualitatively similar.

The hippocampus probably also belongs in the system, though it is included with somewhat less assurance. The equivocation derives from the fact that while hippocampal lesions clearly impair delayed-alternation performance, considerable question remains regarding their effect on delayed-response performance. Mishkin (1954), for example, reported no clear-cut impairment in delayed-response retention after hippocampal ablations; nevertheless, four out of five hippocampal animals accumulated slightly more errors after operation than before. An effect of hippocampal lesions on delayed response may also be suspected in another study (Mishkin & Pribram, 1954), since the only animal of seven to fail to reach criterion was one belonging to the hippocampal group. Similarly, the suggestion of an impairment is present in the performance of hippocampal animals in the more recent study by Orbach et al. (1960). In initial learning after operation five out of six animals with hippocampectomy made more errors at the 5-sec delay than the three similarly treated operated controls. If these minimal and inconsistent effects were the only evidence of hippocampal participation in delayed-response-type performance, they could well be dismissed. That they should be given greater consideration, however, is suggested by the severe and permanent impairment of delayed-response performance found in cats after hippocampal lesions (Karmos & Grastyán, 1962). Perhaps, as with caudate lesions, the effects of hippocampal lesions on delayed response are qualitatively similar to those of frontal lesions, even though they are quantitatively less severe.

While there is still some doubt concerning the effect of hippocampal lesions on delayed-response performance, there is complete agreement that these lesions affect performance on delayed alternation. However, again, the impairment is less severe than after frontal lesions, being more comparable to that after caudate lesions. Thus, Orbach et al. (1960) found that even though all hippocampal animals sustained a retention loss, all but one obtained an error score smaller than would have been expected of frontal animals; in

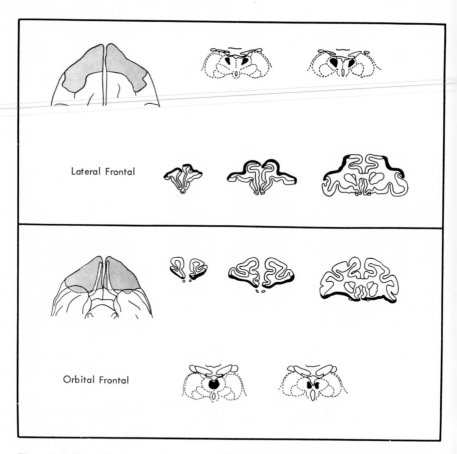

Figure 1.4. Frontal lesions and consequent thalamic degeneration which Brutkowski, Mishkin & Rosvold (1960) used to demonstrate that lesions in orbital frontal cortex were relatively less effective than lesions in dorsolateral frontal cortex in producing delayed-response deficits.

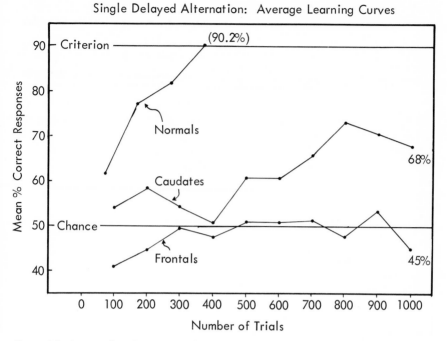

Figure 1.5. Average learning curves of single delayed alternation showing that as compared with normal monkeys, both caudate and frontal animals are impaired.

fact, the loss was very similar to the partial impairment found in caudate animals (Rosvold et al., 1958). Partial effects of hippocampectomy on delayed alternation are also reported by Pribram et al. (1962). In this study, though there was a retention loss in all three hippocampal animals, two reached criterion (one in remarkably few trials) and all made fewer errors than would be expected in frontal, and about the same as would be expected in caudate animals. Furthermore, even under the more difficult condition of postoperative initial learning, one of two animals attained criterion before the limit of training had been reached.

One possible explanation of these partial effects is that maximum impairment results only from total destruction of the hippocampus, and this has not yet been achieved. Thus, in the four studies referred to there was some sparing of tissue in each of the animals tested. If this explanation is correct, it would be expected, as was shown to be the case with caudate lesions (Rosvold et al., 1958), that the severity of the deficit would depend on the extent of the lesion. Accordingly, lesions of various sizes were placed in the hippocampus of 19 monkeys, and the severity of impairment on delayed alternation correlated with the volume of hippocampus involved. It may be seen in Figure 1.8 that when the extent of damage to the hippocampus is increased, the alternation

Delayed Response: No. of Trials to Reach Criterion

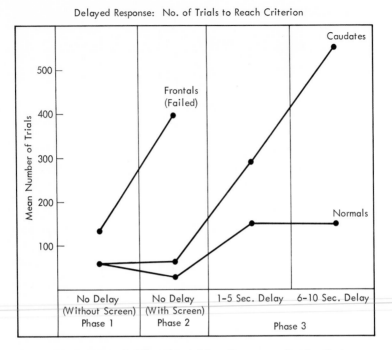

Figure 1.6. Number of trials to learn delayed response showing that as compared with normal monkeys, both caudate and frontal animals are impaired.

errors are also increased; visual-discrimination errors, however, are independent of lesion size (Rosvold et al., 1962). In contrast to this, as shown in Figure 1.9, the scores on visual discrimination but not on alternation reflect the degree to which the visual system (i.e., optic tract, lateral geniculate, visual radiations, inferotemporal cortex) is involved by the lesion.

Another possible explanation for the inconsistent effects of hippocampal damage became apparent in this study. The correlational analysis presented in Figure 1.10 suggests that the hippocampus may not be equipotential in its contribution to delayed-alternation performance. The probability of obtaining a deficit appears to be much greater with anterior than with posterior lesions, and with lesions in regions CA1 and CA4 than in regions CA2 and CA3. Thus, the degree to which delayed-alternation performance is affected may depend not so much on the proportion of total hippocampus involved as on the extent to which specific segments have been damaged.

Only one other subcortical structure has been implicated thus far in the performance of delayed-response tasks. Adey et al. (1962) reported that cats were severely impaired in performance of this task following electrocoagulation of subthalamic zones. Other "frontal" symptoms observed in these animals were great distractibility, increased motor activity, and an inordinate

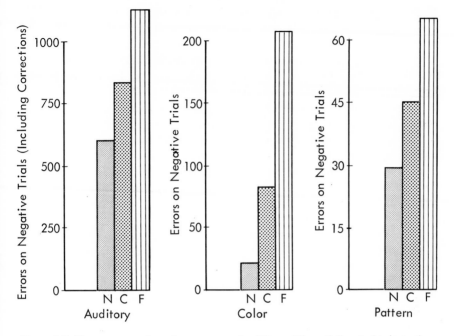

Figure 1.7. The mean number of errors on each of three differentiation tasks. In each of the tasks both caudate and frontal monkeys are inferior to the controls.

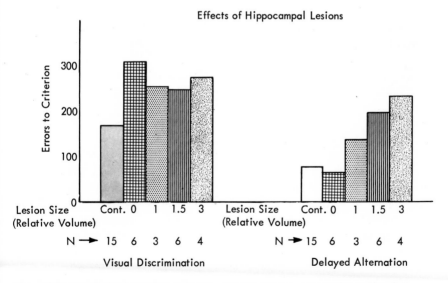

Figure 1.8. Visual-discrimination and delayed-alternation errors relative to the size of hippocampal lesions. The larger lesions result in more delayed-alternation errors, but not in more visual-discrimination errors.

perseveration of position responses. It is not implied that these effects, observed in only two cats, are sufficient for unequivocally establishing a relationship between subthalamus and the frontal cortex. Rather, the intent is to emphasize that, as the search continues, additional components of the system mediating delayed-response functions may be discovered. Indeed, Cianci's (1962) observation that electrical stimulation of the substantia nigra disturbs delayed-response performance suggests that this structure also should be included.

Thus the foregoing evidence that the frontal cortex and certain subcortical structures serve a common behavioral function provides some justification for postulating that these structures may constitute a complex neural system. The following neurophysiological and neuroanatomical evidence, admittedly selective for purposes of exposition, gives further support for this concept.

Consider first the frontal-caudate link in the schematic diagram shown in Figure 1.11. Direct connections between these structures were inferred by Harman et al. (1954) on the basis of a reduction in the size of the head of the caudate nucleus following lateral frontal ablations. Although Akert and his colleagues (Burandt et al., 1961) have failed to confirm this finding on the basis of either a volumetric or retrograde degeneration analysis, Nauta

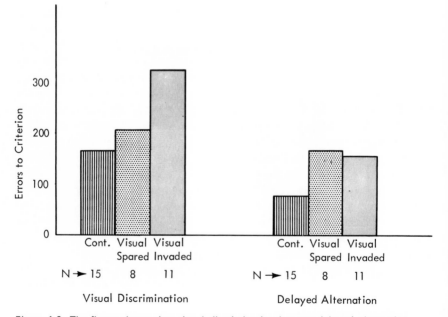

Figure 1.9. The figure shows that visual-discrimination but not delayed-alternation errors reflect the fact that the visual system had been invaded by the hippocampal lesion.

D. A.				V. D.	
Hippo System			Visual System	Hippo System	Visual System
Hippo	A-P	CA			
.59*	-7-3 .34	CA 1 .66ˣˣ	-.32	-.07	.48*
	-2+9 .58*	CA 2 .46			
	+10+16 .62*	CA 3 .45			
		CA 4 .61ˣˣ			

Figure 1.10. Extent to which delayed-alternation and visual-discrimination errors are correlated with the locus of the hippocampal lesions. The anterior posterior (A- P) designations are Horsley-Clarke coordinates, CA designations, the hippocampal regions of Lorente de Nó.

(personal communication) has more recently suggested that direct connections may, in fact, exist. He will probably emphasize the tentative nature of his finding in his paper later in this symposium, but it does appear that degeneration in the head of the caudate after midlateral frontal lesions is evident in his silver-stained material. While anatomists have not finally resolved the issue as to whether or not frontal-caudate connections are direct, neurophysiologists are agreed that the two structures are at least closely related. For example, Forman & Ward (1957) found that simultaneously stimulating cortex and caudate led to effects indicative of interaction between them, although they concluded that it probably takes place through intervening subcortical structures. Poggio et al. (1956) found that cortically induced epileptic discharges are propagated through subcortical structures in such a way as to suggest that there are preferential, if not direct, pathways between frontal cortex and caudate nucleus. Mettler et al. (1952) concluded on the basis of an analysis of the latency of the evoked responses to single shocks that the connections between frontal cortex and caudate are most likely direct.

There is some evidence that the caudate nucleus also interacts with the hippocampus (Figure 1.11). In an extensive study Umbach (1959) demonstrated that direct stimulation of the caudate nucleus induced slow waves in the caudate for a fraction of a second and that during this time the hippocampus was relatively inactive; after this phase, spindle activity developed synchronously in both structures. The hippocampus and caudate nucleus are

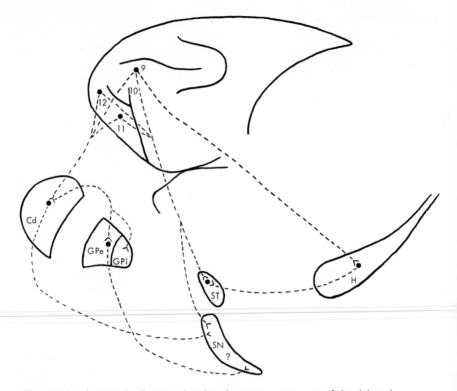

Figure 1.11. Schematic diagram showing the component parts of the delayed-response system. The lines joining the structures are not meant to imply direction of neural activity.

also among the subcortical structures which develop synchronous activity during conditioning (Galambos et al., 1956; John & Killam, 1959). It is also interesting in this context that the hippocampus and caudate nucleus seem to be the only subcortical structures in which spreading depression may be elicited directly (Marshall, 1959; Bureš et al., 1960) and to which a depression may spread, even though minimally, from cortex (Bureš, personal communication). Evidence for the connections between the hippocampus and frontal cortex (Figure 1.11) is provided by Adey & Meyer (1952a), who found that dorsolateral frontal lesions result in degeneration in the hippocampus.

Finally, with respect to the place of the subthalamus in the schema, Adey et al. (1961) have shown that as animals learn delayed response, electrical activity in hippocampus and subthalamus becomes synchronous. In a later study (Adey et al., 1962) it was found that as relearning progressed after a small subthalamic lesion, improvement in the animal's performance was correlated with restoration both of normal activity in the hippocampus and of synchronous activity in the subthalamus. Thus, these two structures appear not only to interact, but even further, to function in tandem. There seems to be ample anatomical basis for such a relationship. Adey (1958) has pointed out that the subthalamus receives fibers from the hippocampus, and Szabo (1962) and Johnson (1961) have shown that the subthalamus is closely related to the caudate by means of major anatomical connections.

Other interrelationships such as, for example, between frontal cortex and substantia nigra (Jung & Hassler, 1960) and between caudate and substantia nigra (Szabo, 1962; Jung & Hassler, 1960) have been described (Figure 1.11). Undoubtedly the structures in Figure 1.11 are interrelated with other nuclei, for example, with centrum medianum, but since the significance of these relationships for delayed-response performance is not known, they are not included in this discussion.

Additional support for the concept of a "frontal lobe system" may be found in similarities in the organization of cellular activity in the parts of the system. Consider, for example, the implication of the finding that damage to the dorsolateral frontal cortex results in similar impairment on delayed response or differentiation tasks irrespective of the sensory modality involved in the test (Rosvold & Mishkin, 1961). One neural model which would satisfactorily account for the nonspecificity of this effect would be one in which afferents from several modalities converge on the same neuron. It is noteworthy that in his reviews of the evidence on convergence, Fessard (1960; Fessard & Szabo, 1961) emphasized that the area which is least specific with regard to sensory modality is the frontal association cortex. Here the rule is an equivalence of effect on the neuron regardless of the source of the stimulus. Convergence also occurs in the caudate, hippocampus, and subthalamus with little preference shown for any one modality. With respect to the caudate nucleus, Albe-Fessard et al. (1960) noted that a large proportion of the cells in this nucleus were unusually responsive to stimulation of either somatic, visual, or auditory afferents. Some cells in the hippocampus also are nonspecific responders and may be activated by excitation of any afferent path (Green & Machné, 1955). Similarly in the subthalamus (Albe-Fessard & Rougeul, 1956) afferents from a variety of sources converge on a single cell.

Although it has been convenient to discuss the subcortical components of the frontal-lobe system as though each were a homogeneous structure entirely concerned with the same function, such apparent simplicity is likely not the case. The caudate nucleus, for example, has at least three distinct segments based on the topical distribution of its efferent connections with the globus pallidus and substantia nigra (Szabo, 1962). At least two of these appear to be differentially related to frontal cortex. Dorsolateral frontal cortical lesions resulted in degeneration only in the anterior and dorsal portion of the head of the caudate nucleus (Nauta, personal communication). It is this part of the caudate which appears to be unresponsive to amygdaloid stimulation (Adey & Dunlop, 1960) and in which electrical stimulation results in delayed-response deficits (Cianci, 1962). On the other hand, the frontal orbital cortex projects to the more ventral portions of the caudate (Wall et al., 1951), which are responsive to stimulation of the amygdala (Adey & Dunlop, 1960) but in which electrical stimulation does not result in delayed-response deficits (Cianci, 1962). Similarly, the hippocampus, as shown earlier (Figure 1.10), is not equipotential with respect to delayed-response performance; instead, there appears to be a principal focus for mediating these functions in region CA4. Adey (1961) found that region CA4 was also the principal focus of the regular rhythmic slow-wave activity which develops as an animal learns the delayed-response task. Perhaps behavioral studies involving selective ablation will reveal that, as in frontal cortex, there is in each subcortical structure a focal area mediating delayed-response functions.

The value to the neuropsychologist of identifying the subcortical structures related to dorsolateral frontal cortex lies in the direction it may give to further analysis of the behavioral effects of interference with frontal lobe functions. Even with the information now available some suggestions may be made in this respect, if only to suggest a reasonable basis for speculation. Consider, for example, the implication of Adey's (Adey et al., 1961, 1962) finding that it is only in the response period of the delayed-response task in which changes in electrical activity of the hippocampus are correlated with improvement and deterioration of performance. Does this not indicate that the delayed-response impairment is associated with dysfunction of a response mechanism rather than of mechanisms related to stimulus presentation or to the delay? However, it is not the response itself (that is, approaching the food wells and searching for the hidden bait) which is impaired after hippocampal lesions; rather, it is probably some central process relating this response to the conditional aspects of the task. Thus, the response is selected, not by the cerebral events initiated by the immediately preceding stimulus, but erroneously by persisting central activity which had been initiated earlier in a similar context. Such a dysfunction could occur in the hippocampus, which not only receives impulses from many widely dispersed sources but also seems to regulate motor functions (Votaw, 1959; Flynn & Wasman, 1960).

Of course, the hippocampus is not the only structure which may regulate efferent activity; in fact, this capability seems to be a common characteristic of the postulated components of the "delayed-response system." The caudate nucleus, for example, has both inhibitory and facilitatory effects (Purpura et al., 1958; Heuser et al., 1961) which are reflected in behavior (Heuser et al., 1961). Thus, low-frequency stimulation of the head of the caudate results in spindle bursts in the EEG, general slowing of locomotor activity, increased reaction times, and decreased rates of bar pressing; high-frequency stimulation results in desynchronization of the EEG, behavioral alerting, increased locomotor activity, and increased rates of bar pressing. It is probable that cerebral activity is modulated not only by the caudate as suggested by Heuser et al. (1961) but by a much more comprehensive system made up at least of frontal cortex, caudate, hippocampus, and subthalamus. It will remain the task of further research to make explicit not only how lesions in these structures result in a failure of the regulating mechanism important for delayed response, but also whether this failure may lead to the various other disorders of behavior which we are to hear more about in this symposium.

Forty years ago Bianchi (1922) summarized his behavioral observations of frontal monkeys thus: " Memory, weak and unreliable, becomes enormously reduced, not only for recent but also for old acquisitions. The mutilated monkey does not utilize past experience; he persists always in repeating the same actions, without profiting from the futility of the previous action, and without making any alteration so as to arrive at a determined object." Bianchi's perceptive descriptions of the behavioral dysfunctions produced by frontal lobe injury will be amplified and analyzed further in many of the papers of this symposium. I should like to emphasize here, at the beginning of our symposium, that while we may confine our discussions to the prefrontal cortex, we are in fact discussing, if only by implication, a complicated cortical-subcortical system of which the frontal cortex is only one, although a most important, component.

REFERENCES

ADEY, W. R. Organization of the rhinencephalon. In H. H. Jasper, L. D. Proctor, R. S. Knighton, W. C. Noshay, & R. T. Costello (Eds.), *Henry Ford Hospital International Symposium: Reticular Formation of the Brain.* Boston: Little, Brown, 1958. Pp. 621–644.

ADEY, W. R., & DUNLOP, C. W. Amygdaloid and peripheral influences on caudate and pallidal units in the cat and effects of chlorpromazine. *Exp. Neurol.,* 1960, **2**, 348–363.

ADEY, W. R., & MEYER, M. An experimental study of hippocampal afferent pathways from prefrontal and cingulate areas in the monkey. *J. Anat.,* 1952, **86**, 58–74.

ADEY, W. R., WALTER, D. O., & HENDRIX, C. E. Computer techniques in correlation and spectral analyses of cerebral slow waves during discriminative behavior. *Exp. Neurol.,* 1961, **3**, 501–524.

ADEY, W. R., WALTER, D. O., & LINDSLEY, D. F. Subthalamic lesions. Effects on learned behavior and correlated hippocampal and subcortical slow-wave activity. *Arch. Neurol.,* 1962, **6**, 194–207.

ALBE-FESSARD, D., ROCHA-MIRANDA, C., & OSWALDO-CRUZ, E. Activités évoquées dans le noyau caudé du chat en répose à des types divers d'afférences. *EEG Clin. Neurophysiol.,* 1960, **12**, 649–661.

ALBE-FESSARD, D., & ROUGEUL, A. Relais thalamiques d'afférences somesthesiques aboutissants à certaines régions localisées du cortex associatif du chat. *J. Physiol.,* 1956, **48**, 370–374.

BATTIG, K., ROSVOLD, H. E., & MISHKIN, M. Comparison of the effects of frontal and caudate lesions on delayed response and alternation in monkeys. *J. Comp. Physiol. Psychol.,* 1960, **53**, 400–404.

BATTIG, K., ROSVOLD, H. E., & MISHKIN, M. Comparison of the effects of frontal and caudate lesions on discrimination learning in monkeys. *J. Comp. Physiol. Psychol.,* 1962, **55**, 458–463.

BIANCHI, L. *The mechanism of the brain and the function of the frontal lobes.* Edinburgh: Livingstone, Ltd., 1922.

BLUM, R. A. Effects of subtotal lesions of frontal granular cortex on delayed reaction in monkeys. *Arch. Neurol. Psychiat.*, 1952, **67**, 375–386.

BRUTKOWSKI, S., MISHKIN, M., & ROSVOLD, H. E. The effect of orbital and dorsolateral frontal lesions on conditioned inhibitory reflexes in monkeys. *Acta Physiol. Polon.*, 1960, **11**, 664–666 (in Polish).

BURANDT, D. C., FRENCH, G. M., & AKERT, K. Relationships between the caudate nucleus and the frontal cortex in *Macaca mulatta. Confinia Neurol.*, 1961, **21**, 289–306.

BUREŠ, J., BUREŠOVÁ, O., & WEISS, T. Functional consequences of hippocampal spreading depression. *Physiol. Bohemoslovenika*, 1960, **9**, 219–227.

CIANCI, S. N. The effects of intracranial electrical stimulation on the delayed-response test in monkeys. Unpublished doctoral thesis, University of Michigan, 1962.

FESSARD, A. Le conditionnement considéré à l'échelle du neurone. In H. H. Jasper & G. P. Smirnov (Eds.) *Moscow colloquium on electroencephalography of higher nervous activity.* Suppl. no. 13, *EEG Clin. Neurophysiol.*, Montreal, 1960.

FESSARD, A., & SZABO, TH. La facilitation de post-activation comme facteur de plasticité dans l'éstablissement des liaisons temporaires. In J. F. Delafresnaye (Ed.), *Brain mechanisms and learning.* Oxford: Blackwell Scientific Publications, Ltd., 1961.

FLYNN, J. P., & WASMAN, M. Learning and cortically evoked movement during propagated hippocampal afterdischarges. *Science*, 1960, **131**, 1607–1608.

FORMAN, D., & WARD, J. W. Responses to electrical stimulation of caudate nucleus in cats in chronic experiments. *J. Neurophysiol.*, 1957, **20**, 230–244.

FRENCH, G. M., & HARLOW, H. F. Variability of delayed reaction performance in normal and brain-damaged rhesus monkeys. *J. Neurophysiol.*, 1962, **25**, 585–599.

GALAMBOS, R., SHEATZ, G., & VERNIER, V. G. Electrophysiological correlates of a conditioned response in cats. *Science*, 1956, **123**, 376–377.

GREEN, J. D., & MACHNÉ, X. Unit activity of the rabbit hippocampus. *Amer. J. Physiol.*, 1955, **181**, 219–224.

HARMAN, P. J., TANKARD, M., HOVDE, C., & METTLER, F. A. An experimental anatomical analysis of the topography and polarity of the caudate-neocortex inter-relationships in the primate. *Anat. Record.*, 1954, **118**, 307–308.

HEUSER, G., BUCHWALD, N. A., & WYERS, E. J. The caudate spindle. II. Facilitatory and inhibitory caudate cortical pathways. *EEG Clin. Neurophysiol.*, 1961, **13**, 519–524.

JACOBSEN, C. F. Functions of the frontal association area in primates. *Arch. Neurol. Psychiat.*, 1935, **33**, 558–569.

JOHN, E. R., & KILLAM, K. F. Electrophysiological correlates of avoidance conditioning in the cat. *J. Pharmacol. Exper. Ther.*, 1959, **125**, 252–274.

JOHNSON, T. N. Fiber connections between the dorsal thalamus and corpus striatum in the cat. *Exp. Neurol.*, 1961, **3**, 556–569.

JUNG, R., & HASSLER, R. The extra-pyramidal motor system. In *Handbook of neurophysiology.* Washington, D.C.: Amer. Physiol. Soc., vol. II, 1960. Pp. 863–928.

KARMOS, G., & GRASTYÁN, E. Influence of hippocampal lesions on simple and delayed conditional reflexes. *Acta Physiol. Hungaricae*, 1962, **21**, 215–224.

MALMO, R. B. Interference factors in delayed response in monkeys after removal of frontal lobes. *J. Neurophysiol.*, 1942, **5**, 295–308.

MARSHALL, W. H. Spreading cortical depression of Leão. *Physiol. Revs.*, 1959, **39**, 239–279.

METTLER, F. A., HOVDE, C., & GRUNDFEST, H. Electrophysiological phenomena evoked by electrical stimulation of caudate nucleus. *Fed. Proc.*, 1952, **11**, 107.

MIGLER, B. The effect of lesions to the caudate nuclei and corpus callosum on delayed alternation in the monkey. Unpublished master's thesis, University of Pittsburgh, Pittsburgh, Pa., 1958.

MISHKIN, M. Visual discrimination performance following partial ablations of the temporal lobe: II. Ventral surface vs. hippocampus. *J. Comp. Physiol. Psychol.*, 1954, **47**, 187–193.

MISHKIN, M. Effects of small frontal lesions on delayed alternation in monkeys. *J. Neurophysiol.*, 1957, **20**, 615–622.

MISHKIN, M., & PRIBRAM, K. H. Visual discrimination performance following partial ablations of the temporal lobe: I. Ventral vs. lateral. *J. Comp. Physiol. Psychol.*, 1954, **47**, 14–20.

MISHKIN, M., & PRIBRAM, K. H. Visual discrimination and delayed alternation after various cerebral lesions in the monkey. Unpublished report, 1958.

ORBACH, J., MILNER, BRENDA, & RASMUSSEN, T. Learning and retention in monkeys after amygdala-hippocampal resection. *AMA Arch. Neurol.*, 1960, **3**, 230–251.

POGGIO, G. F., WALKER, A. E., & ANDY, O. J. The propagation of cortical after-discharge through sub-cortical structures. *Arch. Neurol. Psychiat.*, 1956, **75**, 350–361.

PRIBRAM, K. H., MISHKIN, M., ROSVOLD, H. E., & KAPLAN, S. J. Effects on delayed-response performance of lesions of dorsolateral and ventromedial frontal cortex of baboons. *J. Comp. Physiol. Psychol.*, 1952, **45**, 565–575.

PRIBRAM, K. H., WILSON, W. A., & CONNORS, J. Effects of lesions of the medial forebrain on alternation behavior of rhesus monkeys. *Exp. Neurol.*, 1962, **6**, 36–47.

PURPURA, D. P., HOUSEPIAN, E. M., & GRUNDFEST, H. Analysis of caudate-cortical connections in neuraxially intact and telencèphale isolé cats. *Arch. Ital. Biol.*, 1958, **96**, 145–167.

ROSVOLD, H. E., & DELGADO, J. M. R. The effect on delayed-alternation test performance of stimulating or destroying electrically structures within the frontal lobes of the monkey's brain. *J. Comp. Physiol. Psychol.*, 1956, **49**, 365–372.

ROSVOLD, H. E., & MISHKIN, M. Non-sensory effects of frontal lesions on discrimination learning and performance. In J. F. Delafresnaye (Ed.), *Brain mechanisms and learning*. Oxford: Blackwell Scientific Publications, Ltd., 1961. Pp. 555–576.

ROSVOLD, H. E., MISHKIN, M., & SZWARCBART, M. K. Effects of subcortical lesions in monkeys on visual-discrimination and single-alternation performance. *J. Comp. Physiol. Psychol.*, 1958, **51**, 437–444.

ROSVOLD, H. E., MISHKIN, M., & SZWARCBART, M. K. The effect of hippocampal lesions on delayed alternation performance in monkeys. Unpublished report, 1962.

SZABO, J. Topical distribution of the striatal efferents in the monkey. *Exp. Neurol.* 1962, **5**, 21–36.

UMBACH, W. The electrophysiology of the caudatus of the cat: electrical stimulation and seizure discharge in different structures of the cerebrum and their connection with the caudatus. *Arch. Psychiat.*, 1959, **199**, 553–572 (in German).

VOTAW, C. L. Certain functional and anatomical relations of the cornu Ammonis of the macaque monkey. I. Functional relations. *J. Comp. Neurol.*, 1959, **112**, 353–382.

WALL, P. D., GLEES, P., & FULTON, J. F. Corticofugal connexions of posterior orbital surface in rhesus monkey. *Brain*, 1951, **74**, 66–71.

WEISKRANTZ, L., MIHAILOVIĆ, L. J., & GROSS, C. G., Effects of stimulation of frontal cortex and hippocampus on behavior in the monkey. *Brain*, 1962, **85**, 487–504.

Stimulation of Frontal Cortex and Delayed Alternation Performance in the Monkey

*Lawrence Weiskrantz,
Ljubodrag Mihailović,
and Charles G. Gross*

ABSTRACT. Unilateral or bilateral stimulation of the region surrounding the sulcus principalis of the cortex of the monkey interferes with delayed alternation performance. It is without effect on auditory discrimination performance. Bilateral stimulation is more disrupting than unilateral stimulation. The impairment is limited in time to the period of stimulation and is fully reversible.

That delayed response and delayed alternation performance of monkeys are severely impaired by surgical lesions of the lateral frontal cortex has been firmly established during the past 20 years (*1*). The present report is concerned with the effect of electrical stimulation of regions of the frontal lobes on delayed alternation and discrimination performance. Traditionally, electrical stimulation of the cerebrum has been used as an evoking stimulus, producing such phenomena as "motor maps," "sham rage," and "ergotropic" and "trophotropic" responses. More recently it has been used as a rewarding or punishing stimulus (*2*). Less frequently have its effects on the efficiency of on-going behavior been observed, at least in a systematic fashion; this is especially true where no obvious motor or reward effects are apparent. Such a use of stimulation was adopted by Rosvold and Delgado (*3*), who showed that stimulation of the caudate nucleus impaired delayed alternation behavior. But there have been, as yet, no reports of the effects of stimulation of the

From *Science*, 1960, **131**, 1443–1444. Reprinted with permission of the publisher and authors. Copyright 1960 by the American Association for the Advancement of Science. This research was supported in part by the Air Research and Development Command, U.S. Air Force.

frontal cortex on this type of behavior. The results of the study reported here suggest that the technique might be rather more powerful than surgical lesion for the analysis of cortical function.

The electrodes were designed to permit the fine silver ball contacts (0.8 mm in diameter) to rest upon the cortex near the banks of sulcus principalis and sulcus arcuatus. Each electrode contained 13 points, implanted in each hemisphere according to the technique of Delgado (*4*). The positions of the contacts in one animal, as determined by post-mortem examination, are shown in Fig. 1. Stimulation was applied between the points that are joined by lines. Principalis points are joined by lines ventrally adjacent to the points; arcuatus points, by lines dorsally adjacent. In our study only principalis points *or* arcuatus points were stimulated—never both simultaneously. The stimulus was a unidirectional square wave (duration, 0.2 msec; frequency, 100 cy/sec), generated by a Grass stimulator. During any stimulation condition, pulses were delivered repeatedly for periods of 1 second, with 3 seconds of nonstimulation between presentations. This pattern of stimulation was begun at the beginning of the first trial of a stimulation session and continued without interruption until the end of the last trial; hence, the animal was stimulated both during a trial and between trials. The voltages for each animal for each mode of stimulation (to principalis and to arcuatus) were selected prior to the commencement of formal testing so as to be 1 or 2 volts below the threshold for overt motor responses.

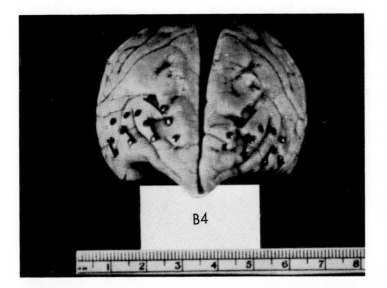

Fig. 1. Position of electrode contacts as determined by post-mortem examination. It should be noted that the markers in the photograph are about 2.5 times the size of the actual contacts, which were 0.8 mm in diameter. Lines ventrally adjacent to pairs of contacts connect arcuatus stimulation points; lines dorsally adjacent connect principalis stimulation points.

Prior to implantation, three young macaque monkeys (each weighing about 3 kg) were trained to perform delayed alternation, auditory discrimination, and visual discrimination tasks (5). All testing was carried out in a Wisconsin general testing apparatus. For the delayed-alternation task the animal was presented with two covered food wells. On successive trials (between trials an opaque screen was lowered for 7 seconds) the animal was required to lift the cover that he had *not* lifted on the prior trial. In the auditory problem the two stimuli to be discriminated consisted of a white noise and a pure tone of 1000 cycles, each interrupted briefly three times per second and each approximately 70 db above the room noise level. The animal was required to lift a food-well cover when the white noise was presented and to refrain from lifting the cover when the tone was presented. Correct responses to either stimulus were rewarded. In both the delay and the auditory tasks, correction trials were run. All animals learned the tasks sufficiently well to satisfy a criterion of 90 correct responses in 100 successive trials (exclusive of correction trials).

After implantation, various orders of testing were employed which cannot be described in detail here. It should be mentioned that the stimulation testing for delayed alternation was carried out intermittently over a period of more than 2 months, during which time the effect was quite stable. Typically, the animal was given 30 control trials without stimulation, then 30 trials with stimulation, followed by another 30 control trials, although the last step was not always taken. Within each session, stimulation and nonstimulation periods followed each other without any time gap between.

In Table 1 are listed the results of stimulation of sulcus principalis and sulcus arcuatus upon delayed alternation and auditory discrimination. It will be seen that there is a very clear effect of bilateral principalis stimulation upon delayed alternation ($P < .0005$). In fact, the behavior is not significantly better than chance. Unilateral stimulation also has a clear but less marked effect ($P < .0005$). Neither arcuatus nor principalis stimulation affected auditory discrimination, a point clearly relevant to results from experiments with surgical lesions (6).

A few points bear emphasizing. Arcuatus stimulation is without effect on delayed alternation; this finding reinforces a view derived from experiments with surgical lesions that the focus for the deficit is to be found near sulcus principalis. However, the division is not made as sharply with surgical lesions. Second, the poststimulation control period for delayed alternation yields scores as good as those of the prestimulation period. Hence, it appears that the deficit literally can be turned on and off at the discretion of the experimenter. Finally, it should be stressed again that no overt motor responses to stimulation were evident, nor could one detect any change in the animals' motivation or willingness to be tested. Indeed, with the parameters of stimulation employed, the only reliable behavioral indication that the stimulation was having any effect whatsoever was the inability of the animals to perform delayed-alternation tasks.

Table 1 Ratios of Correct to Total Trials

ANIMAL	DELAYED ALTERNATION			AUDITORY DISCRIMINATION		
	BEFORE STIMU-LATION	DURING STIMU-LATION	AFTER STIMU-LATION	BEFORE STIMU-LATION	DURING STIMU-LATION	AFTER STIMU-LATION
	Bilateral principalis					
B–2	104/120 [a]	57/120 [a]	52/60	77/90	71/90	28/30
B–3	81/90 [a]	44/90 [a]	30/30	80/90	77/90	22/30
B–4	85/90 [a]	54/90 [b]	27/30	84/90	84/90	26/30
Av. percent	90.4 [a]	51.9 [a]	92.2	90.0	85.9	84.4
	Unilateral principalis					
B–2	178/180 [a]	118/180 [a]	86/90			
B–3	212/230 [a]	153/250 [a]	117/140			
B–4	144/150 [a]	100/150 [b]	29/30			
Av. percent	95.8 [a]	64.5 [a]	92.0			
	Bilateral arcuatus					
B–2	81.90	81/90	29/30	75/90	78/90	29/30
B–3	78/90	84/90	29/30	77/90	77/90	26/30
B–4	80/90	75/90	29/30	84/90	86/90	29/30
Av. percent	88.6	88.9	96.7	87.7	89.3	93.3

[a] $.0005 > P$ (one-tailed chi-square).
[b] $.005 > P > .0005$.

It appears, therefore, that electrical stimulation can reproduce some of the effects of surgical lesions in the frontal region. It also has certain clear advantages over lesions that commend its wider use for the analysis of cortical function. The deficit appears to be fully reversible, and hence each animal can be used as its own control. Indeed, there would seem to be no obstacle to obtaining "double dissociation" within a single organism. Furthermore, electrical stimulation appears to permit a somewhat finer fractionation than is possible with surgical lesions. Finally, certain types of questions, such as those involved in separating the effects on short-term storage from the effects on long-term storage, cannot be unequivocally answered with surgical lesions because these questions are of the form: Is behavior acquired during a "lesion" state altered in a subsequent "nonlesion" state? (7)

REFERENCES AND NOTES

1. K. L. CHOW and P. J. HUTT, *Brain* **76**, 625 (1953).
2. J. OLDS and P. MILNER, *J. Comp. Physiol. Psychol.* **47**, 419 (1954).
3. H. E. ROSVOLD and J. M. R. DELGADO, *ibid.* **49**, 365 (1956).
4. J. M. R. DELGADO, *Clin. Neurophysiol.* **7**, 637 (1955).
5. L. WEISKRANTZ, L. MIHAILOVIĆ and C. G. GROSS, *Brain* **85**, 487 (1962).
6. L. WEISKRANTZ and M. MISHKIN, *Brain* **81**, 406 (1958).
7. We are pleased to acknowledge the assistance of S. Hopkins and R. Hutchison.

Visual Mechanisms Beyond the Striate Cortex

Mortimer Mishkin

I. INTRODUCTION

A monkey that has been trained to discriminate between a pair of visual patterns will lose this ability, and will have great difficulty reacquiring it, after bilateral removal of cortex along the inferior edge of the temporal lobe. The lesion does not encroach on striate cortex, and it need not invade the optic radiations; yet, except for the absence of visual field defects, the resulting deficit is often difficult to distinguish from the effects of just such damage to the visual system. Discrimination of two-dimensional patterns is perhaps the most severely impaired visual ability, but impairment has also been demonstrated in the discrimination of object quality, in color, size and brightness discrimination, and in critical flicker frequency. While the effect would appear from this to be widespread within vision, it does not seem to extend beyond it. Experiments have failed thus far to uncover any deficits analogous to the visual deficits in other sensory modalities.

The evidence leads to the puzzling conclusion that a cortical region some distance removed from the primary visual area, and having no known direct connections with it, is the site of an important focus for visual functions. This chapter describes a search for a neural explanation of this phenomenon. Specifically, the goal was to identify the pathway mediating the presumed interaction between the inferotemporal area and the visual system. Before turning to these recent experiments, however, it would be well to review briefly the history of the problem, beginning with the discovery of a " visual area " in the temporal lobes.

From *Frontiers in Physiological Psychology*, R. W. Russell (Ed.) (New York: Academic Press, 1966), pp. 93–119. Reprinted with permission of the publisher and author, with whose approval certain material has been omitted.

II. LOCALIZATION STUDIES

Two lines of evidence led to the discovery. The first was the report by Klüver and Bucy (1939) of some dramatic changes in the behavior of monkeys following bilateral temporal lobectomy. Perhaps the most striking effect of the operation was the defect which Klüver and Bucy referred to as " psychic blindness," connoting an inability of their monkeys to recognize objects by vision alone. However, symptoms of agnosia were not limited to vision, nor was the temporal lobe syndrome confined to symptoms of agnosia; there were many other complex changes such as increased tameness, changes in dietary habits, and hypersexuality. Klüver (1952) considered the visual disturbance to be but one manifestation of a more profound disturbance in behavior, and he cautioned against the hypothesis that the component symptoms could be independently produced.

The second line of evidence stemmed indirectly from Lashley's (1948) study in monkeys of the effects of preoccipital lesions. In this investigation, Lashley failed to obtain any support for the classical view that the prestriate cortex serves " visuopsychic " or visual associative functions. Partly as a result of these negative findings, Blum, Chow, and Pribram (1950), working in Lashley's laboratory, turned to an investigation of the effects of a more radical removal; their lesion included the preoccipital area, but it also extended anteriorly into other parietal and temporal areas without invading any of the primary sensory projection fields. Using a battery of tests ranging from simple through complex visual, tactual, auditory, and gustatory discriminations, these authors found consistent deficits on the visual problems together with less consistent deficits on the others. Again as with Klüver's interpretation of the temporal lobe syndrome, Lashley (1950) attributed the effects of the extensive neocortical removal to a basic disorder in behavior which could probably not be fractionated further.

Nevertheless, an attempt to locate a more circumscribed area selectively related to visual functions was carried on by a number of investigators (Chow, 1951; Mishkin, 1954; Mishkin & Pribram, 1954). The impetus for the search came from a comparision between the two sets of earlier results which suggested that such an area might be contained in the region of overlap between the temporal lobectomies and the large neocortical lesions. The later experiments confirmed the suggestion and they led, by a series of approxima- tions, to a delineation of the focus as the inferior temporal convexity com- prising the middle and inferior temporal convolutions: Lesions of this area consistently resulted in visual impairments; lesions of the same size sparing this area had either negative or negligible effects. Regions in which damage was found to be relatively ineffective included the superior temporal convolu- tion, the temporal pole, subcortical structures such as the amygdala and hippocampus, the posterior parietal cortex, and, according to some investiga- tors but not all, the prestriate area. The conflicting evidence regarding the effects of prestriate lesions will be considered in detail shortly.

III. BEHAVIORAL ANALYSES

It is important to make clear that the deficit produced by inferotemporal removals is not the dramatic derangement in visually guided behaviour that had been observed after the larger ablations. Monkeys with the selective lesion do not display the signs of visual agnosia, such as repeated and indiscriminate examination of objects, or loss of fear reactions to previously aversive stimuli, seen in animals with temporal lobectomy; nor do they exhibit the signs of spatial disorientation sometimes seen after the extensive posterior neocortical ablations. To gross observation, the inferotemporal monkey is indistinguishable from the normal; its visual discrimination impairment becomes evident only in more formal training situations. In view of the relatively subtle nature of the disorder, the results of the localization studies left open the possibility that inferotemporal lesions had a generalized, cross-modal effect similar to that of the larger lesions but one that would take careful testing to detect.

As already indicated, however, the deficit has turned out on further investigation to be surprisingly specific. Tactual, auditory, and olfactory discrimination, evaluated by methods analogous to those used in evaluating visual discrimination, are apparently unaffected by the lesion (Brown, 1963; Brown, Rosvold, & Mishkin, 1963; P. Pasik, T. Pasik, Battersby, & Bender, 1958; H. Pribram & Barry, 1956; Weiskrantz & Mishkin, 1958; M. Wilson, 1957. It is unlikely that these negative findings in inferotemporal monkeys reflect the use of insensitive or otherwise inadequate tests of discrimination ability, since the same tests have yielded positive findings in monkeys with other cortical lesions. Of particular interest is the fact that discrimination losses in audition and olfaction have been obtained from lesions placed immediately dorsal and rostral, respectively, to the inferotemporal area (Rosvold & Mishkin, 1966; Rosvold, Vest, Mishkin, & Brown, 1966). The absence of such losses after inferotemporal lesions, despite severe and often permanent visual losses, presents a striking contrast indicative of a high degree of functional specialization.

The apparent selectivity of the impairment poses the difficult problem of defining precisely what role this area plays in visual functions. Because the disorder generally is reflected as a failure to retain visual discriminations or as a retardation in acquiring them, it might appear, superficially at least, that the inferotemporal cortex is the locus of visual habit formation. However, as pointed out repeatedly by Lashley (1950), the undeniable complexity of even the simplest memory trace makes it improbable that a small area of association cortex could serve as the storehouse for specific habits or engrams. The anti-localizationist positions of Lashley and Klüver, alluded to earlier, were adopted perhaps more in opposition to this aspect of the classical doctrine than to the view that small cortical fields might turn out to be highly specialized in their functions.

At the opposite extreme from the notion that the inferotemporal cortex contains the engrams for visual habits is the possibility that it contributes significantly to basic sensory processes. However, there is little reason to suppose that an area outside the primary visual system would be fundamentally involved in such functions, and in this instance there is direct behavioral evidence against the supposition. Sensory disturbances such as field defects, acuity losses, or markedly raised visual thresholds have not been demonstrated in inferotemporal animals (Cowey & Weiskrantz, 1963; Mishkin & Weiskrantz, 1959; Weiskrantz & Cowey, 1963; W. A. Wilson & Mishkin, 1959). Furthermore, animals having such defects, as a result, for example, of partial removals of the striate cortex, have been found to be less impaired than inferotemporal animals on a variety of visual tasks (Butter, Mishkin, & Rosvold, 1964; W. A. Wilson & Mishkin, 1959).

These considerations serve to narrow somewhat the limits within which it may be profitable to speculate, but they do not directly suggest a positive formulation of the impairment. Nor have further attempts at behavioral analysis yielded results which provide convincing support for one interpretation over others (Chow & Orbach, 1957; Ettlinger, 1959b; Ettlinger, 1962; Mishkin & Hall, 1955; T. Pasik, P. Pasik, Battersby, & Bender, 1958; Pribram & Mishkin, 1955; Pribram & Mishkin, 1956; Stepien, Cordeau, & Rasmussen, 1960). This difficulty in defining the nature of the inferotemporal area's contribution to vision may reflect, at least in part, the tendency to frame hypotheses in terms of traditional psychological categories such as perception, attention, recent memory, and the like—categories which, just as habit formation, may correspond better to the integrated function of a widespread neural system than to the specific contribution made by a discrete area of the cortex. Should this prove to be the case, it may be extremely difficult to develop the proper behavioral concept without some understanding of the underlying neural mechanisms. Even if such information is not a prerequisite, a description of inferotemporal function is likely to remain imprecise until the particular mechanism by which the function is accomplished has been specified. As a first step toward unraveling these neural processes, the mystery surrounding the inferotemporal area's participation in vision must be resolved. This, too, has proved to be a difficult problem, but one that now seems close to a satisfactory solution.

IV. POSSIBLE NEURAL PATHWAYS

Earlier studies explored the possibility that the interaction between the inferotemporal area and the visual system might be critically dependent on certain subcortical structures. For example, the pulvinar nucleus of the thalamus, which has long been thought to receive direct or indirect visual afferents, sends a projection to the temporal neocortex (Chow, 1950). The temporal neocortex, in turn, sends a projection to the superior colliculus

(Whitlock & Nauta, 1956), an important mesencephalic visuomotor center. However, studies designed to evaluate their roles as essential subcortical relays failed to demonstrate any visual discrimination impairment as a result of damaging these two structures, either singly (Chow 1954; Rosvold, Mishkin, & Szwarcbart, 1958) or in combination (Rosvold & Mishkin, 1966). Because total destruction of these nuclei was not achieved, the negative findings are not necessarily conclusive. At the same time, it may be pointed out that negative results were obtained in cases in which the damage was estimated to be 80% complete. The existence of an essential subcortical relay is placed further in doubt by a recent report (Chow, 1961) that partially undercutting the inferior temporal convexity so as to sever most of its direct subcortical connections leaves visual discrimination performance unaffected.

The evidence presented above against a subcortical pathway is only slightly more convincing than that which may be adduced against a cortical pathway. Although the inferotemporal area does not appear to receive a direct projection from the striate cortex, or to send such a projection to it, data from neuroanatomical (Clark, 1942; Mettler, 1935a; Mettler, 1935b) and strychnine neuronographic studies (Bailey, Von Bonin, Davis, Garol, & McCulloch, 1944; Petr, Holden, & Jirout, 1949; Von Bonin, Garol, & McCulloch, 1942) suggest that the two areas may be interconnected indirectly through prestriate cortex. However, the possibility that the prestriate region mediates the interaction between the inferotemporal area and the visual system was rendered unlikely, even before it became an issue, by the negative results of Lashley's prestriate study referred to earlier. Furthermore, subsequent experiments involving more extensive prestriate destruction than in Lashley's study likewise failed to reveal impairments on visual tasks (Chow, 1952; Evarts, 1952; Meyer, Harlow, & Ades, 1951; Riopelle, Harlow, Settlage, & Ades, 1951; M. Wilson, W. A. Wilson, & Chiang, 1963). Intermixed with these negative findings, however, are several reports indicating that prestriate removals may produce visual impairments under special conditions (Ades, 1946; Ades & Raab, 1949; Riopelle & Ades, 1953; M. Wilson & W. A. Wilson, 1962). Thus, discrimination deficits have been observed in naive animals but not in sophisticated animals, or in postoperative learning but not in retention. These findings have been extremely difficult to interpret. If the prestriate cortex were an essential link in a striate-inferotemporal pathway, damaging this link would be expected to yield effects approximately equivalent to those produced by damaging the areas it interconnects. Instead, prestriate lesions appear to produce, at most, comparatively mild effects, suggesting that the prestriate region is only marginally involved in visual discrimination functions. Even this degree of participation is open to question since such deficits as have been reported could easily have arisen not from the intended lesion, but from encroachment on striate or inferotemporal tissue adjacent to the prestriate area, or on the visual radiations coursing directly below it. Viewed in any of these ways, the findings would seem to argue strongly against a striate-prestriate-inferotemporal pathway.

However, in the absence of any evidence pointing to an alternative pathway, still another interpretation of these minor deficits should be considered. It is conceivable that prestriate cortex is characterized, at least with respect to a relay function, by a high degree of equipotentiality. According to this notion extensive but subtotal damage would impair transmission without disrupting it completely. A similar proposal might be advanced in favor of a subcortical pathway, except that, as already noted, not even minor deficits have been reported after extensive damage to potential subcortical relays. Although the argument was a tenuous one, it indicated that a cortical pathway could not yet be entirely ruled out and that the hypothesis merited reexamination.

V. CROSSED-LESION EXPERIMENT

To attempt once more to interrupt cortico-cortical connections by ablating the prestriate region seemed unprofitable in view of the difficulty of destroying this area completely without critically damaging surrounding visual structures. An alternative approach was therefore adopted (Mishkin, 1958; Mishkin, 1962) which involved the combination of lesions shown in the diagram of Fig. 1. The first stage of the operation consisted of a unilateral inferotemporal resection, followed in the second stage by a contralateral occipital lobectomy. If in such a preparation there is a *cortical* interaction between the intact striate area of one hemisphere and the intact inferotemporal area of the other, then this interaction should be completely disrupted by sectioning the corpus callosum in the third stage. The advantage of the method was that it offered the possibility of severing an essential visual pathway without endangering the primary visual system.

The three-stage experiment was performed in the following way. Unoperated monkeys were trained in a Wisconsin General Test Apparatus (Harlow, 1949) on a simultaneous visual pattern discrimination. The stimuli consisted of a plus sign (the positive cue) and an outline of a square (the negative cue), each a white paper cutout mounted on a 3 by 3 in. gray cardboard plaque. The two plaques served as covers for food wells spaced 14 in. apart, and the positions of the plaques were interchanged from trial to trial in accordance with a Gellerman (1933) series. Training was presented for 30 trials a day to a criterion of 90 correct responses in 100 trials; this was followed two weeks later by a retention test presented to the same criterion. The animals were then given the first-stage lesion—either a unilateral inferotemporal resection or, as a control, a unilateral frontal resection—allowed two weeks to recover, and then retested. Assuming that each striate area has indirect cortical connections with both inferotemporal areas, the first stage of the experiment may be viewed as a test of the effects of destroying two of these four connections. As illustrated in Fig. 2, and in line with results obtained earlier in animals with unilateral inferotemporal lesions (Mishkin & Pribram, 1954), this amount of damage to the system had no detectable effect.

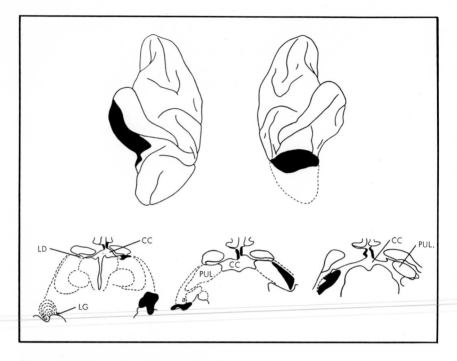

Fig. 1. Reconstructions of the cortical lesions and cross sections through the corpus callosum and thalamus of an experimental animal. Lesions and retrograde degeneration are shown in black. Note the complete degeneration of the lateral geniculate nucleus on the side of the occipital lobectomy, and the degeneration in the posterior tip of the pulvinar on the side of the inferotemporal resection.

After a two-week interval and another retention test, the animals were subjected to the second-stage lesion. The operation involved a partial occipital lobectomy followed by a resection of all the striate cortex spared by the lobectomy, including that portion buried in the rostral part of the medial calcarine sulcus. In half the animals of each of the original groups this second lesion was placed on the same side as the first, while in the others it was placed on the opposite side. The hypothetical cortical connections remaining after the complete unilateral striate removals are shown in the diagrams of Fig. 3. As may be seen by the postoperative retention scores, those control animals in which the lobectomy was presumed to have reduced four connections to two showed little or no impairment. Even a single connection proved adequate provided that it was intrahemispheric. By contrast, when the residual connection crossed from one hemisphere to the other, as was assumed to be the case in the experimental group, a marked impairment appeared. A differential result at this stage of the experiment had not been anticipated. What it seemed to suggest was that crossed striate and inferotemporal areas were less well integrated than uncrossed, and, by implication, that the interaction between the two cortical areas was indeed of considerable importance. However, whether such interaction was mediated by a cortical pathway remained to be determined in the third stage.

To insure that all groups were performing satisfactorily prior to the callosal transection they were given another two-week rest followed by another retention test. As shown in Fig. 4, all groups, including the experimental group, reattained criterion within the minimum number of trials

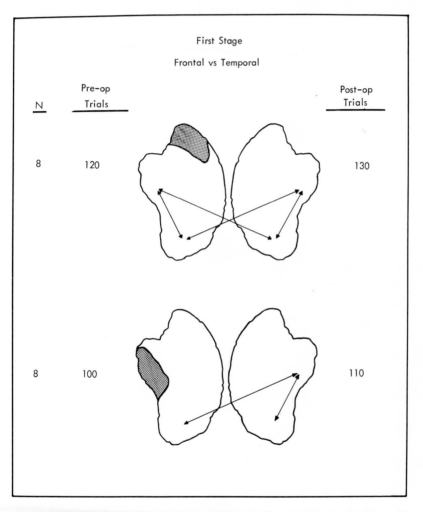

Fig. 2. Discrimination retention before and after the first-stage lesion. In this and in the following figures, *N* equals number of animals; arrows denote hypothetical connections left intact by the lesions; scores are group medians and include the 100-trial criterion run; an underlined score denotes impairment; and *F* indicates failure to relearn within the limits of training.

before the final operation. Furthermore, the three control groups, now left with but one ipsilateral connection each, continued to perform at the same high level after operation. Nevertheless, sectioning the corpus callosum in the experimental animals had the effect of disrupting their performance completely.

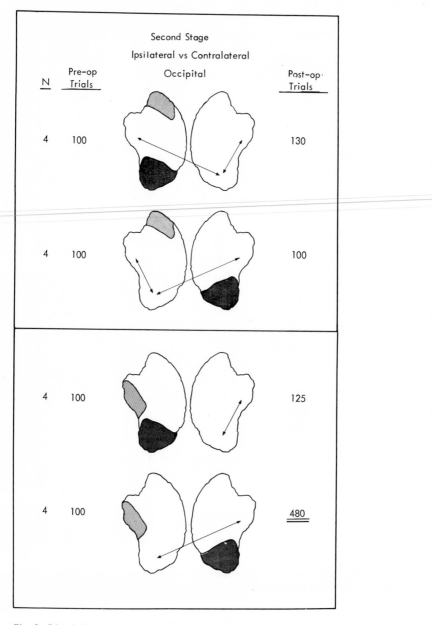

Fig. 3. Discrimination retention before and after the second-stage lesion.

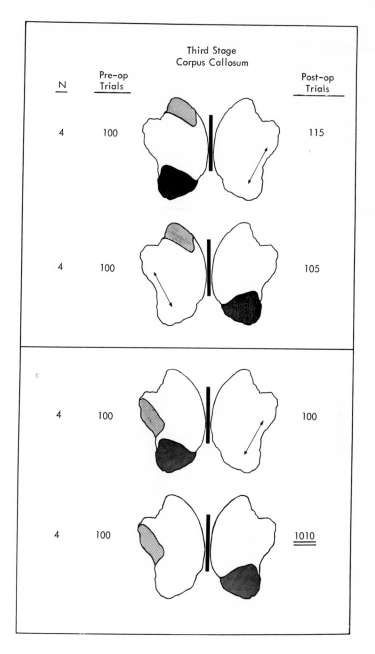

Fig. 4. Discrimination retention before and after the third-stage lesion.

The severity of the effect is shown graphically in Fig. 5. The final result is particularly striking in that, first, all animals had been given identical lesions at this stage, and second, all had met the discrimination criterion several times before. Overtraining to this extent is known to attenuate the effects of bilateral inferotemporal lesions (Chow & Survis, 1958; Orbach & Fantz, 1958), and it

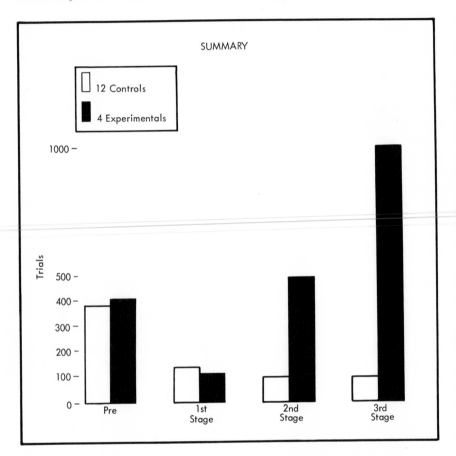

Fig. 5. Recapitulation of results, comparing the experimental animals with all others on initial learning (pre) and on retention after each of the three lesions.

undoubtedly accounts for the gradual improvement in performance shown by the control animals over the course of the present study. Despite the overtraining, however, and despite a combination of lesions which differed only slightly from that given each of the three control groups, the experimental animals showed a stepwise deterioration in performance until at the last they had difficulty in relearning the discrimination at all. The result strongly supported the view that the callosal transection in the experimental group had isolated the inferotemporal area from the visual system by cutting its last cortical connection with the striate area.[1]

VI. CONTROL EXPERIMENTS

[A section describing several series of control experiments has been omitted. The first series was designed to see whether the anterior or posterior corpus callosum was crucial to the interhemispheric transfer. Anterior transections of the corpus callosum, posterior transections of the corpus callosum, and unilateral cingulate ablations were compared as third-stage lesions. Only the posterior transections of the corpus callosum produced the major deficit found in the previous experiments after transection of the entire corpus callosum.

In the next experiments groups with the following lesions were compared to normals on a series of object discriminations: a) anterior section of the corpus callosum, following crossed unilateral striate and inferotemporal lesions, b) posterior section of the corpus callosum, following crossed unilateral striate and inferotemporal lesions, and c) bilateral inferotemporal lesions. The anterior callosal group, with an intact transcallosal pathway between one occipital lobe and the opposite inferotemporal area, though impaired relative to the normal animals, was somewhat less impaired than the bitemporal group. The bitemporal group, in turn, was somewhat less impaired than the posterior callosal group, a finding in line with the supposition that the performance of the latter reflected the combined effects of a unilateral occipital lobectomy *and* a functional bitemporal ablation. The fact that the scores of the two callosal groups differed nearly as much as the scores of the normal and bitemporal groups lends further support to the view that the posterior callosal transection effectively ended the participation of inferotemporal cortex in visual functions.

A third series of experiments demonstrated that the results of the crossed striate and inferotemporal lesions plus section of the corpus callosum could not be attributed to visual neglect produced by the unilateral striate lesions.]

VII. THE PRESTRIATE RELAY

The behavioral evidence that had been gathered up to this point confirmed the existence of the indirect cortical pathway that had been implied by the older

---

[1] In an experiment undertaken independently of the one reported here, Ettlinger (1959a) found a severe deficit in visual pattern discrimination in monkeys given combined callosal transection, unilateral inferotemporal ablation, and (in place of a contralateral occipital lobectomy) complete section of the contralateral optic tract. Ettlinger's results complement those described above and strengthen the argument for the proposed cortical pathway.

neuronographic and neuroanatomical literature. However, inasmuch as the exact source and termination of the connections comprising this pathway were still largely unknown, an anatomical study was undertaken, using the Nauta-Gygax (1954) silver stain technique, in an attempt to delineate the relevant connections more precisely. The results of the experiment have been reported in detail elsewhere (Kuypers, Szwarcbart, Mishkin, & Rosvold, 1965). Of major interest here was the finding that the striate area sends a projection not only to the banks of the lunate sulcus and to the preoccipital gyrus, that is, to the prestriate area as it has commonly been defined, but also to the annectant gyri in the depths of the parieto-occipital junction, to the caudal bank of the upper half of the superior temporal sulcus, and to the banks of the caudal portion of the intraparietal sulcus. This projection field of the striate cortex sends a projection, in turn, to an area in the temporal lobes which corresponds remarkably closely to the inferotemporal "visual area." An example of the cortical distribution of preterminal fiber degeneration in an animal with a partial prestriate lesion is shown in Fig. 10.

The picture which emerges from these findings is that of a complex neural system in which each prestriate area serves as the essential link in a homolateral pathway, and, by virtue of their reciprocal connections across the

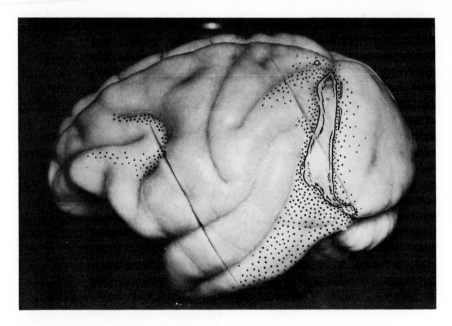

Fig. 10. Photograph of the brain of an operated monkey, showing the unilateral prestriate lesion (outlined) and the cortical distribution of degenerating fibers (stippled). In addition to heavy degeneration in the inferotemporal cortex, this preoccipital lesion led to degeneration in (*a*) the prefrontal area, particularly the prefrontal "eyefields," (*b*) intact portions of the prestriate region, including the area around the intraparietal sulcus, and possibly (*c*) the striate area, though only few scattered fibers were noted here.

posterior portion of the corpus callosum, as part of a dual link in the trans-callosal pathway. The entire system is depicted schematically in Fig. 11 (top), while the residual connection remaining after a crossed striate-inferotemporal lesion is shown in Fig. 11 (bottom). The schema suggests a further test of the proposed pathway, and, simultaneously, a new test of the relay function of the

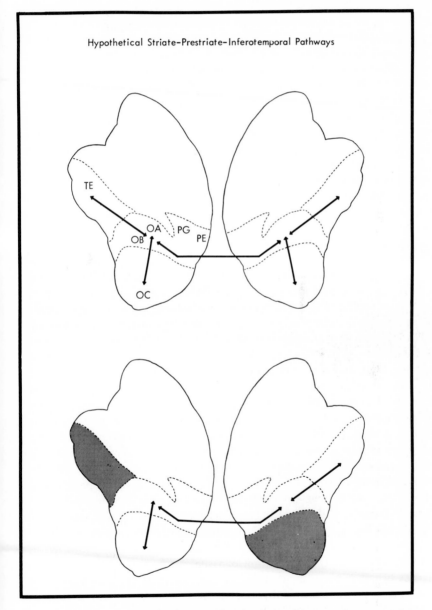

Fig. 11. Hypothetical pathways before and after a crossed striate-inferotemporal lesion. Letters refer to Von Bonin and Bailey's (1947) cytoarchitectural areas.

prestriate region. According to the schema, it should be possible to interrupt the critical connection in a third-stage lesion, not only by sectioning the posterior callosum but also by resecting the prestriate cortex on the side of the occipital lobectomy. The advantage of this method of investigating the postulated relay is that extensive prestriate ablations become possible, including complete destruction of the banks and depths of sulci, without the usual concern for incidental damage to the primary visual system.

That extensive prestriate ablations are necessary was made clear by the following experiments. In one group of crossed-lesion animals, the third-stage resection was limited largely to the preoccipital gyrus in an attempt to reproduce the prestriate lesions that had been performed in earlier studies. As may be seen in Fig. 12, neither a lesion of this type in the lobectomized hemisphere nor the addition of a symmetrical lesion in the opposite hemisphere had any detectable effect on the animals' performance. An impairment was observed, as in the earlier experiments, only when the posterior segment of the corpus callosum was cut. These results led to the attempt in a second experiment to remove not only the preoccipital gyrus but also the entire cortical area to which the striate cortex projects. When this more extensive lesion was made, the predicted effect appeared (see Fig. 13). Of particular interest was the finding that subsequent transection of the posterior callosum in this second series of animals had no additional effect. Taken together, the results of the two experiments demonstrate that negative or negligible effects of prestriate lesions can be traced to a failure to disrupt completely the critical striate-inferotemporal interaction. The difficulty in achieving complete disruption is in accord with the supposition made earlier that multiple pathways exist throughout the prestriate region, investing this area of association cortex with a high degree of equipotentiality. Nevertheless, the fact that an impairment can be produced by a sufficiently extensive ablation favors the view that the prestriate region is an essential part of the system.

In providing an explanation for the involvement of inferotemporal cortex in visual functions, this series of experiments has thus uncovered new evidence pointing to the importance for visual functions of the prestriate cortex. Indeed, the implication of the results is that the inferotemporal cortex cannot function without the prestriate. Although its role in vision has been overshadowed for many years by the more conspicuous role of the inferotemporal area, there is now reason to believe that it is the prestriate area which may provide the key to an understanding of inferotemporal function. In the context of the experiments described in this report, the prestriate region has been considered simply as a relay for transmitting activity between the other components of the proposed cortical visual system. However, if, as now seems likely, the elaboration of visual mechanisms beyond the striate cortex begins in prestriate cortex, then it would seem that renewed efforts to investigate the function of this early stage in the system would yield some important clues to the contribution made by later stages.

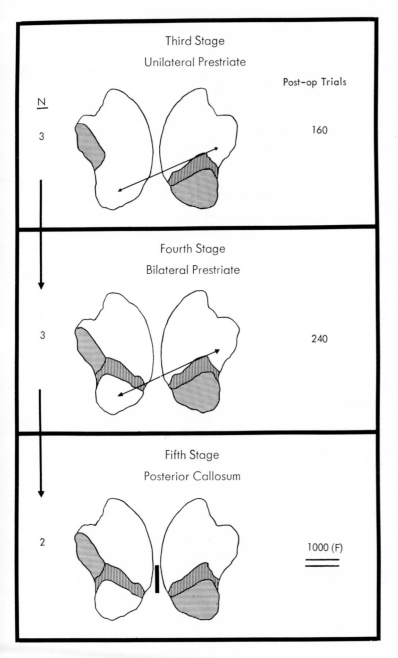

Fig. 12. Failure to interrupt the transcallosal pathway by partial prestriate lesions.

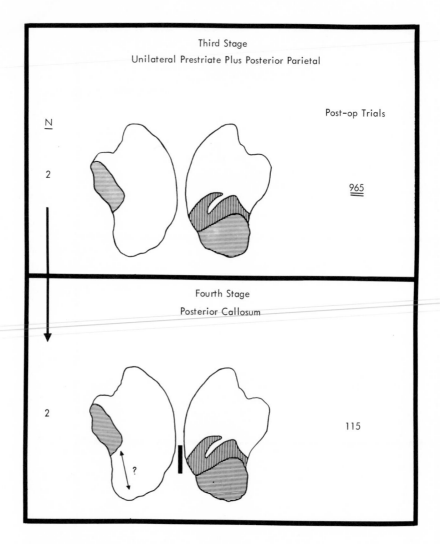

Fig. 13. Interruption of the transcallosal pathway by a unilateral lesion of the cortical projection of the striate area. The possibility that eventual recovery of the discrimination habit is mediated by the remaining prestriate area [a possibility indicated by the arrow in the lower diagram] is currently being investigated.

ACKNOWLEDGMENT

The support and assistance of H. Enger Rosvold in all aspects of the work reported here are gratefully acknowledged.

REFERENCES

ADES, H. W. Effect of extirpation of parastriate cortex on learned visual discriminations in monkeys. *J. Neuropath. exp. Neurol.*, 1946, **5**, 60–65.

ADES, H. W., & RAAB, D. H. Effect of preoccipital and temporal decortication on learned visual discrimination in monkeys. *J. Neurophysiol.*, 1949, **12**, 101–108.

BAILEY, P., VON BONIN, G., DAVIS, E. W., GAROL, H. W., & MCCULLOCH, W. S. Further observations on association pathways in the brain of Macaca mulatta. *J. Neuropath. exp. Neurol.*, 1944, **3**, 413–415.

BATTIG, K., ROSVOLD, H. E., & MISHKIN, M. Comparison of the effects of frontal and caudate lesions on delayed response and alternation in monkeys. *J. comp. physiol. Psychol.*, 1960, **53**, 400–404.

BLUM, J. S., CHOW, K. L., & PRIBRAM, K. H. A behavioral analysis of the organization of the parieto-temporo-preoccipital cortex. *J. comp. Neurol.*, 1950, **93**, 53–100.

BROWN, T. S. Olfactory and visual discrimination in the monkey after selective lesions of the temporal lobe. *J. comp. physiol. Psychol.*, 1963, **56**, 764–768.

BROWN, T. S., ROSVOLD, H. E., & MISHKIN, M. Olfactory discrimination after temporal lobe lesions in monkeys. *J. comp. physiol. Psychol.*, 1963, **56**, 190–195.

BUTTER, C. M., MISHKIN, M., ROSVOLD, H. E. Stimulus generalization following inferotemporal and lateral striate lesions in monkeys. In D. Mostofsky (Ed.), *Stimulus generalization.* Stanford, Calif.: Stanford Univer. Press, 1964.

CHOW, K. L. A retrograde cell degeneration study of the cortical projection field of the pulvinar in the monkey. *J. comp. Neurol.*, 1950, **93**, 313–340.

CHOW, K. L. Effects of partial extirpation of posterior association cortex on visually mediated behavior in monkeys. *Comp. Psychol. Monogr.*, 1951, **20**, 187–217.

CHOW, K. L. Further studies on selective ablation of associative cortex in relation to visually mediated behavior. *J. comp. physiol. Psychol.*, 1952, **45**, 109–118.

CHOW, K. L. Lack of behavioral effects following destruction of some thalamic association nuclei in monkey. *A.M.A. Arch. Neurol. Psychiat.*, 1954, **71**, 762–771.

CHOW, K. L. Anatomical and electrographical analysis of temporal neocortex in relation to visual discrimination learning in monkeys. In J. F. Delafresnaye (Ed.), *Brain mechanisms in learning.* Oxford, England: Blackwell, 1961.

CHOW, K. L., & ORBACH, J. Performance of visual discriminations presented tachistoscopically in monkeys with temporal neocortical ablations. *J. comp. physiol. Psychol.*, 1957, **50**, 636–640.

CHOW, K. L., & SURVIS, J. Retention of overlearned visual habit after temporal cortical ablation in monkey. *A.M.A. Arch. Neurol. Psychiat.*, 1958, **79**, 640–646.

CLARK, W. E. LEGROS. The visual centers of the brain and their central connections. *Physiol. Rev.*, 1942, **22**, 205–232.

COWEY, A., & WEISKRANTZ, L. A perimetric study of visual field defects in monkeys. *Quart. J. exp. Psychol.*, 1963, **15**, 91–115.

CROSBY, E. C., & HENDERSON. J. W. The mammalian midbrain and isthmus regions. Part II. Fiber connections of the superior colliculus. B. Pathways concerned in automatic eye movements. *J. comp. Neurol.*, 1948, **88**, 853–892.

ETTLINGER, G. Visual discrimination following successive temporal ablations in monkeys. *Brain*, 1959, **82**, 232–250.(a)

ETTLINGER, G. Visual discrimination with a single manipulandum following temporal ablation in the monkey. *Quart. J. exp. Psychol.*, 1959, **11**, 164–174.(b)

ETTLINGER, G. Relationship between test difficulty and the visual impairment in monkeys with ablations of temporal cortex. *Nature*, 1962, **196**, 911–912.

EVARTS, E. V. Effects of ablation of prestriate cortex in auditory-visual association in monkeys. *J. Neurophysiol.*, 1952, **15**, 191–200.

GELLERMAN, L. W. Chance orders of alternating stimuli in visual discrimination experiments. *J. genet. Psychol.*, 1933, **42**, 206–208.

GLICKSTEIN, M., ARORA, H. A., & SPERRY, R. W. Delayed-response performance following optic tract section, unilateral frontal lesion, and commissurotomy. *J. comp. physiol. Psychol.*, 1963, **56**, 11–18.

HARLOW, H. F. The formation of learning sets. *Psychol. Rev.*, 1949, **56**, 51–65.

KLÜVER, H. Brain mechanisms and behavior with special reference to the rhinencephalon. *Lancet*, 1952, **12**, 567–577.

KLÜVER, H., & BUCY, P. C. Preliminary analysis of functions of the temporal lobes in monkeys. *Arch. Neurol. Psychiat.*, 1939, **42**, 979–1000.

KUYPERS, H. G. J. M., SZWARCBART, M. K., MISHKIN, M., & ROSVOLD, H. E. Occipitotemporal corticocortical connections in the rhesus monkey. *Exp. Neurol.*, 1965, **11**, 245–262.

LASHLEY, K. S. The mechanism of vision: XVIII. Effects of destroying the visual "associative areas" of the monkey. *Genet. Psychol. Monogr.*, 1948, **37**, 107–166.

LASHLEY, K. S. In search of the engram. *Sympos. Soc. exp. Biol.*, 1950, **4**, 454–482.

METTLER, F. A. Corticofugal fiber connections of the cortex of Macaca mulatta. The occipital region. *J. comp. Neurol.*, 1935, **61**, 221–256.(a)

METTLER, F. A. Corticofugal fiber connections of the cortex of Macaca mulatta. The parietal region. *J. comp. Neurol.*, 1935, **62**, 263–291.(b)

MEYER, D. R., HARLOW, H. F., & ADES, H. W. Retention of delayed responses and proficiency in oddity problems by monkeys with preoccipital ablations. *Amer. J. Psychol.*, 1951, **44**, 391–396.

MISHKIN, M. Visual discrimination performance following partial ablations of the temporal lobe: II. Ventral surface vs. hippocampus. *J. comp. physiol. Psychol.*, 1954, **47**, 187–193.

MISHKIN, M. Visual discrimination impairment after cutting cortical connections between the inferotemporal and striate areas in monkeys. *Amer. Psychologist*, 1958, **13**, 414. (Abstract)

MISHKIN, M. A possible link between interhemispheric integration in monkeys and cerebral dominance in man. In V. B. Mountcastle (Ed.), *Interhemispheric relations and cerebral dominance.* Baltimore: Johns Hopkins Press, 1962.

MISHKIN, M. Perseveration of central sets after frontal lesions in monkeys. In J. M. Warren & K. Akert (Eds.), *The frontal granular cortex and behavior.* New York: McGraw-Hill, 1964.

MISHKIN, M., & HALL, M. Discrimination along a size continuum following ablation of the inferior temporal convexity in monkeys. *J. comp. physiol. Psychol.*, 1955, **48**, 97–101.

MISHKIN, M., & PRIBRAM, K. H. Visual discrimination performance following partial ablations of the temporal lobe: I. Ventral vs. lateral. *J. comp. physiol. Psychol.*, 1954, **47**, 14–20.

MISHKIN, M., & WEISKRANTZ, L. Effects of cortical lesions in monkeys on critical flicker frequency. *J. comp. physiol. Psychol.*, 1959, **52**, 660–666.

NAUTA, W. J. H., & GYGAX, P. A. Silver impregnation of degenerating axons in the central nervous system. A modified technic. *Stain Tech.*, 1954, **29**, 91–94.

ORBACH, J., & FANTZ, R. L. Differential effects of temporal neo-cortical resections on overtrained and non-overtrained visual habits in monkeys. *J. comp. physiol. Psychol.*, 1958, **51**, 126–129.

PASIK, P., PASIK, T., BATTERSBY, W. S., & BENDER, M. B. Visual and tactual discrimination by Macaques with serial temporal and parietal lesions. *J. comp. physiol. Psychol.*, 1958, **51**, 427–436.

PASIK, T., PASIK, P., BATTERSBY, W. S., & BENDER, M. B. Target size and visual form discrimination in monkeys with bitemporal lesions. *Fed. Proc.*, 1958, **17**, 481. (Abstract)

PETR, R., HOLDEN, L. B., & JIROUT, J. The efferent intercortical connections of the superficial cortex of the temporal lobe in Macaca mulatta. *J. Neuropath. exp. Neurol.*, 1949, **8**, 100–103.

PRIBRAM, H., & BARRY, J. Further behavioral analysis of the parieto-temporo-pre-occipital cortex. *J. Neurophysiol.*, 1956, **19**, 99–106.

PRIBRAM, K. H., & MISHKIN, M. Simultaneous and successive discrimination by monkeys with inferotemporal lesions. *J. comp. physiol. Psychol.*, 1955, **48**, 198–202.

PRIBRAM, K. H., & MISHKIN, M. Analysis of the effects of frontal lesions in monkey: III. Object alternation. *J. comp. physiol. Psychol.*, 1956, **49**, 41–45.

RIOPELLE, A. J., & ADES, H. W. Visual discrimination performance in rhesus monkeys following extirpation of prestriate and temporal cortex. *J. genet. Psychol.*, 1953, **83**, 63–77.

RIOPELLE, A. J., HARLOW, H. F., SETTLAGE, P. H., & ADES, H. W. Performance of normal and operated monkeys on visual learning tests. *J. comp. physiol. Psychol.*, 1951, **44**, 283–289.

ROSVOLD, H. E., & MISHKIN, M. Effects of combined pulvinar and superior colliculus damage on visual discrimination in monkeys. Unpublished manuscript.

ROSVOLD, H. E., & MISHKIN, M. Further analysis of the effects of frontal and temporal cortical lesions on auditory discrimination in monkeys. Unpublished manuscript.

ROSVOLD, H. E., MISHKIN, M., & SZWARCBART, M. K. Effects of subcortical lesions in monkeys on visual-discrimination and single-alternation performance. *J. comp. physiol. Psychol.*, 1958, **51**, 437–444.

ROSVOLD, H. E., VEST, B., MISHKIN, M., & BROWN, T. S. Olfactory discrimination impairment after medial temporal cortical lesions in monkeys. Unpublished manuscript.

STEPIEN, L. S., CORDEAU, J. P., & RASMUSSEN, T. The effect of temporal lobe and hippocampal lesions in auditory and visual recent memory in monkeys. *Brain.* 1960, 83, 470–489.

VON BONIN, G., & BAILEY, P. *The neocortex of Macaca mulatta.* Urbana, Ill.: Univer. of Illinois Press, 1947.

VON BONIN, G., GAROL, H. W., & MCCULLOCH, W. S. The functional organization of the occipital lobe. *Biol. Sympos.*, 1942, **7**, 165–192.

WAGMAN, I. H. KRIEGER, H. P., & BENDER, M. B. Eye movements elicited by surface and depth stimulation of the occipital lobe of Macaca mulatta. *J. comp. Neurol.*, 1958, **109**, 169–193.

WEISKRANTZ, L., & COWEY, A. Striate cortex lesions and visual acuity of the rhesus monkey. *J. comp. physiol. Psychol.*, 1963, **56**, 225–231.

WEISKRANTZ, L., & MISHKIN, M. Effects of temporal and frontal cortical lesions on auditory discrimination in monkeys. *Brain*, 1958, **81**, 406–414.

WHITLOCK, D. G., & NAUTA, W. J. H. Subcortical projections from the temporal neocortex in Macaca mulatta. *J. comp. Neurol.*, 1956, **106**, 183–212.

WILSON, M. Effects of circumscribed cortical lesions upon somesthetic and visual discrimination in the monkey. *J. comp. physiol. Psychol.*, 1957, **50**, 630–635.

WILSON, M., & WILSON, W. A. Intersensory facilitation of learning sets in normal and brain operated monkeys. *J. comp. physiol. Psychol.*, 1962, **55**, 931–934.

WILSON, M., WILSON, W. A., & CHIANG, H. M. Formation of tactual learning sets. *J. comp. physiol. Psychol.*, 1963, **56**, 732–734.

WILSON, W. A., & MISHKIN, M. Comparison of the effects of inferotemporal and lateral occipital lesions on visually guided behavior in monkeys. *J. comp. physiol. Psychol.*, 1959, **52**, 10–17.

Psychological Defects Produced by Temporal Lobe Excision

Brenda Milner

Although experimental ablation studies in monkeys have failed to reveal any significant or consistent behavioral change after unilateral temporal lobectomy (in contrast to the marked deficits (10) which follow a bilateral lesion), in man the manifest non-equivalence of the two hemispheres, at least with respect to language, and the greater range and sensitivity of behavioral measures available encourage the search for clues to human temporal lobe function through a study of unilateral lesions. In fact we find that unilateral epileptogenic lesions of the temporal lobe dating from birth or early life are accompanied by certain cognitive defects which vary in kind depending on whether the lesion is in the dominant (left)[1] or non-dominant (right) temporal lobe. In such cases when unilateral partial temporal lobectomy is carried out for the relief of seizures, these characteristic defects persist and may even be accentuated, despite the fact that over-all intellectual efficiency is apt to increase if the patient is no longer having seizures. These specific defects form the main topic of the present paper.

During the last five years over a hundred patients with temporal lobe seizures have been subjected to formal psychological testing immediately before unilateral operation and again about 18 days later, at the time of the patient's discharge from hospital. Wherever possible, long-range follow-up studies have also been carried out, but these unfortunately have not been very numerous as yet. Twenty-two control cases consisting of patients with atrophic epileptogenic lesions of frontal or parietal cortex have been similarly studied before and after brain operation, in order to determine how far the deficits found are specific to the temporal lobe. All the patients in the series have been operated upon either by Dr. Wilder Penfield or by Dr. Theodore Rasmussen. In the course of the investigation the test battery has gradually changed and expanded, and we do not have complete data for all patients on all tests.

From *The Brain and Human Behavior*, 1958, **36**, 244–257. Reprinted with permission of the publisher and author.

[1] For the purpose of this study cases of right hemisphere speech representation are excluded.

Temporal lobe seizures are notoriously difficult to control by anti-convulsant medication. In such cases unilateral partial temporal lobectomy constitutes a reasonably successful method of treatment. It is usually followed by upper quadrantic homonymous hemianopsia but by no other neurological deficit. As Penfield and Baldwin (14) have pointed out, the abnormal sclerotic area of cortex which must be removed usually lies deep to the surface in the most inferior and mesial portion of the temporal lobe, adjacent to the mid-brain. It is believed that in most cases this sclerosis is produced by herniation through the incisura of the tentorium and compression of the arteries of supply at the time of birth (3), although seizures may not occur until much later. At operation the surgeon typically finds objective evidence of atrophy in the region of the uncus and anterior portion of the first temporal convolution and also in the hippocampus and hippocampal gyrus, and it is unusual to obtain lasting relief from seizures if these structures are spared. A typical removal is shown in figure VIII.I: the shading indicates abnormality of the

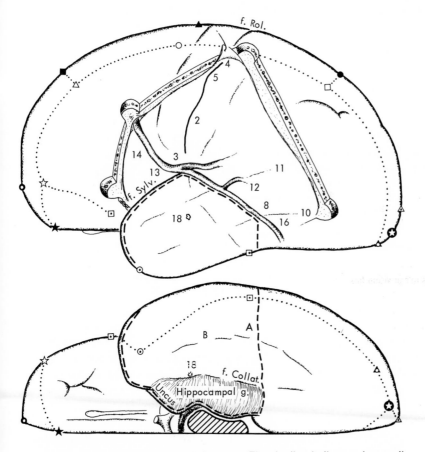

Fig. VIII.1. Typical partial temporal lobectomy. The shading indicates abnormality of the hippocampal zone.

hippocampal zone which was therefore excised together with the overlying cortex, the dotted line showing the total extent of excision. The fact that abnormality deep to the surface is typically found and that the excisions include both temporal neocortex and allocortex may well have an important bearing on the deficits seen.

RESULTS

General Intelligence

These patients with focal cortical epilepsy constitute a young group (the average age is 26 years, with a range from 14 to 45), and they are not intellectually retarded. During the last two years, in addition to more specialized tests, the Wechsler Intelligence Scale has been administered to all patients, Form I before operation and Form II after operation. Table 1 shows the mean intelligence ratings before operation for 30 consecutive temporal lobe cases, 15 left-sided and 15 right-sided, all with speech representation in the left hemisphere. The mean Full-Scale, Verbal, and Performance I.Q. ratings all fall within the normal range, and there is no significant difference between the two groups on these various measures. There is, however, a significant difference (t = 2.57, P < .05) between the Verbal and Performance I.Q. ratings for the right temporal group, with the Performance Quotient (based on non-verbal tests) averaging 9 points lower than the Verbal. A relative inefficiency on non-verbal tests has been reported by various workers for miscellaneous lesions of the right hemisphere (1, 9, 11, 16, 20): our observations extend these findings to the right temporal lobe specifically, thus corroborating Hebb's findings in a single case of right temporal lobectomy (6).

Table 1   Preoperative Mean I.Q. Ratings

GROUP	N	FULL SCALE	VERBAL	PERFORMANCE
Left temporal	15	108.5 (86–129)	107.2 (87–122)	107.3 (87–133)
Right temporal	15	103 (87–127)	107.1 (94–143)	97.6 (78–117)

After operation the patients were re-tested with Form II of the Wechsler scale which is a slightly harder test, yielding ratings lower rather than higher than Form I in a normal population (4). Thus practice effects can safely be ignored. Table 2 summarizes the findings three weeks after unilateral temporal lobectomy. There is no significant change in Full-Scale, Verbal, or Performance I.Q. ratings for the right temporal group. There were, however, some marked individual changes, a few patients improving by as much as 11 points in Full-Scale I.Q. rating and others showing a corresponding deterioration. The left temporal lobe group all showed some postoperative dysphasia

Table 2   Mean Fall in I.Q. Rating 3 Weeks After Unilateral Partial Temporal Lobectomy

GROUP	NO. OF PATIENTS	FULL SCALE	VERBAL	PERFORMANCE
Left temporal	15	10.3	16.6	2.3
Right temporal	15	1.5	2.5	1.4

due to the effects of cerebral edema upon neighboring speech areas although of course no primary speech area had been destroyed. This dysphasia is a transient phenomenon, usually developing from one to three days after operation and beginning to clear by about the tenth postoperative day. Marked individual differences in the severity and duration of the dysphasia are found, and these are reflected in varying degrees of impairment on verbal tests three weeks after operation. Thus we see in Table 2 that the left temporal lobe group shows a pronounced postoperative deficit in Verbal I.Q. rating, and hence some deficit also in Full-Scale I.Q. rating, changes which are significant beyond the .001 level of probability. There is, however, no impairment on performance tests even during this dysphasic period. Furthermore when these patients return for follow-up study a year or more later, we find that the I.Q. rating has returned at least to the preoperative level, provided they are no longer having seizures. Thus we can conclude that no lasting impairment of general intelligence follows unilateral anterior temporal lobectomy in either hemisphere.

Specific Defects

Against this background of general intellectual competence certain specific deficits stand out: verbal for the left temporal lobe group, perceptual for the right. These deficits, which differentiate between right and left temporal lobe cases even before operation, will now be described.

   a. Verbal Recall and the Left Temporal Lobe.   Although before operation the patients with left temporal lobe lesions showed no consistent impairment on verbal intelligence tests and no dysphasia, it was possible to demonstrate a specific deficit in verbal learning and retention at this time. As a result of this specific deficit the Wechsler memory quotient fell far below the I.Q. level for the left temporal lobe group, whereas no difference was found for the right temporal lobe cases. Patients with frontal lobe lesions are intermediate between the two temporal lobe groups and do show some relative memory impairment before operation, but the deficit is both different in kind and less severe than that shown by patients with left temporal lobe lesions. Table 3 gives the mean intelligence and memory quotients for these three groups of patients before and after brain operation. Analysis of variance yielded F-values significant beyond the .001 level, and subsequent t-tests showed the three groups to differ significantly one from another both before and after operation, the left temporal lobe patients consistently showing the

Table 3   Comparison of Mean Intelligence and Memory Quotients
(Before and Three Weeks After Operation) for Left
Temporal, Right Temporal and Frontal Lobe Cases

		PREOPERATIVE MEANS (FORM I)			POSTOPERATIVE MEANS (FORM II)		
GROUP	N	I.Q.	M.Q.	I.Q.-M.Q.	I.Q.	M.Q.	I.Q.-M.Q.
Left temporal	9	106.6	91.2	15.4	95.1	77.4	17.7
Right temporal	12	102.5	102.2	0.3	102.8	107.8	−5.0
Frontal	9	101.6	94.8	6.8	93.0	92.6	0.4

largest discrepancy between intelligence and memory quotients. The inter-group differences remain the same after operation, but Form II of the memory scale appears to be a somewhat easier test than Form I.

The Wechsler memory quotient is based on a heterogeneous sample of subtests, not all of which show impairment in the left temporal lobe group. There is, for example, no impairment in the recall of geometrical drawings. Moreover, although the patients with left temporal lobe lesions tend to do poorly on all verbal memory tests, the defect shows up most clearly and characteristically when they are asked to recall simple prose passages (stories a mere paragraph in length) which have been read to them some time before. Such measures of delayed recall do not contribute to the conventional memory quotient, yet they provide our most valuable localizing sign. It is our current practice to read the patient the two stories of the Logical Memory subtest of the memory scale, obtaining immediate reproductions of each in the usual manner, and then about one and a half hours later and without any previous warning we ask the patient to tell us the stories once more. Under these conditions the left temporal lobe group makes very low scores, as can be seen from Table 4 which gives the percentage of material recalled after an

Table 4   Delayed Recall of Stories (Preoperative)

		PERCENT RECALL	
GROUP	N	MEAN	RANGE
Left temporal	15	13	6–21
Others	29	25	8–42

interval by the left temporal group as compared with a mixed group of frontal, parietal and right temporal lobe cases. The left temporal lobe patients remember only half as much of the stories as do patients with lesions in other areas, a difference which is significant well beyond the .001 level of probability. It is of interest that the patients with frontal lobe lesions showed no impairment on this particular memory task.

All this is before operation, the effect of a focal epileptogenic lesion of the dominant temporal lobe. After operation these patients show the transient dysphasia noted above, at which time scores on all verbal tests, and not merely on verbal memory tests, are seriously impaired. But even after the dysphasia has cleared, the verbal memory difficulty persists, and there is now a detectable impairment even in the initial comprehension of stories. This is illustrated in Table 5, which gives average scores for four patients tested

Table 5   Specific Postoperative Impairment of Story Reproduction 1–3
          Years After Partial Left Temporal Lobectomy (Means for 4 Cases)

		BEFORE OPERATION	FOLLOW-UP
Wechsler I.Q.		104	110
Story Recall	Immediate	30	20
(percent)	Delayed	13.8	9.2

before left anterior temporal lobectomy and again in follow-up study from one to three years later, at which time they were free of seizures and had achieved a mean I.Q. level slightly higher than before operation. All four patients show a residual postoperative impairment in the immediate recall of stories. Quantitatively this falling-off is significant (P < .02), and there are corresponding qualitative changes also, the postoperative versions being more fragmentary and losing the distinctive pattern of the original story. It appears that only a very limited amount of verbal material can be assimilated in one sequence although any specific sentence or question taken in isolation is readily understood. This is a defect of which a patient of good intelligence is well aware. A student will report that he cannot follow lectures; a stenographer that she cannot keep up with her dictation; a bank clerk that he cannot handle the rapid give-and-take of conversation in the business world. Such individuals are apt to be less successful in their work than their intelligence and high motivation would lead one to predict. It is interesting that Meyer and Yates (12), working with similar case material in England, have also emphasized the severe learning difficulty of patients undergoing partial temporal lobectomy in the dominant hemisphere. However they regard this primarily as a postoperative phenomenon, whereas the results of the present study show that there are marked verbal recall deficits present even before operation. These differences in emphasis probably reflect differences in the measures used.

    b. Pictorial Comprehension and the Right Temporal Lobe.   Patients with epileptogenic lesions of the right, non-dominant, temporal lobe have none of these verbal difficulties, but they show a clear, specific and reliable impairment on a pictorial test, the McGill Picture Anomaly Series. In this test the subject is shown a number of sketchily drawn scenes and has to point to what is most incongruous in each. A relatively easy item from this test is shown in figure VIII.2. In this instance the picture on the wall of the monkey's cage is immediately recognized as inappropriate by most normal subjects, and also by patients with lesions of frontal, parietal, or left temporal cortex. However, a patient with a right temporal lobe lesion might have difficulty identifying the various parts of the drawing and so might, for example, point to the woman's head in the foreground as " unidentifiable" and therefore "wrong." The error scores for the various groups on this test are shown diagrammatically in figure VIII.3, different forms of the test being used before and after operation to eliminate practice effects. The right temporal lobe patients make significantly more errors (P < .01), both before and after operation, than other brain-injured subjects, who do not differ significantly from normal control subjects (a regrettably small group). It is particularly noteworthy that the patients with parietal lobe lesions made excellent scores. This pictorial test, whatever it measures, is not to be confused with tests such as Kohs Blocks which are primarily dependent upon spatial ability and are known to be peculiarly sensitive to parietal lobe injury (2, 8).

Fig. VIII.2. Representative item from the McGill Picture Anomalies test.

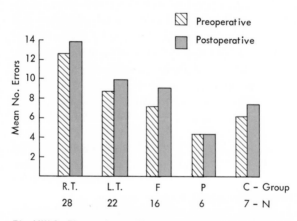

Fig. VIII.3. Picture Anomalies test: error scores for right temporal (R.T.), left temporal (L.T.), frontal (F) and parietal lobe (P) cases before and after operation, and for normal control subjects (C) tested twice.

The Picture Anomalies test was originally intended as a power test only, time of response not being recorded; but it became increasingly clear that the right temporal lobe patients were abnormally slow and hesitant, and not merely inaccurate, in their responses, and therefore time scores for the whole test are now unobtrusively recorded. The results to date are shown in figure VIII.4. The right temporal lobe group is slower than either the left temporal lobe or the frontal lobe groups even before operation, and after operation a significant further slowing occurs. Thus on this test we find a defect specific to the minor temporal lobe, and one which is heightened by removal of the epileptogenic area.

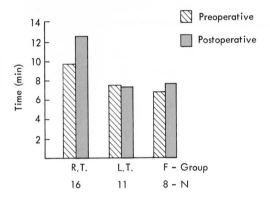

Fig. VIII.4. Picture Anomalies test: time scores, showing significant postoperative slowing for the right temporal lobe group only.

c. Auditory Discrimination—Preliminary Observations. The original test battery did not include any auditory tasks, but during the past year the Seashore tests of musical ability have been administered to all patients before and after operation. Despite the small number of cases, we already have some evidence of auditory deficits after unilateral temporal lobe excisions, the evidence so far being most clear for the right temporal lobe group. Unilateral temporal lobectomy, not necessarily including Heschl's gyrus, has consistently resulted in impairment on the Seashore tonal memory test, a test in which the subject listens to a simple melody of three or four notes played twice in rapid succession and has to indicate which note is changed at the second playing. After operation, scores of the right temporal group fall sharply on this test although other auditory tests, including simple pitch and intensity discrimination, may be unimpaired. In two patients seen for follow-up study this deficit was still present though not quite to the same degree. So far we do not see so consistent a deficit from the left temporal lobe, but the numbers are too small and the excision size too variable to permit any final conclusion to be drawn from this. Meanwhile it appears that right temporal lobectomy is in itself sufficient to cause a lasting deficit in the discrimination of tonal patterns. The fact that this deficit only appears after operation, whereas the visual difficulty is present even before operation, suggests that different parts of the temporal cortex are implicated in the visual and auditory tasks.

General Versus Specific Defects and the Nociferous Effects of Epileptogenic Cortex

The data so far presented have emphasized specific defects shown by patients with long-standing epileptogenic lesions of one temporal lobe, defects which tend to increase rather than decrease when the epileptogenic area is excised. Apart from these specific defects, most patients show normal intellectual functioning both before and after operation. However, there are marked individual differences in this respect, differences which may well be related to differences in degree of electrographic abnormality and seizure frequency before operation, though this has still to be demonstrated. Certainly some patients with unusually active electrographic foci before operation show general intellectual impairment which we attribute to widespread interference with cortical functioning rather than to the temporal lobe lesions specifically (7, p. 282). Unlike the specific defects, this more general intellectual inefficiency is apt to disappear after removal of the epileptogenic area. The following case is chosen to illustrate this point.

CASE M. L. This 22-year-old man presented a lifelong history of major and minor seizures, the latter occurring as often as 16 times a day. The attacks were ushered in by a warm, empty sensation in the umbilicus, followed by grunting, chewing and automatic behavior for which there was subsequent amnesia. Repeated electroencephalographic studies showed a very clear right temporal focus which was extraordinarily active, with sharp waves and slow wave sequence present continuously. On December 16, 1953, Dr. Penfield carried out a right temporal lobectomy, finding marked abnormality beginning in the first temporal convolution deep anteriorly and extending into the uncus and hippocampus and along the inferior surface of the temporal lobe. The removal extended roughly 4 cm. along the first temporal convolution and 5.5 cm. along the inferior surface, including the anterior portion of the hippocampal gyrus. Since this operation failed to stop the patient's attacks, three weeks later Dr. William Feindel extended the removal to include a further 1½ cm. of the hippocampus and adjacent inferior temporal cortex together with the insula. The patient has had no further seizures, and his family considers that his memory has improved greatly and that he is far less irritable than before.

PSYCHOLOGICAL FINDINGS. Preoperative psychological examination on December 12, 1953, showed the characteristic right temporal lobe deficits. The Performance I.Q. rating was only 84, as compared with a Verbal I.Q. rating of 95, and he made poor time and error scores on the Picture Anomalies test. But in addition to these specific and expected deficits he showed abnormal variability on other tests, giving careless answers to simple questions, failing easy items on the mental arithmetic test only to succeed a moment later on more difficult ones, and showing a very restricted attention span. There was marked impairment on short-term memory tests, resulting in a memory quotient of only 79, 10 points lower than the I.Q. rating. When tested for delayed recall of stories and drawings, further distortions and omissions occurred. We took these deficits as indicative of widespread interference with intellectual functioning due to the extremely active discharging lesion in the right temporal lobe, and hoped that improvement would follow surgical treatment. This in fact occurred. Fifteen days after the second operation the I.Q. level had risen from 89 to 99, the improvement being most marked on verbal tests. There was also a remarkable all-round improvement on short tests of memory and attention so that the memory quotient rose from 79 to 101, the most marked rise in the whole right temporal lobe group. Yet at the same time there was the typical further slowing on the Picture Anomalies test and also a falling off to chance scores on auditory discrimination tests, from which there has been little improvement to the present time.

This case has been selected to show the non-specific deficits which may result from an extremely active epileptogenic lesion in one temporal lobe. Removal of the epileptogenic focus in such a case may increase all-round intellectual efficiency, as shown for example by an appreciable rise in I.Q. rating, but will at the same time tend to aggravate the deficits specific to the area removed. This same principle of course could have been illustrated equally well by a left temporal lobe lesion, but the specific deficits would have been different.

The Memory Defect in Bilateral Hippocampal Lesions

So far we have been considering only the effects of lesions strictly lateralized to one temporal lobe, cases in which the opposite temporal lobe is, we believe, functioning normally. In such cases only minor deficits are seen: a specifically verbal difficulty from the left temporal lobe, a perceptual difficulty from the right. But in two instances in our temporal lobe series unilateral partial temporal lobectomy in the dominant hemisphere was followed by a major impairment: a grave, persistent and totally unexpected loss of recent memory, fortunately unaccompanied by other changes of intellect or personality (15). In one instance the temporal lobe removal had been carried out in two stages, separated by a five-year period, and the memory loss followed the second operation only, at which time the uncus, hippocampus, and hippocampal gyrus alone were excised. Interestingly enough, although the patient had been aphasic for a time after the first operation, the second operation caused no language disturbance. The memory loss seen in these two cases appeared to be qualitatively quite distinct from the verbal learning difficulty normally seen in unilateral lesions of the dominant temporal lobe since it affected all postoperative events and not merely verbal material. We believe this distinction to be of fundamental importance.

Both these amnesic patients have continued to earn their living, one as a glove cutter, the other as a draughtsman; and their professional skills are well maintained. There is no defect of attention, concentration, or reasoning ability and no aphasia. Both patients show some retrograde amnesia for a period before the operation (four years in the first patient, three months in the second), but their memory for events before the period of retrograde amnesia is apparently normal. They show a very gross impairment of memory for all events subsequent to operation, and they are unable to recall test material after a lapse of five minutes or less if their attention has been diverted to another topic in the meantime. The retention difficulty is not specific to any one kind of material, but is quite general, affecting stories, drawings and numbers, and cutting across any distinction between verbal and perceptual material or between one sense modality and another.

To account for the severe memory loss in these two patients we have assumed that, in addition to the known epileptogenic lesion of the left hippocampal region, there was a second and preoperatively unsuspected destructive lesion of the opposite (right) hippocampal zone at the time of birth, so that when the surgeon removed the left hippocampal area, the patient was functionally deprived of that zone on both sides. And in fact both patients now show continuing electrographic abnormality in the unoperated temporal lobe. This view then attributes a key role to the hippocampal zone (hippocampus and hippocampal gyrus) in the retention and subsequent recall of current experience. A similar view was advanced by Glees and Griffith in 1952 (5) to account for memory loss seen in one patient with bilateral destruction of hippocampus and hippocampal gyrus by vascular accident. Strong and direct support for this interpretation comes from Dr. William Scoville who in 1954 (17) reported a grave loss of recent memory as a sequel to bilateral medial temporal lobe resection in one psychotic patient and one patient with intractable seizures. These operations had been radical ones, undertaken only when more conservative forms of treatment had failed. The removals extended posteriorly along the mesial aspect of the temporal lobes for a distance of about 8 cm. from the temporal tips, and the excisions were made by bisecting the tips of the temporal lobes and removing bilaterally the inferior portions of each temporal lobe which lay mesial to the inferior horn of the ventricle. These ablations must then have included the major portion of the hippocampus and hippocampal gyrus bilaterally, as well as uncus and amygdala,[2] but of course spared the lateral neocortex. Dr. Scoville has very generously allowed us to study these patients, and they present exactly the same type of memory disturbance as our two cases had shown (18). Interestingly, I think, they do not have any perceptual difficulty or any disturbance of initial comprehension. The impairment is specifically one of retention.

[2] In his experience, bilateral removals limited to the uncal and amygdaloid regions cause no memory loss.

CONCLUSIONS

What do these findings as a whole tell us of the normal function of the temporal lobes? The data on unilateral lesions show that the left temporal lobe contributes to the rapid understanding and subsequent retention of verbally expressed ideas. Deprived of this area a man is not dysphasic, but he remains an inefficient listener and a poor reader since he can assimilate less verbal information in one sequence than formerly and forgets this little abnormality quickly. The right, minor, temporal lobe, on the other hand, appears to be more critically involved in perceptual than in verbal skills.[3] When the right temporal lobe is removed, pictures and representational drawings lose some of their former distinctiveness, and the separate parts are less easily identified although there is never anything approaching a true visual agnosia. It seems that the right temporal lobe facilitates rapid visual identification, and that in this way it enters into the comprehension of pictorially expressed ideas.

These data on unilateral lesions have underlined the differences in function between the two temporal lobes, differences which relate to the functional asymmetry of the two hemispheres, the left being primarily concerned with verbal, the right with non-verbal skills. But it is clear that there must still be a considerable overlap of function between the two temporal lobes, the extent of which can only be revealed by bilateral lesions (19). We have no experience of bilateral lesions of the temporal neocortex, but the discovery of generalized memory loss, apparently independent of type of material or sense modality, after bilateral destruction of the hippocampus and hippocampal gyrus suggests that this hippocampal zone plays an essential part in the consolidation of the effects of current experience so that they endure beyond the moment of primary attention.

SUMMARY

Formal psychological testing before and after unilateral partial temporal lobectomy in over 100 cases of temporal lobe epilepsy has yielded the following results.

1. Intelligence as measured by the Wechsler-Bellevue I.Q. rating is not permanently affected by these operations although there is a deficit on verbal subtests in the left temporal group during the period of postoperative dysphasia.

2. Long-standing epileptogenic lesions of the temporal lobe are associated with defects on certain specialized tests, these defects varying in kind

---

[3] Dr. Sean Mullan's observations, reported by Dr. Penfield (13) at these meetings, provide further evidence of the importance of the minor temporal lobe for perceptual functions. He finds that visual illusions of changes in the appearance of objects, whether occurring during epileptic discharge or as a result of cortical stimulation, arise almost invariably from the non-dominant rather than the dominant temporal lobe.

depending on whether the lesion is in the dominant or non-dominant hemisphere.

3. Unilateral epileptogenic lesions of the dominant (left) temporal lobe are accompanied by difficulties in verbal recall although recall of non-verbal material is normal.

4. Unilateral epileptogenic lesions of the non-dominant (right) temporal lobe are accompanied by impairment in the comprehension of pictures although verbal skills are intact.

5. When unilateral partial temporal lobectomy is carried out for the relief of seizures, these specific deficits persist and in fact tend to be accentuated. This is true even in those cases which show a postoperative increase in I.Q. rating and complete cessation of seizures.

6. In contrast to the relatively mild deficits which accompany unilateral lesions, bilateral damage to the hippocampal zone causes profound and generalized loss of recent memory, unaccompanied by other intellectual changes.

7. These findings suggest that (a) the left temporal lobe contributes to the understanding and retention of verbally expressed ideas; (b) the right temporal lobe aids in rapid visual identification; (c) the hippocampus and hippocampal gyrus (either separately or together) play a crucial role in the retention of new experience.

REFERENCES

1. ANDERSON, A. L.: The effect of laterality localization of brain lesions on the Wechsler-Bellevue subtests. J. Clin. Psychol., *7;* 149–153, 1949.
2. CRITCHLEY, M.: The Parietal Lobes. Edward Arnold Ltd., London, 1953.
3. EARLE, K. M., BALDWIN, M., & PENFIELD, W.: Incisural sclerosis and temporal lobe seizures produced by hippocampal herniation at birth. Arch. Neurol. & Psychiat., *69;* 27–42, 1953.
4. GERBOTH, R.: A study of the two forms of the Wechsler-Bellevue Intelligence Scale. J. Consult. Psychol., *14;* 365–370, 1950.
5. GLEES, P., & GRIFFITH, H. B.: Bilateral destruction of the hippocampus (cornu Ammonis) in a case of dementia. Monatsschr. Psychiat. u. Neurol., *123;* 193–204, 1952.
6. HEBB, D. O.: Intelligence in man after large removals of cerebral tissue; defects following right temporal lobectomy. J. Gen. Psychol., *21;* 73–87, 1939.
7. HEBB, D. O.: The Organization of Behavior: A Neuropsychological Theory, Wiley, New York, 1949.
8. HÉCAEN, H., PENFIELD, W., BERTRAND, C., & MALMO, R.: The syndrome of apractognosia due to lesions of the minor cerebral hemisphere. Arch. Neurol. & Psychiat., *75;* 400–454, 1956.
9. HEILBRUNN, A. B., JR.: Psychological test performance as a function of lateral localization of cerebral lesions. J. Comp. & Physiol. Psychol., *49;* 10–14, 1956.
10. KLÜVER, H., & BUCY, P. C.: Preliminary analysis of functions of the temporal lobe in monkeys. Arch. Neurol. & Psychiat., *42;* 979–1000, 1939.
11. MCFIE, J., & PIERCY, M. F.: Intellectual impairment with localized cerebral lesions. Brain, *75;* 292–311, 1952.

12. MEYER, V., & YATES, A. J.: Intellectual changes following temporal lobectomy for psychomoter epilepsy. J. Neurol. Neurosurg. & Psychiat., *18:* 44–52, 1955.
13. PENFIELD, W.: Functional localization in temporal and deep Sylvian areas. Res. Publ. Assn. Res. Nerv. Ment. Dis., 1957.
14. PENFIELD, W., & BALDWIN, M.: Temporal lobe seizures and the technique of sub-total temporal lobectomy. Ann. Surg., *136:* 625–634, 1952.
15. PENFIELD, W., & MILNER, B.: The memory deficit produced by bilateral lesions in the hippocampal zone. Arch. Neurol. & Psychiat., 1957 (in press).
16. REITAN, R. M.: Certain differential effects of left and right cerebral lesions in human adults. J. Comp. & Physiol. Psychol., *48:* 474–477, 1955.
17. SCOVILLE, W. B.: The limbic lobe in man. J. Neurosurg., *11:* 64–66, 1954.
18. SCOVILLE, W. B., & MILNER, B.: Loss of recent memory after bilateral hippocampal lesions. J. Neurol. Neurosurg. & Psychiat., *20:* 11–21, 1957.
19. TERZIAN, H., & DALLE ORE, G.: Syndrome of Klüver and Bucy produced in man by bilateral removal of the temporal lobes. Neurology *5:* 373–380, 1955.
20. WEISENBERG, T., & MCBRIDE, K.: Aphasia: A Clinical and Psychological Study. Commonwealth Fund, New York, 1936.

Some Alterations
in Behavior
After Cerebral Lesions
in Man

Hans-Lukas Teuber

With the present paper, we enter upon the last section of the reports on evolution of nervous control. We thus tried within this symposium to ascend from the earliest forms of nervous organization to the complexities of the human brain. Such attempt on our part might seem blasphemous: it took the Creator seven days, or, according to more recent readings of the Scripture, over two billion years to accomplish what we have tried to recapitulate in so little space. No wonder that our understanding is somewhat limited in scope and that this last part should deal less with evolution and more with *dissolution* of nervous systems, with decay in behavior in the presence of ablation, injury, or disease.

The evolutionary method is based on studying variations in the structure of nervous systems of different species and on the search for correlated differences in their behavioral repertoire. The method based on studying dissolution of the nervous system has the same objectives. Pathology in animals or man is studied because by it normal physiology is "laid bare" (cf. ref. 24). The ultimate question is here, again, how does the nervous system (or specifically, the brain) mediate behavior? Or, more cautiously put: in what ways is behavior permanently altered in the presence of a lesion in the brain?

Studies of disordered physiology face a number of difficulties. It is often hazardous to go from symptoms (i.e., dysfunction) to inferences about the

From *Evolution of Nervous Control from Primitive Organisms to Man* (Washington, D.C.: American Association for the Advancement of Science, 1959), pp. 157–94. Reprinted with permission of the publisher and author. Copyright 1959 by the American Association for the Advancement of Science. The work reviewed in this paper has been made possible by grants from the Commonwealth Fund of New York. In its earlier stages, the work has also been supported by the U.S. Veterans Administration and the Office of the Surgeon General, Department of the Army, under Contract DA-49-007-MD-312.

neural bases of normal function, doubly so since many changes after cerebral lesions are transient rather than permanent. From previous speakers we have heard about complexity and regulatory capacity in "simple protoplasm" (51). The human central nervous system presents a degree of complexity of still higher order; resiliency after lesions is therefore part of the story and just as important perhaps as the presence of lasting impairment.

The greatest difficulty in the use of abnormal physiology stems from incomplete or incorrect description of behavioral changes. We tend to substitute casual observation or clinical beliefs for the necessary analyses of altered performance. As a result, our attempts at correlating particular cerebral lesions with particular changes in behavior become inconsistent or impossible to apply to the study of normal relations between function and structure of the brain. To make this point, we shall cite four propositions, corresponding to common beliefs about effects of cerebral lesions in man; we shall then review some evidence to show that each of these propositions is wrong (though some are more wrong than others).

SOME PROPOSITIONS

Let me start with a proposition that was held to be true not so many years ago, but is patently wrong:

I. *Changes in behavior, after penetrating brain wounds in man, are obvious, gross, and detectable by routine tests.* This is quite wrong; they are often subtle, elusive, require very special tasks for their discovery, and even then might go undiscovered.

A second proposition can be put in the form of a dichotomy:

II. *Changes where they do occur are either specific* (tied to a given locus in the brain), *or generalized,* reflecting a diffuse alteration in mode of functioning; rarely, if ever, does one see both types of change. This dichotomy we believe to be wrong. Studies of men with penetrating brain lesions suggest to us that both types of effect—specific and general—occur together. The relative prominence of one or the other kind of effect may differ from case to case, but it differs even more markedly with the kinds of test employed.

The third proposition can again be stated as a dichotomy; we consider it misleading, and probably untrue:

III. *Changes in behavior occur either on some elementary level,* e.g., in basic sensory processes, or motor function, *or on some much "higher" level,* so that we might be able to see after a brain lesion, but fail to recognize what we are seeing ("agnosia"), or might be able to move, but do not know how to perform skilled acts ("apraxia").

The existence of such a dichotomy of "lower" and "higher" functions has been widely accepted among clinicians. Only recently have serious questions been raised (5, 28, 59, 68). Changes in so-called elementary functions do no longer appear quite as elementary as claimed, and there are doubts whether the supposed higher functions can ever be as selectively impaired as the classical notion of agnosia would suggest.

A fourth and final proposition is, in a sense, merely a special form of the third. It is the old belief in the preeminent function of the frontal lobes. Thus:

IV. As we ascend phylogeny, function steadily shifts toward the frontal end of the forebrain, so that in man *the highest functions are selectively impaired by lesions of the frontal lobes.*

Again, we cannot believe that, even though our denial is easily misunderstood. We do not mean to say that man's frontal lobes can be removed with impunity. Changes do occur, even after restricted frontal lesions in man, but some of these changes result quite as readily from lesions elsewhere in the brain, and others are of a curious sort, involving primarily sensorimotor aspects of behavior rather than specific, "higher" intellectual functions.

Let us now turn to the evidence we possess with regard to each of these four propositions.

POPULATION STUDIED

The principal observations are based on work with a group of patients we have followed for a varying number of years (from ten years in the majority of cases down to two years in a few, with an average of seven). There are 232 men in this group, all with penetrating battle injuries of the brain. In each case, the fact of penetration of missiles into the brain substance has been established on the basis of surgical history and roentgenographic evidence.

The group differs from those observed in earlier studies in that none of the cases are included for clinical reasons. That is, these men are called to our laboratory because they are known to have a brain injury, and they come regardless of whether they need clinical attention or not. This fact may account for the higher incidence of seemingly "negative" cases in our work, in contrast to earlier studies which had to concentrate, automatically, on patients who had severe symptoms or thought they did. As we have pointed out in the past (67), the group includes an estimated 80% of all men with battle wounds of the brain who reside in or around Greater New York.

The group of control patients comprises at the present time 118 cases of battle injury to one or more peripheral nerves, in the absence of brain injury. These control patients are studied in the same fashion as the brain-injured, in numerous individual testing sessions. Needless to say, the work exceeds what one person might do alone. I have had the help, for many years, of a number of collaborators, notably (for the work to be reported here) that of Dr. Josephine Semmes, Dr. Sidney Weinstein, and Dr. Lila Ghent. All of us, however, owe our greatest debt to the patients themselves; they have volunteered, in many instances, for two to three dozen testing sessions, and they are doing this in the hope of helping us rather than of getting help.

I. RESILIENCY OF PERFORMANCE AND INADEQUACY OF ROUTINE PSYCHOMETRIC TESTS

Let us begin with an illustration of our first proposition, viz., that the defects are gross and detectable with the usual kind of test.

At the time of induction into the armed services, our men had all been given a routine test of " general intelligence," the Army General Classification Test (AGCT). For 62 men who subsequently sustained brain injuries, pre-injury scores could be obtained, with the help of the Surgeon General's Office (U.S. Army Medical Department). All these men were retested, on the average, ten years after their wounding with an equivalent form of the test (AGCT, First Civilian Edition).

The same was done for 50 of our controls, i.e., men with battle injuries of peripheral nerves, but without brain injury. The results are illustrated in Figs. 1 and 2. As the first figure shows, 48 of the 50 controls (without brain

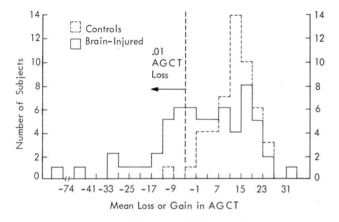

Fig. 1. Distribution of losses and gains on the AGCT for 62 brain-injured patients (solid lines) and 50 controls with peripheral nerve injury, but without brain injury (dotted lines). The original test scores were obtained at the time of induction into the armed services in World War II. Subsequently these men sustained brain or nerve injury in combat; they were retested on the average ten years after their wounding.

injury) have markedly increased their score; on the average they have gained 13 points, even though ten years have intervened between the first and second testing session. (Only 2 controls showed losses on retest—one had lost 1 point and another 9.) Such gains, rather than losses in performance with advancing age, are unexpected if one relies on earlier beliefs of psychometrists (79), but they are in agreement with recent long-term retest studies summarized by Lorge (42). The retest reliability for our control group was considerable, since the correlation (Pearson's r) between scores earned on test and retest was .902.

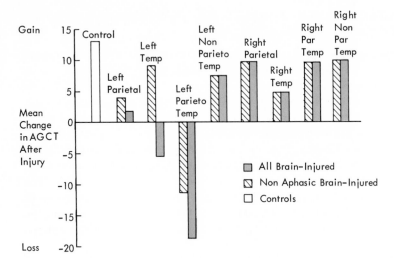

Fig. 2. Average gains or losses in AGCT scores for 50 controls (open bar) and 62 brain-injured subjects. The brain-injured group has been subdivided according to location of lesion. In this particular comparison, e.g., men with known involvement of the left parieto-temporal region are contrasted with all those men who fail to have a known injury implicating that region (left nonparieto-temporal). Results are shown separately for all brain-injured (solid tint bars) and for the brain-injured exclusive of the aphasic subjects (striped bars).

Much less expected, however, was the fact that among the brain-injured, nearly two-thirds improved their scores, many as much as the controls (see Fig. 1, solid lines). Only 20 men of the 62 brain-injured showed a significant loss in scores. The question immediately arises: which ones among the brain-injured tend to show this decline. Figure 2 presents a breakdown of test results for separate groups among the brain-injured, set up according to wound of entrance, whether in the frontal, parietal, temporal, or occipital regions, and whether in the left or right hemispheres of the brain. It is apparent that the instances of significant decline in AGCT performance after brain injury are found among those with penetration into the left parietal and temporal regions.

Injury to these regions in the left hemisphere is known to result frequently in disturbances of language functions (aphasia); one might ask, therefore, whether the relatively focal nature of the loss might not reflect merely a higher incidence of lasting aphasia following left parieto-temporal lesion. Tests such as the AGCT are notoriously dependent on language skills: the subject has to read and grasp each question regardless of whether the content of the test question is itself concerned with vocabulary, with arithmetic, or with a visuo-spatial task (block counting).

The results grouped by wound of entrance were therefore re-analyzed (84), omitting all those patients who had a history of aphasic disorder. The resulting pattern is seen in Fig. 2, which shows that even when obviously aphasic cases have been excluded, the decline in AGCT performance is most pronounced for the group with left parieto-temporal lesions (cf. also ref. 46).

These results of our second analysis (exclusive of the obviously aphasic patients) can be interpreted in two ways: if one accepts scores on a routine psychometric test, such as the AGCT, at their face value, one would be inclined to conclude that losses in test intelligence are rare or absent unless the injury encroaches upon the left parieto-temporal region. The second and more parsimonious interpretation would emphasize the negative findings first, namely that the AGCT seems insensitive to many of the actual changes that might occur after brain injury *unless* these changes include some subtle but significant loss of verbal skills. This second interpretation would then stress that a paper-and-pencil test so intimately tied to language functions as the AGCT would be expected to bring out traces of language trouble even in those patients with left hemisphere lesions who appear to be without aphasia on clinical interview.

Regardless of which of these interpretations one selects, the results of our test-retest study with the AGCT clearly indicate the remarkable resiliency of test intelligence in the majority of our brain-injured patients. At the same time, such an outcome shows that contrary to common expectations, the intellectual effects of penetrating brain wounds need be neither gross nor obvious. Instead of routine psychometric instruments such as paper-and-pencil tests of intelligence, one needs special procedures in order to define the various characteristic if subtle changes following injuries to different lobes.

II. SPECIFICITY AND GENERALITY OF EFFECTS

Granting that the behavioral effects of brain lesions need not be obvious, we might still ask whether those that can be demonstrated are necessarily general (appearing in the same way with lesions in any part), or quite specific (appearing like the losses on the AGCT with lesions in focal, restricted regions of the brain). As we said initially, the after-effects of nearly any lesion sufficient to produce some noticeable change are always specific as well as general, so that local signs are found in an obligatory association with signs of general or nonspecific involvement.

Vision

Specific (Focal) Symptoms: Visual Field Defects. We can illustrate this nondichotomous result by referring to some of our older studies on effects of lesions in the central visual pathways (66, 70–72). Figure 3 depicts a typical effect on the visual field of a penetrating rifle bullet wound implicating the left lower occipital region. The resulting area of acquired blindness is a wedge-shaped island in the right upper quadrant of the field, a striking instance of specific effect of a lesion, since there is direct correspondence between a gap in the neural structure and a gap in the visual field. It is difficult to conceive of any other consequences of cerebral lesions which would be as static, localizable, and circumscribed.

It is remarkable that the scotoma in the case illustrated should be wedge-shaped, with the tip of the wedge pointing toward the center of fixation in each eye. In the past, it has been claimed that such sector defects tapering toward the fovea are practically nonexistent after brain injury. Their supposed nonexistence was used as an argument against any direct correspondence between defect in structure and defect in visual field (37, 55). Actually, such sector defects are anything but rare. They have been seen by us in four additional instances out of our total group of 52 patients with field defects, and they have been described independently by Spalding on the basis of a survey of field defects in an even larger series of cases observed in England (64, 65).

Project A - Case 66

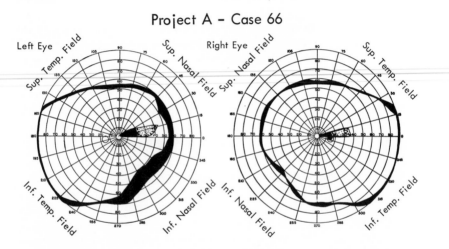

Fig. 3. Homonymous field defects (wedge-shaped scotoma tapering toward fovea), due to gunshot wound implicating left lower occipital pole. Solid black indicates inability to discriminate presence from absence of a stationary 1° target (white), at 330 mm from the cornea, under 7-foot-candle illumination. Area of stippling indicates amblyopia (abnormal fluctuation in visibility of 1° target).

A few words might need to be said about the permanence of field defects and the reliability of the perimetric method. In taking the visual field by perimetry, parameters of stimulation have to be rigorously controlled. These are known to include illumination, size, and distance of the targets; duration of exposure; stationary or moving presentation. However, if these factors are properly controlled, different examiners obtain essentially identical visual fields, independently, from the same patient over periods of many years. To be sure, during the early posttraumatic period, the visual field can be observed to change. We can confirm the classical descriptions of development from an initial complete blindness (in some instances) to diffuse nonlocalizable light perception, and thence to the gradual return of first color and then contour vision. Such progressive changes can occur within hours, days, and (very rarely) weeks or months. However, before the end of the first year after wounding, the patient's field appears essentially as it always will, so that it makes no difference whether a scotoma like the one shown in Fig. 3 is recorded two years or twenty years after the trauma.

Diffuse Visual Symptoms (*Changes in Critical Flicker Fusion, Motion Perception, Dark Adaptation*). Quite a different picture is given by those visual symptoms which occur in permanent and obligatory association with visual field defects, but are not restricted to areas of demonstrable scotoma. As we have shown in the past, reduction in fusion thresholds for flickering light, impairment of motion perception, or dark adaptation, and of tachistoscopic vision, all are present when there is a field defect, yet involve the visual field as a whole (for summary, see ref. 68; for earlier studies, see refs. 3, 33, 34, 70–72). In this respect, these effects of penetrating occipital injury are diffuse, since they appear even in those parts of the visual field which seem intact on routine perimetry. However, the effects are restricted to cases with visual field defect, suggesting that occipital lesions produce two-fold effects: those that are focal (scotoma), and those that are less focal, involving visual function over the entire field, and many aspects of visual performance.

Nonspecific Symptoms (*Performance on Hidden-Figure Tasks*). Further analysis of performance on visual tasks has permitted us to draw one additional conclusion (78). Men with visual field defects also exhibit increased difficulty in the discovery of " hidden " figures, i.e., of line drawings concealed by embedding them in interlacing contours [after Gottschaldt (18, 19)] (see Fig. 4). However, while field defects are sufficient to produce some deficit on such tasks, they are not necessary, since men without field defect perform equally badly. Moreover, men with injuries in any lobe, in either or both hemispheres, show approximately the same impairment (Fig. 5). We thus have a deficit which is not specific for locus of lesion, despite the seemingly "visual" character of the task. Nor do men with somatosensory or motor symptoms perform any more poorly than those without such symptoms, though all fall below the level of our controls (Fig. 6). Only the aphasic patients, as a group, do significantly worse than the other brain-injured who in turn do significantly worse than the controls.

Visual symptoms after lesions of the higher visual pathways thus range from those that are most specific to those most general, with other symptoms in between. Some dysfunctions (scotomata) are specific and circumscribed, others (lowered flicker fusion, impaired dark adaptation) exist in the presence of scotoma, but involve the entire field. Still others (impairment on hidden figures) exist irrespective of location of lesion and presence or absence of other symptoms, thus indicating a general deficit (cf. for the rodent ref. 36). For our present purpose, the decisive finding is the absence of any dichotomy: our cases show specific as well as general effects. The common view that effects of lesions should be either all general or all specific cannot be maintained.

Somesthesis

Specific Somatosensory Symptoms. Analogous findings are now available for somesthesis (62). Extended testing of so-called elementary somatosensory functions (passive motion and position sense, light touch thresholds, two-point discrimination, and point localization) have confirmed the classical notion that lesions in the central sector of the brain (pre- and postrolandic areas) can impair somatosensory performance in a permanent and circumscribed fashion. Thus, tactile deficits of the contralateral hand following lesions of one hemisphere (right or left) show essentially the same direct relation to the "gap" in the cerebral substrate which is manifested by the scotomata found in the visual field after lesion of higher visual pathways.

In the course of these studies, however, we encountered an unexpected feature of representation in somesthesis (62). For cases with unilateral involvement of the *left* hemisphere, lesions of central (i.e., pre- and postrolandic) sectors and of midparietal regions produced significantly more frequent and more severe sensory changes in the contralateral hand than lesions elsewhere in the brain. This is the expected pattern. Corresponding tests of the left hand, i.e., the one contralateral to the *right* hemisphere, revealed a different pattern of representation: defects of the left hand were just as frequent as those of the right, but the defects did not seem to occur with significantly higher frequency with lesions in the classical sensorimotor area

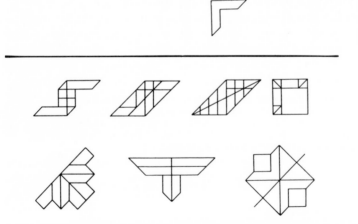

Fig. 4. Hidden-figure test (sample page), modified after Gottschaldt. The subject is required to find the figure at the top within each of the lower (embedding) figures. [Reproduced with permission from Teuber and Weinstein, *A.M.A. Arch. Neurol. Psychiat.,* 76 (1956).]

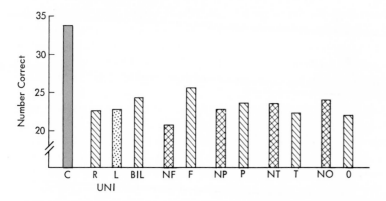

Fig. 5. Mean number of figures correctly traced by controls (C) and brain-injured subjects grouped according to location of lesion. R, right unilateral lesion; L, left unilateral lesion; Bil, bilateral lesion; F, P, T, O, frontal, parietal, temporal, and occipital, respectively; NF, NP, NT, NO, nonfrontal, nonparietal, etc. [Reproduced with permission from Teuber and Weinstein, *A.M.A. Arch. Neurol. Psychiat., 76* (1956).]

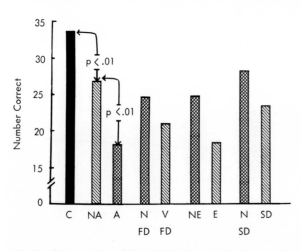

Fig. 6. Mean number of figures traced correctly by controls (C), and by brain-injured subjects, grouped according to presence or absence of aphasia (A), visual field defect (VFD), epilepsy (E), and somatosensory defect (SD). Absence of a given defect is indicated by N. [Reproduced with permission from Teuber and Weinstein, *A.M.A. Arch. Neurol. Psychiat., 76* (1956).]

than with lesions outside these areas. It seemed as if sensory representation were less focal in the right hemisphere than in the left.

Less Specific Symptoms in Somesthesis: Difficulties in Discrimination of Object Qualities. Such apparent differences between hemispheres aside, our tests of " elementary " sensory function reveal lasting and specific changes in thresholds limited to parts of the body opposite a unilateral lesion. By their very nature, these deficits might be expected to interfere with the perception of what are traditionally known as "higher" or complex aspects of objects presented through the sense of touch. However, the classical concept of "astereognosis" suggests that recognition of object qualities within a given modality can be impaired in the absence of any "primary" or "elementary" deficit in that sense modality (54). This claim is in effect yet another statement of dissociation of "lower" and "higher" aspects of sensation, rather than of individual, "elementary" sense modalities.

Accordingly, we investigated performance on a series of tasks involving discrimination of tactile object qualities. The tasks included discrimination of two-dimensional patterns, tridimensional forms (solids), and textures (14, 15). On these tests, the subject palpated a given object with one hand, and then tried to find a replica of this object in an array of objects offered for comparison (see Figs. 7 and 8). Vision was always excluded by the simple

Fig. 7. Discrimination of two-dimensional patterns (one of five discrimination tasks). On each trial one of the forms is placed for 5 seconds on subject's palm, as shown. Immediately afterwards, subject attempts to identify this form by palpating the entire array.

device of placing the test object behind a black curtain, but within the patient's reach. On all tests each hand was tested singly for an equal number of trials; on certain additional tests, further trials were run in which both hands were tested together, so that one received the standard and the other the comparison object, either simultaneously (cf. refs. 6, 35), or in rapid alternation. These conditions of testing had systematically different effects: testing either hand alone produced significantly smaller errors in all groups (controls as well as brain-injured), then testing both hands together, either simultaneously or in rapid succession. Analogous results were obtained in tests of discrimination of weights (73, 81, 82).

Fig. 8. Discrimination of solid forms. Subject palpates a sample form (front), and attempts to find the identical form within the array (in back).

The most general finding, however, was the following: men with sensory impairment of one hand (established by prior administration of "basic" sensory tests), showed significantly poorer performance in object discrimination in both hands, not only the one opposite their injury but also their ipsilateral hand, which had seemed intact on all "primary" tests of sensory function (Figs. 9 and 10).

This unexpected finding shows that discrimination deficits are associated with more basic sensory defects, but transcend these basic defects by involving seemingly unimpaired parts of the patient's body. The observations are strikingly parallel to those made on visual functions after lesions of the central visual pathways; there too, specific defects (scotomata) are restricted to certain regions, while the more subtle deficits, such as lowered flicker-fusion, go beyond the area of primary defect, and involve the entire visual field.

General Involvement: Performance on Formboard and Other Complex Tactile Tasks.   Are there deficits in the somatosensory modality analogous to the nonspecific changes revealed by hidden-figures tasks? We have no data, as yet, on a tactile analogue of the Gottschaldt test, but we would predict that men with lesions in any lobe would show impairment on such a test of tactile hidden figures. The prediction is based on the essentially "nonspecific" outcome of a series of complex tactual tasks (60). These tasks were constructed to represent logical, if not perceptual, analogues of various visual complex tests (sorting tests and their variants) (69). Impairment on these complex tactual tasks was found for *all* groups of men with brain injury. Similarly, all groups with brain injury, regardless of particular locus of lesion, performed significantly below the level of the controls on a modified Seguin-Goddard form-board test (77).

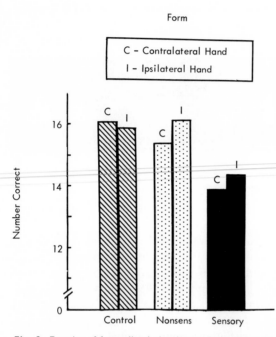

Fig. 9. Results of form discrimination task. In the control group, C and I hands are left and right, respectively. Note the reduction in score for both hands in the group with sensory defect (as defined by "basic" sensory tests). The brain-injured group without such "basic" sensory defect (nonsensory) does not differ from the controls.

Disturbances in somesthesis thus range from those that are most specific and circumscribed to those that are neither; which kind of symptom appears is a matter of the tasks employed. Many of the classical sensory tests yield relatively specific and circumscribed deficits, restricted to a body region opposite to a unilateral brain injury: tests of discrimination, however, reveal bilateral deficits (both hands) in these same cases of seemingly unilateral sensory loss. Finally, tasks can be devised which are not susceptible to localization, i.e., which reveal losses with injury in any lobe, in either hemisphere, or both.

Texture

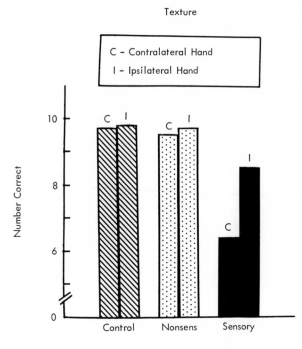

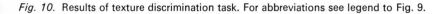

Fig. 10. Results of texture discrimination task. For abbreviations see legend to Fig. 9.

III. THE DICHOTOMY OF "HIGHER" AND "LOWER" LEVELS OF PERFORMANCE: THE PROBLEM OF AGNOSIA

Our findings in vision and somesthesis thus fail to conform to the traditional dichotomy of specific versus general effects. Considered under a slightly different aspect, the same findings cast doubt on yet another dichotomy, the dichotomy of higher versus lower functions. It has been assumed that a given cerebral lesion might produce selected losses in sensation, while some other lesion, differently placed, would interfere with recognition within that sense modality, in the absence of any significant disturbance in sensation. Thus, visual agnosia is considered as a disturbance of "higher" aspects of vision. The patient can see, but fails to understand what he is seeing. In tactile agnosia, he can feel, but fails to recognize objects through the sense of touch.

It is one of the strangest features of this complicated field that at the present moment no one really knows whether visual or tactile agnosia does ever occur in man. Positive reports were quite numerous in the literature before the turn of the century. However, the closer one moves to the present time, the less frequent are the cases reported. In our own group with gunshot wounds of the brain, not one case of agnosia in the classical sense was found, either because gunshot wounds rarely or never produce the necessary kind of lesion, or because agnosia becomes the harder to demonstrate the more detailed the examination.

The criterion of true agnosia is dissociation of higher and lower aspects of sensation. Elementary sensation needs to be intact before one can speak of a selective loss on a gnostic level (29). However, in our cases, such difficulties with recognition were never completely dissociated from "primary sensory deficit," except in the very special sense that difficulties with tactile recognition of object qualities (see above) appeared in *both* hands of those patients who had defects of primary tactile sensations in *one* of their hands. In that sense a primary sensory defect turned out to be one of the necessary conditions for the presence of agnosia-like disturbances; at the same time, the primary sensory defect was not in itself sufficient to account for the disturbance, since the agnosia-like difficulties appeared in parts of the body not directly involved in the primary deficit. One could say that agnosia appeared as a penumbra around an area of sensory defect, a result which is neither compatible with a complete rejection of the concept of agnosia, nor with its acceptance in the classical sense, viz., as a solitary loss of recognition in a particlar sense modality.

The classical concept of agnosia (as originally formulated by Freud) included the further criterion that the difficulty should be specific for a given sense modality. In visual agnosia, recognition through sight is disturbed, but the same objects are recognized as soon as the patient is allowed to touch and handle them. We have investigated this aspect of modality specificity with regard to a special form of agnosia, a form commonly manifested in disorders of route finding and map reading (13, 47, 87), and described in the clinical literature as a disturbance of spatial orientation (1, 41, 44). This disturbance is usually designated a "visuo-spatial" agnosia; however, patients with such difficulties are often more disoriented in the dark. It is conceivable that the disorder transcends vision and is present even if the patient has to orient himself to other than visual cues.

To test this possibility, the following set of fifteen maps was constructed (61) (Fig. 11). As can be seen from the figure, each map contains nine dots; these dots correspond to larger ones painted in the same arrangement on the floor of a large room. Five of these maps are presented visually: the patient is required to hold the map in front of him, and to walk along a path on the floor of the room corresponding to the lines connecting the dots on the map. He is given a score based on the number of turns required by his map and forfeits the score for that map as soon as he takes a wrong turn. The remaining ten maps are presented through the sense of touch; they are made from cord connecting nine tacks on a square board. These tactile maps are presented to the patient in a black-curtained box which he carries around with him without ever seeing the pattern. In palpating five of these maps the patient uses the hand ipsilateral to his brain injury (the presumably less affected hand); for the remaining five, he uses the hand opposite the injury.

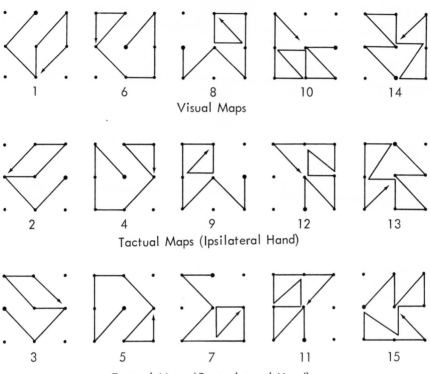

Visual Maps

Tactual Maps (Ipsilateral Hand)

Tactual Maps (Contralateral Hand)

Fig. 11. Diagrams of maps used in spatial orientation test. The 9 dots on each of the maps represent 9 circular red dots painted on the floor of a large room. In the room, adjacent dots are 137 cm apart, center to center. The subject was given each map in turn in the order shown in figure, and required to walk through the indicated path. [Reproduced by permission from Semmes, Weinstein, Ghent, and Teuber, *J. Psychol., 39* (1955).]

The results of the fifteen trials can be seen in Fig. 12. It turned out that the mode of presentation, whether through the sense of sight or touch, had no effect on the outcome of this experiment. Men with parietal lobe injuries (right or left) as a group showed significant defect in performance, while men with lesions elsewhere in the brain showed little or no defect as compared with a group of controls.

These results were further analyzed by Weinstein (83) in an effort to determine whether particular sensory deficits or other definable symptoms (such as aphasia) were significantly related to impaired performance on the route-finding test. A close association was found to exist between impaired two-point discrimination and defective performance on route finding. Again, however, the alteration of tactile two-point threshold could not by itself account for our patients' failure on the route-finding task. Men with defective two-point threshold did just as badly on the visual as they did on the tactile

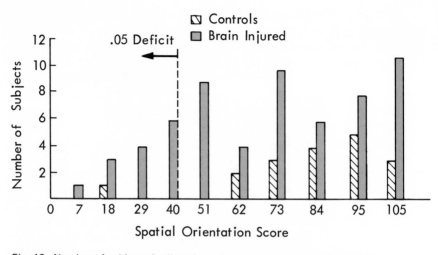

Fig. 12. Number of subjects (ordinate) earning a given score on the spatial orientation test (abscissa). Bars referring to 18 control subjects (without brain injury) have stripes. Bars referring to the 62 brain-injured subjects are solid tint. Low scores (on abscissa) indicate poor performance.

parts of the test. Apparently, some cerebral focus crucial for good performance on the orientation test overlaps with that for two-point discrimination.

In any event, it would seem to us difficult to maintain that route-finding difficulties of the kind here tested can be described as a visuo-spatial agnosia. The disorder is neither specific for vision nor for somesthesis; it transcends these two modalities, thus lacking the modality-specific character of an agnosia in the classical sense. Nor can we maintain that the complex or "higher level" disturbance represented by route-finding disorders is completely dissociated from more elementary sensory deficits. The parietal lesions studied here produced impairment on higher as well as lower levels, even though it seemed impossible to explain the deficit on either level by that on the other.

IV. THE RIDDLE OF FRONTAL LOBE FUNCTION

If our results do not support, so far at least, the existence of agnosia, they nevertheless show that complex and serious disturbances may follow parietal lesions. Such persistent consequences of parietal involvement have been noted repeatedly in our work; they seem to be at variance with traditional opinion which assigned a preeminent role to the frontal lobes rather than any other region of the brain. As we have pointed out elsewhere (67, 69) this belief in the crucial dependence of higher intellectual functions on the integrity of the frontal lobes may have historical rather than logical reasons.

In tracing the evolution of the human brain, much has been made of the "all-surpassing development of the frontal lobes" (10). In point of fact, parietal and temporal structures have developed just as much (8). Nevertheless a number of investigators who have dealt with behavioral sequelae of frontal lesions in man have insisted that many of these lesions are followed by losses in some of the highest aspects of intellectual performance (9, 21, 58). We have already cited enough results of our studies to show that, at least for our group of cases, the traditional view cannot possibly be correct.

In our group, resiliency of function was noted particularly for men with lesions in the frontal lobes: they did not show significant losses on the AGCT (see Fig. 2), and their performance on the hidden-figure task showed them neither better nor worse than men with lesions elsewhere in the brain. Contrary to earlier claims (21), they showed no persistent losses in flicker fusion (3), and they did as well as men with postcentral lesions on comparatively lifelike tasks of problem solving (4). Similarly, we have been unable to confirm the common claim that tests of sorting and concept formation (e.g., 20, 80) should be selectively sensitive to frontal lobe damage. Deficits on tests of this sort have turned out to be essentially nonspecific, i.e., of about equal severity with lesions in any lobe (60, 69). For certain variants of these tasks, more focal results were obtained, but these tended to point to the left parieto-temporal region rather than to the frontal lobes (85).

Such patterns are of particular interest, since they were demonstrated with sorting tests that had been modified in order to eliminate all overt reliance on language. In effect, the tasks had been redesigned in analogy to those in use with nonverbalizing (subhuman) primates (23, 30, 38, 63). The nonverbal administration of the task permitted us to present the problems under comparable conditions to patients with and without aphasia. As might be expected, aphasics tended to show maximal deficits (85), thus underscoring the conclusion we had already reached on the basis of other tasks, viz., that the essential disorders in aphasia, with few exceptions, transcend the sphere of language as such (16, 17, 25, 45, 50, 53, 86). However, even if the scores of the aphasic patients are eliminated from these analyses, our men with frontal lesions fail to do worse than those with lesions of different localization; in many instances they do better.

Negative findings are particularly striking with regard to certain individual cases. Thus, the man whose injury is illustrated in Figs. 13, 14, and 15 attacked one of the classical tests of concept formation (a modified Weigl card sorting test) (20) with immediate and correct analysis of the three principles built into the test. He took one look at the material and then asked calmly whether the examiner wanted him to sort according to color, form, or number.

It is true that over the years our laboratory has displayed something like a perverse pride in not knowing what the specific alterations after frontal lobe damage should be (4, 67). Admittedly the frontal lobes are not a unitary

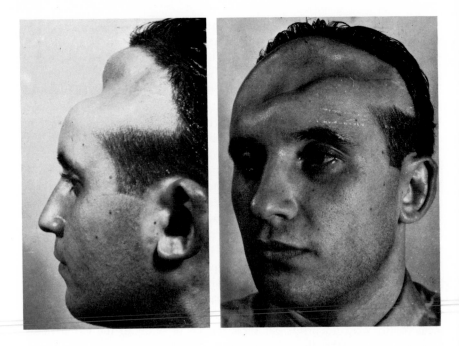

Fig. 13. Patient with healed pistol wound (bilateral) of frontal areas.

structure; the search for a single " frontal lobe syndrome " may be unreasonable from the outset. Nevertheless, we know that our men with frontal lobe lesions are impaired in certain nonspecific ways (see above), and it would seem reasonable to expect, in addition, certain more focal signs of frontal penetration if one could only formulate the appropriate behavioral questions.

The search for focal frontal lobe signs in man derives some encouragement from studies on subhuman primates. In the experimental monkey, bilateral removal of cortex surrounding the sulcus principalis in the frontal lobes leads to a characteristic impairment on tests of delayed response* (7, 23, 27, 56; see also 32 and 40 for dogs). Conversely, lesions of equal or greater·extent in both temporal lobes, while producing deficits on visual discrimination tasks (12, 22, 31, 57), nevertheless leave the animals' performance on delayed response tests intact (48). We thus have a specific sign of

---

* In the delayed response test (11, 26), the monkey is confronted with two food wells. A bait (raisin, piece of banana) is placed in full view of the animal in one of the two wells, both are covered with lids, and an opaque screen is interposed between the animal and the display. After a specified number of seconds (usually 5 sec), the screen is raised and the animal is permitted to displace one of the lids. If he removes the correct one on the first trial, he is scored for success; if he removes the incorrect one, he is scored for failure on this trial. Following bifrontal cortical removals, monkeys fail to exceed chance levels on this test, their failure persisting in many instances for years.

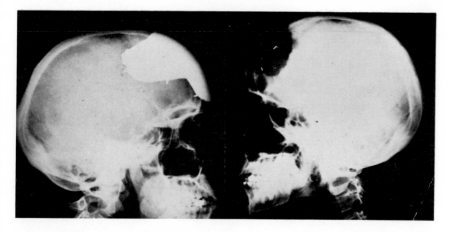

Fig. 14. Skull X-rays of patient shown in Fig. 13 before (right) and after (left) tantalum cranioplasty.

Fig. 15. Appearance of patient shown in Figs. 13 and 14 before and after repair of large frontal defect by tantalum cranioplasty.

frontal damage in the monkey, although one has to admit that the meaning of the task is obscure; it has not been possible to identify completely those aspects of the delayed response task which make the problem insoluble for the bifrontal monkey (49).

In earlier studies the impairment has been attributed to disturbances in memory (27). However, the macaque with bifrontal lesions undoubtedly remembers without difficulty which one of two visually distinct containers is hiding a reward. From time to time alternative interpretations of the delayed response deficit have been offered to supplant the hypothesis of altered memory functions (e.g., 43). Lashley (39) has repeatedly stressed the close proximity between the so-called frontal eye fields (whose electrical stimulation elicits eye movements) and those frontal areas whose destruction leads to interference with delayed response. It is tempting to consider the delayed response deficit in the monkey as some rather specific disturbance in visual fixation.

Such speculations on the nature of the delayed response deficit, even though tenuous, might help in finding some analogous task for man, i.e., some task on which men with certain types of frontal damage would show characteristic and specific deficits. This analogous task, if it can be found, cannot be the delayed response test itself, since the test is much too simple for human subjects, whether their frontal lobes are intact or not. The lead we have followed derives from an extension of those interpretations of the delayed response deficit which stress the possible oculomotor component.

Some years ago Mishkin and I proposed (76) that certain frontal lesions in man might produce abnormal interaction between posture and vision: the patient might have specific difficulties in maintaining visual orientation in the face of altered or unusual posture. To test this hunch, we have fallen back upon a classical perceptual phenomenon, originally demonstrated in 1861 by H. Aubert (2). If a normal adult is asked to adjust a luminous line in a dark room to the vertical position, he will do so with great accuracy as long as his head and body are upright. However, as soon as his head or body is tilted, there appear constant errors in the setting of the visual vertical. When the observer's body is tilted, say 30° to his left, he will judge a luminous line as vertical when the line is actually tilted from 2° to 6° in a direction opposite to his body tilt (Fig. 16). The converse error appears with body tilts in the opposite direction. We suspected that the effect should be abnormally exaggerated in men with frontal lesions. We predicted further that this abnormality would not appear as long as the patient's body was upright and that it would be found to depend crucially on the interaction between vision and abnormal posture.

We accordingly undertook a series of experiments shown diagrammatically in Fig. 17. We selected for these experiments 20 controls without brain injury but with peripheral nerve wounds, 20 men with anterior (frontal) lesions (6 right, 6 left, and 8 bilateral), and correspondingly 20 men with posterior (parieto-temporo-occipital) lesions. Each man was placed in a tilting chair in a dark room (Fig. 16) and asked to set a luminous line to the vertical, first with body and head upright (Experiment I, see Fig. 17, 1) and then with body tilted 30° to the left and to the right (Experiment II, see Fig. 17, 2). We expected that the first experiment should yield little or no group differences, and that the second experiment (body tilted) would show maximal errors for frontals, less errors for parietals, and least for controls. As is apparent from Fig. 18, the outcome of these two experiments confirmed the predictions.

Fig. 16. Experimental procedure for demonstrating tilted-line effects. The actual experiment is performed in a dark room.

The possibility remained, however, that any kind of perceptual conflict (not only between vision and posture, but within a single modality such as vision itself) might have led to the same results. We therefore devised Experiment III (see Fig. 17, 3), in which the patient, with body upright, had to set a black thread to the vertical, while the thread appeared against an interfering obliquely striped background. On this task the normal error consists in

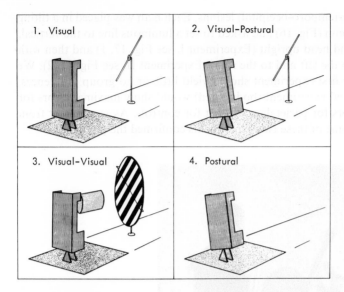

Fig. 17. Diagram of four experimental situations used in differentiating frontal and posterior syndromes. For explanation, see text. [Reproduced by permission from Teuber and Mishkin, *J. Psychol., 38* (1954).]

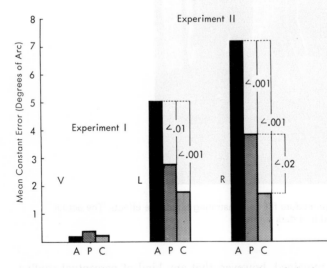

Fig. 18. Average constant errors (in degrees of arc) made in the setting of a luminous line to the vertical by 20 men with anterior brain lesions (Group A), 20 men with posterior brain lesions (P), and 20 controls without brain injury (C). In Experiment I subjects in all groups adjusted the line with their body upright; the resulting errors are small and there are no differences among the groups. In Experiment II, however, significant differences among the groups appear. Here the luminous line was adjusted under conditions of body tilt to the left (L), and to the right (R). The significance of the group differences is indicated on the right-hand side of the graphs.

setting the subjective vertical slightly off the true vertical, in the direction of the background tilt. As Fig. 19 shows, the resulting errors turned out to be maximal for the parietal group, less for the frontals, and least for the controls, so that, on this task, the role of parietal and frontal groups was reversed. Thus, conflict within a single modality, a visuo-visual interaction, did not seem sufficient to bring out characteristic frontal lobe deficits.

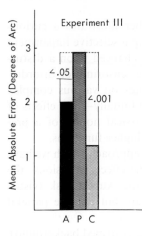

Fig. 19. Results of Experiment III: the setting of a black thread to the vertical (with body upright) with the thread appearing against an obliquely striped background. Scores for right and left tilt of stripes have been combined. For abbreviations, see legend to Fig. 18.

Finally, we wished to ascertain whether the abnormal performance of our frontal group in the classical Aubert task (Experiment II) might be understood in terms, not of visuo-postural interaction, but of some simple abnormality in their appreciation of posture. Accordingly, all three groups were subjected to a fourth test in Experiment IV (see Fig. 17, 4). Each patient, blindfolded, was placed in a tilted position (30° right and 30° left) on the tilting chair. After specified periods of time (2 minutes for each trial) the patient's body was slowly raised until he judged himself upright. Here, the normal response consists in "undershooting" the true vertical: the observer considers himself upright when he is still in fact several degrees off the vertical in the direction of his former tilt. On this final task, no group differences appeared among controls, men with frontal, and men with parietal penetrations. Thus, abnormalities in the appreciation of posture could not account for the unusual performance of the frontal group when asked to set the visual vertical while their bodies were tilted.

We are currently engaged in an extension of these studies and are substituting an auditory signal for the visual line to be judged (74, 75). This is done in order to see whether the abnormality in our frontal group is limited to interaction between posture and vision, or whether it would appear equally when posture interacts with other distance receptors. Even though this program is still incomplete, we have described the four earlier experiments in some detail, since we hoped to illustrate what we understand by an experimental analysis of abnormal performance. The emphasis is not so much on the discovery of focal signs and symptoms, but rather on the behavioral analysis of symptoms once they are found.

The work with the Aubert phenomenon further illustrates a curious aspect of frontal symptoms in man. Instead of finding a selective impairment in higher and highest intellectual functions, we have chanced upon a disturbance which could be classified as a relatively simple sensorimotor disorder. Taken together with our essentially negative findings on various complex tasks (60, 69), these results underscore what we said initially—that effects of frontal lobe lesions in man fail to support the classical notion of a preeminent role of these structures in the mediation of higher functions.

Finally, the series of experiments exemplifies an approach which we have found increasingly useful in our inquiry into specific effects of lesions: the search for double dissociation of symptoms. On the Aubert task (visual judgment with abnormal posture), the frontal group, but not the parietal group, showed marked departure from normal performance. On the visuo-visual task (setting of a black thread against an obliquely striped background), the error of the parietals exceeded that of the frontals. Such double dissociation requires that symptom A appear with lesions in one structure but not with those in another, and that symptom B appear with lesions of the other but not of the one. Wherever such dissociation is lacking, specificity in the effects of lesions has not been demonstrated.

We have come to the end of our survey of methods and results. As will be apparent, analysis of altered behavior after cerebral lesions is still in a rudimentary stage. We believe nevertheless that such work adds to our understanding of cerebral function. In this respect, we disagree with Dr. Page (52). We see no reason to inhibit our intellectual curiosity when we consider the highest levels in the evolution of nervous control. Admittedly, we may be in a better position to say why the brain does not work properly when it does not, than to say why it works when it does. Eventually, however, we may be able to specify the necessary neural correlates of behavior. For unless we can take this step from the neural substrate to the behavior it supports, all our inquiries into structure and function of the nervous system remain incomplete.

SUMMARY

It is difficult to summarize a paper that is in itself an epitome. We have cited four propositions commonly made about changes in behavior after brain injury in man. We have tried to show that each of these propositions is wrong:

1. Changes in behavior after cerebral lesions are often thought to be so obvious that they can be detected by routine tests. By contrast, we found that nearly two-thirds of a group of men with penetrating brain wounds showed gains rather than losses in intelligence test scores when performance before, and 10 years after, injury was compared.

2. Changes in behavior after brain injury, in animal or man, are often interpreted in a dichotomous way, as being either specific (i.e., restricted to lesions in a particular area), or nonspecific (i.e., unrelated to the area injured). Studies of more than 200 men with penetrating brain wounds have convinced us that these lesions produce specific as well as nonspecific effects, and that the two kinds of symptoms exist together in the same groups of patients.

In the visual sphere, field defects (scotomata) represent exquisitely specific (and localizable) effects of lesions; in the same cases, however, more diffuse changes (involving the entire visual field) are revealed by tests of flicker-fusion, dark adaptation or motion perception. Finally, performance on certain " hidden figure tasks " is impaired in *all* subgroups of the brain-injured population, regardless of presence or absence of visual field defect, and irrespective of whether the lesion is in the occipital, parietal, temporal or frontal lobes. Analogous findings are available for the somatosensory sphere.

3. These observations on obligatory association of specific and general deficits raise questions about the third proposition, viz., that brain injuries produce abnormalities, selectively, either on lower (sensorimotor), or higher (cognitive) levels, and that there exist syndromes such as visual or tactile agnosia, so that recognition of objects through a particular sense modality be lost, while basic sensation is preserved. An experimental analysis of certain route-finding disturbances (characteristic of men with parietal lesions) suggested to us that this particular disorder, at least, should not be labeled an agnosia, and that " higher " and " lower " deficits may not be dissociable.

4. Lastly, we turned to the old proposition that the highest functions of man are selectively impaired after lesions of the frontal lobes. The evidence presented indicated rather that deficits after frontal lesions are either non-specific, or of a curious sort, involving an altered interaction between vision and posture.

These analyses of behavior after brain injury in man are incomplete, but illustrate how studies of disordered function might shed light on the neural organization underlying normal performance. The comparative resiliency of higher functions and the persistence of deficits in more elementary forms of sensation suggest different modes of cerebral representation for these two aspects of behavior.

The most general finding, however, concerns the obligatory association of specific and nonspecific symptoms in all our brain-injured groups. This association is consistent with the view that specific cerebral systems mediate not only their own, but other, activity, and that the highest levels of neural control require the interaction of both.

REFERENCES

1. AJURIAGUERRA, J. DE, & H. HÉCAEN, *Le Cortex Cérébral.* Masson, Paris, 1949.
2. AUBERT, H., Eine scheinbare bedeutende Drehung von Objekten bei Neigung des Kopfes nach rechts oder links. *Virchow's Arch. pathol. Anat. u. Physiol.*, *20*, 381–393 (1861).
3. BATTERSBY, W. S., The regional gradient of critical flicker frequency after frontal or occipital lobe injury. *J. Exptl. Psychol.*, *42*, 59–68 (1951).
4. BATTERSBY, W. S., H.-L. TEUBER, & M. B. BENDER, Problem-solving behavior in men with frontal or occipital brain injuries. *J. Psychol.*, *35*, 329–351 (1953).
5. BAY, E., Disturbances of visual perception and their examination. *Brain, 76,* 515–550 (1953).
6. BENDER, M. B., Extinction and precipitation of cutaneous sensations. *A.M.A. Arch. Neurol. Psychiat.*, *54*, 1–9 (1945).
7. BLUM, R. A., Effects of subtotal lesions of frontal granular cortex on delayed reaction in monkeys. *A.M.A. Arch. Neurol. Psychiat.*, *67*, 375–386 (1952).
8. BONIN, G. V., The frontal lobe of primates: cytoarchitectural studies, Chap. III in *The Frontal Lobes, Research Publs. Assoc. Research Nervous Mental Disease, 27,* 67–83 (1948).
9. BRICKNER, R., *The Intellectual Functions of the Frontal Lobes.* The Macmillan Company, New York, 1936.
10. BRODMANN, K. *Vergleichende Lokalisationslehre der Grosshirnrinde.* J. A. Barth, Leipzig, 1925.
11. CARR, H. A., cited by Hunter, 1913.
12. CHOW, K. L., Further studies on selective ablation of associative cortex in relation to visually mediated behavior. *J. Comp. Physiol. Psychol.*, *45*, 109–118 (1952).
13. CRITCHLEY, M., *The Parietal Lobes.* Williams & Wilkins, Baltimore, 1953.
14. GHENT, LILA, JOSEPHINE SEMMES, S. WEINSTEIN, & H.-L. TEUBER, Tactile discrimination after unilateral brain injury in man. *Am. Psychologist, 10,* 408 (1955).
15. GHENT, LILA, S. WEINSTEIN, JOSEPHINE SEMMES, & H.-L. TEUBER, Effect of unilateral brain injury in man on learning of a tactual discrimination. *J. Comp. Physiol. Psychol.*, *48*, 478–481 (1955).
16. GOLDSTEIN, K. *The Organism.* American Book, New York, 1939.
17. GOLDSTEIN, K., & M. SCHEERER, Abstract and concrete behavior: An experimental study with special tests. *Psychol. Monograph, 53,* No. 20, 1941.
18. GOTTSCHALDT, K., Über den Einfluss der Erfahrung auf die Wahrnehmung von Figuren. I. *Psychol. Forschung., 8,* 261–317 (1926).
19. GOTTSCHALDT, K., Über den Einfluss der Erfahrung auf die Wahrnehmung von Figuren. II. *Psychol. Forschung., 12,* 1–87 (1929).
20. GRANT, A. D., & ESTA A. BERG, A behavioral analysis of degree of reinforcement and ease of shifting to new responses in a Weigl-type card-sorting problem. *J. Exptl. Psychol.*, *38*, 404–411 (1948).
21. HALSTEAD, W. C., *Brain and Intelligence: A Quantitative Study of the Frontal Lobes.* University of Chicago Press, Chicago, 1947.
22. HARLOW, H. F., R. T. DAVIS, P. H. SETTLAGE, & D. R. MEYER, Analysis of frontal and posterior association syndromes in brain-damaged monkeys. *J. Comp. Physiol. Psychol.*, *45*, 419–429 (1952).
23. HARLOW, H. F., and P. H. SETTLAGE, Effect of extirpation of frontal areas upon learning performance of monkeys. *Research Publs. Assoc. Nervous Mental Disease, 27,* 446–459 (1948).
24. HEAD, H., *Studies in Neurology.* 2 vols., Oxford Medical Publications, London, 1920.

25. HEAD, H., *Aphasia and Kindred Disorders of Speech.* Cambridge University Press, Cambridge, England, 1926.
26. HUNTER, W. S., The delayed reaction in animals and children. *Behavior Monographs, 2,* 86 (1913).
27. JACOBSEN, C. F., Functions of frontal association area in primates. *A.M.A. Arch. Neurol. Psychiat., 33,* 558–569 (1935).
28. JUNG, R., Symposion über die Grundlagen der Hirnpathologie. *Nervenarzt, 19,* 518–529 (1948).
29. KLIEST, K., *Gehirnpathologie.* Barth, Leipzig, 1934.
30. KLÜVER, H., *Behavior Mechanisms in Monkeys.* University of Chicago Press, Chicago, 1933.
31. KLÜVER, H., & P. C. BUCY, Preliminary analysis of functions of the temporal lobes in monkeys. *A.M.A. Arch. Neurol. Psychiat., 42,* 979–1000 (1939).
32. KONORSKI, J., Analiza nadmiernej ruchliwosci zwierzat po uszkodzeniach okolic czolowych kory mozgowej (Analysis of hyperactivity of animals after the removal of prefrontal areas of the cerebral cortex). *Neurol. Neurochir. Psychiat. Pol., 6,* 865–873 (1956).
33. KRIEGER, H. P., Effects of retrochiasmal lesions upon variability of the absolute visual threshold. *Am. Psychologist, 7,* 255 (1952).
34. KRIEGER, H. P., & M. B. BENDER, Dark adaptation in lesions of the optic pathways. *Federation Proc., 8,* 89 (1949).
35. KRUEGER, E. G., P. A. PRICE, & H.-L. TEUBER, Tactile extinction in parietal lobe neoplasm. *J. Psychol., 38,* 191–202 (1954).
36. LASHLEY, K. S., *Brain Mechanisms and Intelligence.* University of Chicago Press, Chicago, 1929.
37. LASHLEY, K. S., Basic neural mechanisms in behavior. *Psychol. Rev., 37,* 1–24 (1930).
38. LASHLEY, K. S., The mechanism of vision. XVIII. Effects of destroying the visual "associative areas" of the monkey. *Genet. Psychol. Monograph, 37,* 107–166 (1948).
39. LASHLEY, K. S., in *Cerebral mechanisms in behavior* (Hixon Symposium), edited by L. A. Jeffress, John Wiley & Sons, New York, 1951, pp. 272–273.
40. LAWICKA, W., Physiological analysis of the disturbances of the delayed responses in dogs after prefrontal ablation. *Bull. Acad. Pol. Sci. Cl. 6, 5,* No. 3, 107–110 (1957).
41. LHERMITTE, J., & J. O. TRELLES, Sur l'apraxie pure constructive. Les troubles de la pensée spatiale et de la somatognosie dans l'apraxie. *Encéphale, 28,* 413–444 (1933).
42. LORGE, I., Aging and intelligence. Chap. V, pp. 46–60 in *Neurologic and Psychiatric Aspects of the Disorders of Aging. Research Publs. Assoc. Research Nervous Mental Disease, 35,* 1956.
43. MALMO, R. B., Interference factors in delayed response in monkeys after removal of frontal lobes. *J. Neurophysiol., 5,* 295–305 (1942).
44. MARIE, P., & B. BÉHAGUE, Syndrome de désorientation dans l'espace consécutif aux plaies profondes du lobe frontal. *Rev. neurol., 26,* 1–14 (1919).
45. MARIE, P., & C. FOIX, Les aphasies de guerre. *Rev. neurol., 26,* 3–87 (1917).
46. MCFIE, J., & M. F. PIERCY, Intellectual impairment with localized cerebral lesions. *Brain, 75,* 292–311 (1952).
47. MCFIE, J., M. F. PIERCY, & O. L. ZANGWILL, Visual-spatial agnosia associated with lesions of the right cerebral hemisphere. *Brain, 73,* 167–190 (1950).
48. MISHKIN, M., & K. H. PRIBRAM, Visual discrimination performance following partial ablations of the temporal lobe. I. Ventral vs. lateral. *J. Comp. Physiol. Psychol., 47,* 14–20 (1954).

49. MISHKIN, M., & K. H. PRIBRAM, Analysis of the effects of frontal lesions in monkey: I. Variations of delayed alternation. *J. Comp. Physiol. Psychol.*, *48*, 492–495 (1955).

50. MONAKOW, C. V., *Die Localisation im Grosshirn.* J. F. Bergman, Wiesbaden, 1914.

51. NIU M. C., this volume.

52. PAGE, I. H., this volume.

53. PICK, A., *Die agrammatischen Sprachstörungen.* I. *Monograph Neurol Psychiat.*, 7 (1913).

54. PIÉRON, H., *Le Cerveau et la Pensée.* Felix Alcan, Paris, 1923.

55. POPPELREUTER, W. *Die psychischen Schädigungen durch Kopfschuss im Kriege 1914–16.* Voss, Leipzig, 1917.

56. PRIBRAM, K. H., M. MISHKIN, H. E. ROSVOLD, & S. J. KAPLAN, Effects on delayed-response performance of lesions of dorsolateral and ventromedial frontal cortex of baboons. *J. Comp. Physiol. Psychol.*, *45*, 565–575 (1952).

57. RIOPELLE, A. J., R. G. ALPER, P. N. STRONG, & H. W. ADES, Multiple discrimination and patterned string performance of normal and temporal-lobectomized monkeys. *J. Comp. Physiol. Psychol.*, *46*, 145–149 (1953).

58. RYLANDER, G., *Personality Changes after Operations on the Frontal Lobes.* Oxford, London, 1939.

59. SEMMES, JOSEPHINE, Agnosia in animal and man. *Psychol. Revs.*, *60*, 140–147 (1953).

60. SEMMES, JOSEPHINE, S. WEINSTEIN, LILA GHENT, & H.-L. TEUBER, Performance on complex tactual tasks after brain injury in man: analyses by locus of lesion. *Am. J. Psychol.*, *67*, 220–240 (1954).

61. SEMMES, JOSEPHINE, S. WEINSTEIN, LILA GHENT, & H.-L. TEUBER, Spatial orientation in man after cerebral injury. I. Analyses by locus of lesion. *J. Psychol.*, *39*, 227–244 (1955).

62. SEMMES, JOSEPHINE, S. WEINSTEIN, LILA GHENT, & H.-L. TEUBER, *Changes in Somatic Sensation after Penetrating Brain Injury in Man.* Monograph for the Commonwealth Fund, Harvard University Press, Cambridge, Mass., in press.

63. SETTLAGE, P., M. ZABLE, & H. F. HARLOW, Problem solutions by monkeys following bilateral removal of the prefrontal areas. VI. Performance on tests requiring contradictory reactions to similar and to identical stimuli. *J. Exptl. Psychol.*, *38*, 50–65 (1948).

64. SPALDING, J. M. K., Wounds of the visual pathway. Pt. I. The visual radiation. *J. Neurol. Neurosurg. Psychiat.*, *15*, 99–109 (1952).

65. SPALDING, J. M. K., Wounds of the visual pathway. Pt. II. The striate cortex. *J. Neurol. Neurosurg. Psychiat.*, *15*, 169–183 (1952).

66. TEUBER, H.-L., Neuropsychology, in *Recent Advances in Psychological Testing*, C C Thomas, Springfield, Ill., 1950, Chap. 3, pp. 30–52.

67. TEUBER, H.-L., Some observations on the organization of higher functions after penetrating brain injury in man, in *The Biology of Mental Health and Disease.* Paul B. Hoeber, New York, 1952, pp. 259–262.

68. TEUBER, H.-L., Physiological psychology. *Ann. Rev. Psychol.*, *6*, 267–296 (1955).

69. TEUBER, H.-L., W. S. BATTERSBY, & M. B. BENDER, Performance of complex visual tasks after cerebral lesions. *J. Nervous Mental Disease*, *114*, 413–429 (1951).

70. TEUBER, H.-L., & M. B. BENDER, Critical flicker frequency in defective fields of vision. *Federation Proc.*, *7*, 1 (1948).

71. TEUBER, H.-L., & M. B. BENDER, Alterations in pattern vision following trauma of the occipital lobes in man. *J. Gen. Psychol.*, *40*, 37–57 (1949).

72. TEUBER, H.-L., & M. B. BENDER, Perception of apparent movement across acquired scotomata in the visual field. *Am. Psychologist*, *5*, 271 (1950).

73. TEUBER, H.-L., M. B. BENDER, & W. S. BATTERSBY, Discrimination of weights by men with penetrating lesions of the parietal lobes. *Federation Proc.*, *9*, 125–126 (1950).
74. TEUBER, H.-L., & S. DIAMOND, Effects of brain injury in man on binaural localization of sounds. Paper read at EPA meetings in Atlantic City, March, 1956.
75. TEUBER, H.-L., & R. S. LIEBERT, Effects of body tilt on auditory localization. *Am. Psychologist*, *11*, 430 (1956).
76. TEUBER, H.-L., & M. MISHKIN, Judgment of visual and postural vertical after brain injury. *J. Psychol.*, *38*, 161–175 (1954).
77. TEUBER, H.-L., & S. WEINSTEIN, Performance on a formboard-task after penetrating brain injury. *J. Psychol.*, *38*, 177–190 (1954).
78. TEUBER, H.-L., & S. WEINSTEIN, Ability to discover hidden figures after cerebral lesions. *A.M.A. Arch. Neurol. Psychiat.*, *76*, 369–379 (1956).
79. WECHSLER, D., *Measurement of Adult Intelligence*, 3rd edition, Williams & Wilkins, Baltimore, 1944.
80 WEIGL, E., On the psychology of so-called processes of abstraction. *J. Abnormal Social Psychol.*, *36*, 3–33 (1941).
81. WEINSTEIN, S., Weight judgment in somesthesis after penetrating injury to the brain. *J. Comp. Physiol. Psychol.*, *47*, 31–35 (1954).
82. WEINSTEIN, S., Time-error in weight judgment after brain injury. *J. Comp. Physiol. Psychol.*, *48*, 203–207 (1955).
83. WEINSTEIN, S., JOSEPHINE SEMMES, LILA GHENT, & H.-L. TEUBER, Spatial orientation in man after cerebral injury. II. Analysis according to concomitant defects. *J. Psychol.*, *42*, 249–263 (1956).
84. WEINSTEIN, S., & H.-L. TEUBER, Effects of penetrating brain injury on intelligence test scores. *Science*, *125*, 1036–1037 (1957).
85. WEINSTEIN, S., H.-L. TEUBER, LILA GHENT, & JOSEPHINE SEMMES, Complex visual task performance after penetrating brain injury in man. *Am. Psychologist*, *10*, 408 (1955).
86. WEISENBURG, T. H., & K. E. MCBRIDE, *Aphasia: A Clinical and Psychological Study*. Commonwealth Fund, New York, 1935.
87. ZANGWILL, O. L., Discussion on parietal lobe syndromes. *Proc. Roy. Soc. Med.* (*Sect. Neurol.*), *44*, 343–346 (1951).

Some Developments in Brain Lesion Studies of Learning

R. W. Sperry

The following is a rapid survey of some of the things we've been doing in recent years in following up what for present purposes may be called "the split-brain approach to the learning problem." The general idea involved is simple enough: we first split the brain longitudinally down the middle to separate the right and left hemispheres, one of which is then reserved for the use of the animal, while the other is donated to science for application of the ablation and other methods of analysis.

In the surgery, we first sever the large corpus callosum, the main connecting link between the hemispheres. Along with this we generally cut also the smaller hippocampal and anterior commissures (see fig. 1). If vision is to be involved, the optic chiasm is divided in the midline or one of the optic tracts. For other purposes the following may also be sectioned: the massa intermedia, the habenular commissure, the posterior commissure, the quadrigeminal plate containing the commissures of the colliculi, and, in some of our more recent cases, also the cerebellum. The fibers of the small supraoptic commissures are presumed to be cut also.

This is as far as we have carried the midline sections to date, but this does not necessarily represent a limit from the surgical standpoint. It would be quite feasible to continue cutting into the upper end of the tegmentum, but here one soon begins to encounter important decussating fiber systems that connect structures up and down the brain, the cutting of which, of course, is quite a different thing from the cutting of commissural cross connections between homologous pairs of control centers.

It can be seen that these midline sections, except for loss of part of the visual inflow, leave nearly all the sensory, motor and other brain-stem relations intact. Also the great bulk of the internal organization of each

From *Federation Proceedings*, 1961, **20**, 609–616. Reprinted with permission of the publisher and author. Original work reported here has been supported by the National Science Foundation, the National Institutes of Health, and the Frank P. Hixon Fund of the California Institute of Technology.

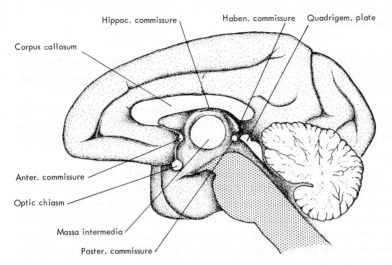

Hippoc. commissure   Haben. commissure   Quadrigem. plate

Corpus callosum

Anter. commissure

Optic chiasm

Massa intermedia

Poster. commissure

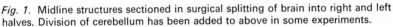

Fig. 1. Midline structures sectioned in surgical splitting of brain into right and left halves. Division of cerebellum has been added to above in some experiments.

hemisphere is preserved. Accordingly, the two separated hemispheres following recovery from the surgery continue to carry on most of their regular functions and the subsequent behavior is remarkably normal in character. In fact, monkeys so operated upon are hardly distinguishable from their normal cage mates under most ordinary circumstances, especially if the cerebellar section is not included. One does not notice any paralyses, spasticity, ataxia, no forced circling or other asymmetries, no hyperactive pacing nor apathy, automatisms nor mutism, nor have we observed to date any autonomic dysfunctions. Some slight changes in eye movements may be noticed in cases with section of the posterior commissure and/or quadrigeminal plate. Those with the cerebellum divided have shown some weakness and unsteadiness especially noticeable during the first months after surgery but it diminishes gradually. For the most part the monkeys appear normal and are quite suitable for behavioral testing.

However, when one studies more carefully the learning and memory of such "split-brain" animals under special training conditions where the inflow of sensory information to each hemisphere can be separately restricted and controlled, it is possible to show that each of the divided hemispheres now has its own separate gnostic or cognitive system: its own separate perceptual, learning, and memory processes. It is as if neither hemisphere any longer has any direct knowledge of what the other is doing, nor any direct memories of what has been going on in the other hemisphere subsequent to the time of section.

Although there were some intimations that this might be the case in the earlier literature on the corpus callosum, they were outweighed by confusing and contradictory observations (1). The first convincing demonstration was obtained by Ronald Myers in a nice series of experiments beginning about

1953 (16) which he carried out on the functions of the corpus callosum and on interocular transfer in the cat. In brief, Myers showed that a cat with mid-line section of the optic chiasm and forebrain commissures is unable to remember with one eye visual pattern discriminations learned with the other eye (12–14). In fact, with the second eye such a cat easily learns a discrimination habit that conflicts directly with what it had just previously learned with the first eye.

At this point the question immediately arose as to how separate in their function the two hemispheres really are: For example, might it be that the unblinded side in a commissurotomized cat is simply much more dominant than is usual with the corpus callosum intact and tends to drain the attention off to the unblinded side? In partial answer to this we find that extensive cortical removals on the unblinded side, that would be expected to depress severely any dominance of this hemisphere, still do not force visual learning of pattern discriminations over into the other separated hemisphere (20, 24). Also, when we compared the learning curves of the second eye with those of the first eye on a statistical basis, we found no significant carry-over from the training of the first eye to that of the second (25). Thus the visual learning of the second eye seemed to benefit in no way from that of the first. It was as if in using the second eye, the cat had a selective visual amnesia for the learning experience with the first eye.

The training and testing in these experiments is carried out in a type of discrimination box that I had designed earlier for studies of detailed pattern perception in the cat. The basic principle involves putting the animal inside a darkened box where the only light enters at one end through a pair of trans-lucent stimulus patterns that the animal is being trained to discriminate. The cat walks up to and pushes its head into the stimulus figures, mounted in swinging doors, the correct one of which will open and give access to a bit of food on a tray outside the box. And the final technical point—the stimulus figures are of a size roughly the same or slightly smaller than that which will admit passage of the animal's head. Whatever the critical factors, the apparatus has enabled us to get extremely refined pattern and size discriminations, and to quantify the cat's perceptual performance with test scales based on graded reduction of dissimilarity. Vision of one eye is occluded during the training sessions by having the cat wear a rubber eye patch as devised by Myers.

Let me emphasize at this point that I am serving pretty much as a spokes-man here, for work that has been very much a group effort. In addition to Myers who got the project off the ground to a good start, there have since been a dozen or so research fellows, graduate students and assistants who have all made their important contributions.

In another apparatus engineered by John Stamm, we found that the same kind of functional independence prevailed in the separated hemi-spheres with respect to the learning of somesthetic discriminations that involved touch and pressure on the surface of the forepaw (26). The cats were trained to push the correct one of two pedals which they were unable to see and had to discriminate entirely on the basis of touch. Again, a comparison of the learning curves revealed that the strong transfer of training from the first paw to the second in normal control cases was entirely lacking in those cats in which the corpus callosum had first been sectioned. This lack of transfer applied as well to the motor learning that was involved in gaining proficiency in the operation of the pedals. Hence it was inferred that in the split-brain cat " the left forepaw knoweth not what the right forepaw doeth."

With respect again to learning and memory in the visual sphere, the findings in the cat have been confirmed also for the monkey by both Dr. Downer (2) and myself (21) quite independently. Perhaps it should be mentioned here that the attempt to test the effect upon visual learning and memory of combined section of both the optic chiasm and corpus callosum is something that has been tried a number of times in the past and abandoned, largely because of the surgical problems. The present-day success can be attributed in large measure, in our own case at least, to the carry-over to the mammalian brain of the surgical procedures of experimental embryology adapted originally to salamander larvae and frog tadpoles. In the main this involves the use of a high-powered stereoscopic microscope for most of the finer aspects of the surgery along with correspondingly delicate instruments. In our own case it also includes adaptation of the operating table for use in the sitting position, not only because of the fatigue factor, but also for the increased support, steadiness, and prolonged concentration that it favors.

The monkey is much less inclined to be cooperative than is the cat about the wearing of an eye patch, and accordingly I devised a training box by which we can restrict vision to one or the other eye. Essentially it has two eye apertures so positioned with reference to head restraints that one of the peepholes is accessible only to the right eye, and the other only to the left eye (fig. 2). Either or both eye apertures can be opened or closed from trial to trial. In addition, there is a sliding panel that controls the use of the arms and allows the pairing of either eye with either hand from trial to trial. This has the advantage over the use of an eye patch, corneal occluders, or sewing of the eyelids in that it is possible to switch easily back and forth from one eye to the other in a given series of trials.

One can give a few trials to the right eye and then a few trials to the left eye, and so on. If this is done while the monkey is in the process of learning two conflicting pattern discriminations with right and left eyes, it is possible to show that while one brain half is learning to select, say a triangle and avoid a square, the other hemisphere can be learning at the same time to do exactly the reverse. Under these conditions the two learning curves then rise in parallel concurrently in the separated hemispheres, with no particular retardation nor cross interference apparent (23). Needless to say, the normal monkey brain does not operate in this way.

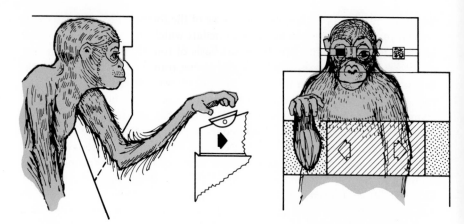

Fig. 2. Profile and front diagrams of visual discrimination training apparatus for controlling use of different eye-hand combinations.

More recently we've been trying to carry this a step farther in an effort to find out if such reversed discrimination learning could proceed in the separated hemispheres, not only concurrently but really simultaneously. Instead of switching alternately from one to the other eye, both eyes are used on all trials and the training conditions are arranged so that each single trial feeds back conflicting data simultaneously into the separate hemispheres. To state the problem another way: does the split-brain monkey, while learning new visual habits under these conditions, have to pay attention to what's coming into only one eye at a time—or, can the monkey attend to what is coming into both eyes simultaneously, deal with both sets of conflicting information, file them in two separate memories, and so on, thus learning simultaneously and in parallel the two reversed discriminations?

A method by which this can be tested based on the use of polarized light (27) had already been devised by Colwyn Trevarthen for studies on conflict. In his apparatus diagrammed in figures 3 and 4 the pair of patterns to be discriminated is shown through two projectors, one for each eye. Each of the projectors has a polarizing filter in front of it, the one filter set at right angles to the other. These two filters are interchanged at random, right to left, from trial to trial. Both sets of patterns from each projector are projected on top of each other on two plastic screens, one of which the monkey pushes in order to obtain a reward. Another filter in front of each eye cuts out the patterns from one or the other projector from trial to trial.

With this set-up the two plastic screens appear to one eye as if, for example, there is a circle on the left and a cross on the right, while to the other eye it appears just the reverse, as if the cross were on the left and the circle on the right. Thus, while one eye sees the hand reach out and push the circle on the left, the other eye views the same act as a reaching out and pushing of the cross on the left. Any kind of projectable figure can be used and the pairs of patterns can be simply different as well as reversed. Essentially the apparatus is a monkey automat; a correct choice activating a micro-switch that releases a peanut, dehydrated banana tablet, or other monkey delicacy.

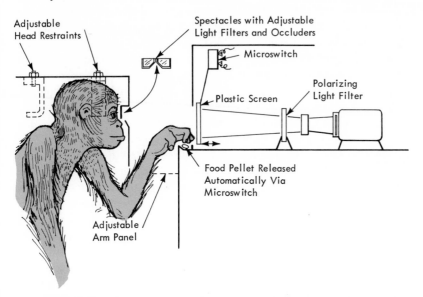

Fig. 3. Diagram illustrating use of polarizing light filters to present different visual problems to right and left eyes simultaneously. Inversions produced by projector and ocular lenses are omitted.

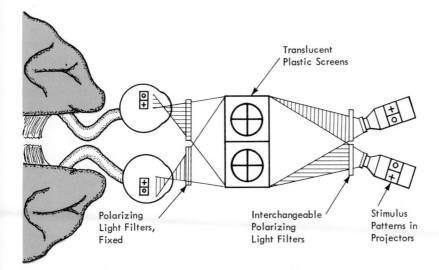

Fig. 4. Profile sketch of same apparatus illustrated in fig. 3.

The procedure is to allow learning to progress under these conditions with both eyes open until the learning curve reaches a level of 85 or 90% correct. At this point each eye is tested individually to find out if the learning has been taking place in one hemisphere only, or in both, and to what degree. In his tests to date involving three split-brain animals, Trevarthen has found that the proportion of learning found in the right and left eye varies: a) One eye may learn fully, the other only partly or not at all. b) In some cases neither eye can perform the discrimination alone, but together they are successful, suggesting that different components of the same habit complex may be learned on right and left sides and that the neural changes of an engram may be complex and divisible. c) Each eye may fully learn its own problem. Although chance is largely against such an equal balance of the learning on both sides, occasional instances have emerged in which both eyes have fully learned, simultaneously, their opposed discriminations.

In other words, in these instances, in approximately the same order of time that it takes a plain ordinary-brained monkey to learn one discrimination habit, the altered, double-brained monkey may successfully master two such problems. This result is less favored during the first few problems than it is later after the monkey has become proficient in the use of the box and in the pairing of either hand with either eye.

This evidence of simultaneous reversed learning in the separated hemispheres, gives us some things to think about with respect to learning theory, and the role in learning of the attention process referred to above and of other components of learning, such as the motivational background and mental, perceptual and motor sets. Are all these constituents of learning duplicate, or perhaps bifurcate in structure, with prongs qualitatively different in the two hemispheres? The next step calls for tachistoscopic (quick flash) presentation of the stimulus figures to further reduce the attention span.

When the monkey has been trained through the left eye to select a circle and avoid a cross and through the right eye to do just the reverse, the two hemispheres get along harmoniously enough so long as what looks like a circle to the right eye appears like a cross to the left. But now suppose that we rotate one of the eye-filters 90°, so that each eye sees the same set of patterns from the same projector. With one brain trained to reach for the left plaque containing the circle and the other trained to reach for the right plaque containing the cross, what kind of mental conflict will arise? Will each hemisphere try to decide for itself, or will one follow the decision of the other? Actually, what Trevarthen finds is that the monkey in this situation may exhibit some extra hesitancy and indecision, but no extreme conflict. One or the other brain tends to take over to select consistently either crosses or circles. The dominance shifts from time to time from one hemisphere to the other as a result of factors that only in part can now be predicted or controlled. This would seem to be just another example of the fact that brain organization from the highest to the lowest level tends to be an "either/or" kind of thing. Either one excitation pattern prevails or another; but it is the rare exception that competing patterns produce a confused mixture.

So much for the evidence for independent learning and memory in the two separated hemispheres. Given now these two independent learning and memory systems operating in parallel, let's turn back to our original proposition: that is, to leave one of the learning systems for the use of the animal, while we take the other for experimental analysis.

Briefly, what are some of the kinds of things that have been and can be done with this approach? Especially what are some of the advantages of using the half brain for analysis instead of the whole brain? The advantages to the animal over the usual bilateral invasion are obvious; the gains are also considerable from the experimental standpoint. But first in this connection, it is worth our remembering that the half brain is, after all, nearly a whole brain in the sense that it contains a full complement of all the cerebral integration centers and cortical areas and all their interrelationships excepting only the right-left cross connections. Practically the entire pattern and most of the problems of cerebral organization above the midbrain level are there for the unravelling within the half brain.

One obvious advantage of the split-brain preparation lies in the factor of built-in controls—of many kinds, of the homozygous, identical-twin quality with additional common denominators in experiential factors—not only for the testing of learning and memory, but also for acute physiological studies as well. By restricting the sensory inflow to one side, or by other procedures that cause the animal to attend in, and use, one hemisphere, the effect of unilateral lesions, drugs, shock and anesthetic administrations can be checked and compared with the function of the normal side.

Another advantage lies in the possibility of investigating the role in learning of cerebral structures such as the caudate, the primary motor cortex, and others, the bilateral ablation of which produces incapacitating or other secondary effects that act to obscure or confuse possible contributions to learning. Each control center tends to be involved in a whole spectrum of different functions, and in many cases only the more basic impairments can be inferred after bilateral removals, the others being hidden or untestable in the presence of the former.

The split preparation similarly offers the possibility of using much larger ablations even to the extreme of removing most of the neocortex and working with isolated functional remnants. We have isolated the visual cortex of the cat in this way (see fig. 5) and found that extremely little vision survives such isolation (20, 24). A next step is to go back and to restore in other animals different portions of the removed cortex to determine the respective contributions of each to visual learning and memory. Comparison of the effects of temporal and frontal removals indicates that in the cat the temporal lobes are not as important for visual discrimination as they are in the monkey (11).

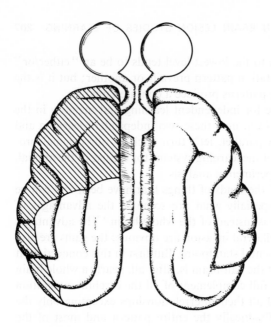

Fig. 5. Central visual cortex is surgically isolated in left hemisphere; right hemisphere serves as control.

A very different result was found to follow similar surgical isolation of the frontal cortex including the somatic areas. In this case the isolated remnant was found to be capable of mediating excellent learning and memory of new somesthetic discrimination habits performed in a pedal-pressing apparatus (22). The elusive engrams or memory trace for these new habits would seem to have been, if not trapped, at least cornered within the local cortical area indicated in figure 6. It should be possible to further localize the engram by paring away the anterior, medial, and ventral edges of the area, and also to test the contribution of various subcortical centers that remain undegenerated like the caudate, amygdala, and hippocampus by prior placement of deep stereotaxic lesions. The preparation thus furnishes a promising means for determining the critical minimum cerebral apparatus essential for learning and memory of somesthetic discrimination in the mammalian brain.

To further assure in the foregoing experiment that the habits were not being mediated by the contralateral somatic cortex, a complementary removal of the same area was made on the opposite side. To start making lesions in the hemisphere that was set aside for the use of the animal may not seem exactly fair, but at least a "trade" was made. At any rate, the feasibility of adding complementary lesion patterns in the intact hemisphere of the split brain offers further possibilities for the analysis of functional relationships.

There are other promising angles in the foregoing "somatic island preparation" for the investigation of learning: For example, we could test its proven pedal-pressing learning capacity using visual or auditory instead of tactile stimuli; that is, we could ask, "Could such a cat learn to press a pedal that activates the correct one of two different tone patterns, first, with the auditory cortex in the opposite hemisphere?" If not, could it then do so if an isolated patch of auditory cortex were to be left on the same side as the somatic island? Should the answer still be no, then what kind of intracortical bridges and connections are needed to satisfy the learning requirements?

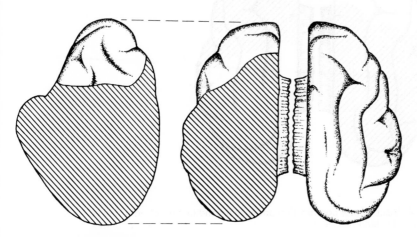

Fig. 6. Capacity for high-level somesthetic discrimination learning and memory survives isolation of the frontal cortex as shown.

Figure 7 illustrates a basic type of complementary lesion preparation we've been using with a number of variations to study visuo-motor coordination. The experimental question here was: "Can visual information that is processed in one hemisphere serve as a guide for limb responses, the cortical centers for which lie in the opposite hemisphere and surgically separated from the visual inflow?" And, in another experiment with the same type of preparation, "Could a visual signal be used as the conditioning stimulus for a conditioned flexion response of the forelimb in question?" The evidence so far indicates that the answer will be "yes" to both of these questions (unpublished observations of R. E. Myers, R. W. Sperry and Nancy Miner, and of T. J. Voneida and R. W. Sperry), but there are qualifications and of course each new answer raises four new questions.

The visual guidance of a limb, the main cortical control centers for which lie in the hemisphere opposite that of the visual inflow presents certain problems. The split-brain monkey with unilateral vision shows a tendency to prefer to use the arm governed from the same hemisphere, i.e., the contralateral arm. However, this is only a tendency and it is easily overcome in a matter of hours in most of our training situations (23, 27, and unpublished observations of R. E. Myers, R. W. Sperry and Nancy Miner). On the other

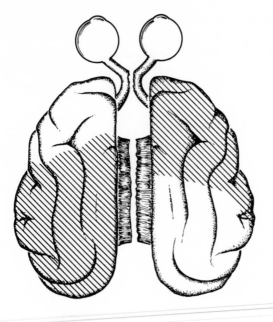

Fig. 7. Visuo-motor coordination and visual conditioning of right foreleg response survive this kind of surgical separation of visual and limb areas of cortex.

hand, this tendency can be enhanced in other testing circumstances to the point where use of the ipsilateral arm may appear extremely difficult or impossible for a prolonged period (3). However, preference for the ipsilateral arm may prevail when the given arm is strongly dominant either naturally or as a result of training in a particular apparatus.

It was found that the split-brain cat readily uses either forepaw to carry out visual directives in the learning of visual discriminations with one eye (19). Monkeys also are able to use either hand under similar conditions, but there is a difference between the ipsilateral and contralateral performance, the contralateral arm having the advantage (27).

Analogous to the above sensori-motor type of integration, there are various sensori-sensory integrations that can be analyzed to advantage with the split-brain technique. Figure 8 illustrates an approach to a form of visuo-tactile association. The monkey is trained to perform a discrimination problem that requires in each trial an association of both visual plus somesthetic cues. By controlling the hand and the eye used, and thereby the cortical receptor centers involved, we can test intra- and inter-hemispheric integration with and without different parts of the corpus callosum, and then with various types of separating cuts and ablations to analyze the kind of neural association required for such a performance.

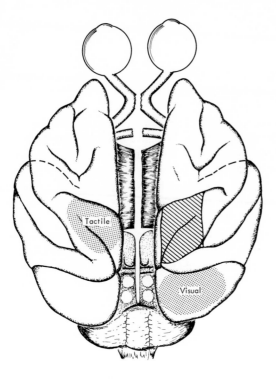

Fig. 8. Capacity to integrate visual stimuli with somesthetic stimuli from right hand survives surgical splitting and cortical removal as indicated.

It was somewhat of a surprise to find that with somesthetic stimuli entering the hemisphere opposite that of the visual inflow, the monkey was still able to perform the visuo-tactile integration. I first used color and weight (largely proprioceptive) discriminations (23) and have now repeated the results with black and white pattern and cutaneous rough-smooth stimuli. Performance with the latter is retained even after midline section of the habenular and posterior commissures, the massa intermedia, and the quadrigeminal plate in addition to the corpus callosum and anterior and hippocampal commissures. Removal of the bulk of somatosensory arm cortex, on the side of the visual input as indicated in the figure, abolishes the performance with the affected hand for several weeks. Meantime, however, the other hand continues to perform above 95% correct. This puzzling result is under further investigation.

In this connection I am reminded that it is perhaps as important as anything to point out that in working with this twin brain preparation we have often been forced into new patterns of thinking. That is, not only does one see new approaches to old problems, but in many cases one is forced into asking entirely new kinds of questions about brain physiology, questions of a sort that I, at least, would never even have thought of asking with the usual bilateral approach.

When we turn to the evidence regarding intermanual transfer of somesthetic discriminations and of motor learning in the primates, the results have not been entirely consistent (4, 6–8, 10, 15, 21, 23). In our own experience, section of the cerebral commissures may lead to failure of intermanual transfer but not in all cases nor under all conditions. We have observed intermanual transfer in chiasm-callosum sectioned monkeys that were sophisticated in using either hand with either eye and were trained with pairs of objects that were left in sight because they were distinguishable only by touch not vision, the one being harder, or heavier, or looser than its mate and this being discernible only upon palpation. Also, removal of the somatosensory arm cortex as shown in figure 8 has been found to evoke transfer on subsequent testing in split-brain monkeys that had formerly failed to exhibit transfer on problems tested prior to the cortical removal (10). The interpretation of this is complicated at present by the fact that a trained reversal of the transferred task consistently fails to transfer back again to the first hand (10).

Some transfer effects also show up in visual learning, according to data obtained by Trevarthen in monkeys with presumably complete section of the callosum, anterior and hippocampal commissures and optic chiasm. So far the transfer influences seem to be confined to brightness, general color and possibly very simple forms of pattern discrimination. All these may be aspects of visual stimulation that cross at the collicular level of the midbrain and hence cases are being tested with more extensive midline sections that include the posterior commissure and quadrigeminal plate.

In figure 9A may be recognized a unilateral approach to the classical Klüver-Bucy temporal lobe syndrome and some of its subsequent fractionations (5) and in 9B the same for the old prefrontal lobe syndrome and its role in visual delayed response. In the former case the operation may make the monkey "unilaterally tame" for a while, i.e., placid in its response to touch and stroking of its limbs and body parts contralateral to the temporal lesion (John Steiner, unpublished observations). In the latter case (9) the delayed response performance is impaired in the absence of the usual hypermotility and distractibility that have followed bilateral removals and that for years have tended to confuse the interpretation. In each instance one gains new data and information as to whether certain of the symptoms involve direct intrahemispheric relations or are perhaps more distant secondary effects stemming from hyperactivity, temperament changes, and the like, involved in the bilateral removals.

The so-called *encephale isolée*, and *cerveau isolé* preparations of Bremer and his group (1) have found considerable use in physiology. It should not be out of the question to go further and prepare isolated half-brains of different forms and degrees of isolation that would be used in the chronic condition, i.e., carried around by the animal *in vivo* in the brain's natural habitat under normal biochemical conditions, and recovered from the acute effects of diaschisis for use in implanted electrode conditioning and other physiological studies.

By combining various ablations and sections like those described above with local stereotaxic lesions in subcortical nuclei, it is possible today with methods now available to attain a fairly extensive surgical dissection of the mammalian brain, and to set up a large variety of combinations and permutations of cerebral centers in chronic preparations for functional testing and analysis. Combine with this the analytic possibilities brought by the chronically implanted electrode for recording, stimulating, and self-stimulating plus the new automated training and programming techniques, and those of us working in the physiology of behavior find ourselves today surrounded by seemingly endless new possibilities just waiting for the doing.

In the outlook for physiology, particularly that of the younger people, perhaps even those top-level secrets of brain function that to Professor Herrick were always primary and which gave a perspective and an added

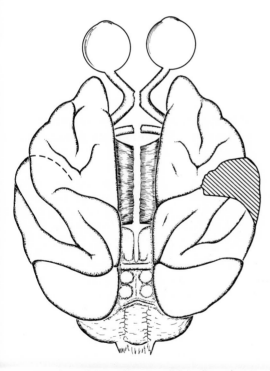

Fig. 9a. One of the various possible unilateral approaches to the classical temporal and prefrontal lobe syndromes.

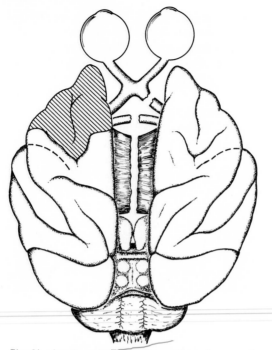

Fig. 9b. Another of the possible unilateral approaches to the classical temporal and prefrontal lobe syndromes.

meaning to all his observations, whether he was looking at a synapse or at a hemisphere, need not remain so much longer, "impossibly remote and out of reach."

Our brain surgery on monkeys has been performed during the past 18 months almost exclusively by Dr. Harbans Arora. Lois MacBird has carried the major responsibility for the training and medication of the animals and for general laboratory assistance. I wish also to thank Colwyn Trevarthen and Drs. Mitchell Glickstein and John Steiner for permission to mention some of their unpublished findings.

REFERENCES

1. BREMER, F., J. BRIHAYE and G. ANDRÉ-BALISAUX. *Arch. Swiss. Neurol. Psychiat.* 78: 31, 1956.
2. DOWNER, J. L. DE C. *Fed. Proc.* 17: 37, 1958.

3. DOWNER, J. L. DE C. *Brain* 82: 251, 1959.
4. EBNER, F. and R. E. MYERS. *Fed. Proc.* 19: 288, 1960.
5. ETTLINGER, GEORGE. *Brain* 82: 232, 1959.
6. GLICKSTEIN, M. and R. W. SPERRY. *Physiologist* 2 (No. 3): 45, 1959.
7. GLICKSTEIN, M. and R. W. SPERRY. *Amer. Psychol.* 14: 385, 1959.
8. GLICKSTEIN, M. and R. W. SPERRY. *J. Comp. Physiol. Psychol.* 53: 322, 1960.
9. GLICKSTEIN, M. and R. W. SPERRY. *Physiologist* 3 (No. 3): 66, 1960.
10. GLICKSTEIN, M. and R. W. SPERRY. *Amer. Psychol.* 15: 485, 1960.
11. MISHKIN, M. *Amer. Psychol.* 13: 414, 1958.
12. MYERS, R. E. *Jour. Comp. Physiol. Psychol.* 48: 470, 1955.
13. MYERS, R. E. *Brain* 79: 358, 1956.
14. MYERS, R. E. In: *Brain Mechanisms and Learning,* edited by J. F. DELAFRESNAYE. Oxford: Blackwell, 1961, pp. 481–505.
15. MYERS, R. E. *Fed. Proc.* 19: 289, 1960.
16. MYERS, R. E. and R. W. SPERRY. *Anat. Rec.* 115: 351, 1953.
17. MYERS, R. E. and R. W. SPERRY. *Fed. Proc.* 15: 134, 1956.
18. MYERS, R. E. and R. W. SPERRY. *A.M.A. Arch. Neurol. Psychiat.* 80: 298, 1958.
19. SCHRIER, A. M. and R. W. SPERRY. *Science* 129: 1275, 1959.
20. SPERRY, R. W. Physiological plasticity and brain circuit theory in *Biological and Biochemical Bases of Behavior,* edited by H. R. Harlow and C. N. Woolsey. Madison: Univ. of Wisconsin Press, 1958.
21. SPERRY, R. W. *Anat. Rec.* 131: 297, 1958.
22. SPERRY, R. W. *J. Neurophysiol.* 22: 78, 1959.
23. SPERRY, R. W. *Transactions of the Macy Conference on Central Nervous System and Behavior,* 1958.
24. SPERRY, R. W., R. E. MYERS and A. M. SCHRIER. *Quart. J. exper. Psych.* 12: 65, 1960.
25. SPERRY, R. W., J. S. STAMM and NANCY MINER. *J. Comp. Physiol. Psychol.* 549: 29, 1956.
26. STAMM, J. S. and R. W. SPERRY. *J. Comp. Physiol. Psychol.* 50: 138, 1957.
27. TREVARTHEN, C. B. *Amer. Psychol.* 15: 485, 1960.

Observations on Visual Perception After Disconnexion of the Cerebral Hemispheres in Man

M. S. Gazzaniga,
J. E. Bogen,
and R. W. Sperry

INTRODUCTION

In earlier reports we have outlined some of the functional effects produced in man by surgical disconnexion of the cerebral hemispheres as effected by a complete transection of the corpus callosum and the anterior and hippocampal commissures, with separation of the massa intermedia (Gazzaniga et al., 1962, 1963). The observations were based on a case operated by Drs. Philip Vogel and Joseph Bogen at the White Memorial Medical Center in Los Angeles (Bogen and Vogel, 1962).

The present paper in the main is an account of some of the further findings obtained to date in the same person in tests directed principally at visual functions and also reports confirmatory findings on a second case similarly operated. The tests were aimed at determining the extent and kinds of interaction, if any, between the perceptual and mnemonic activities of the separated hemispheres, at detecting differences in performance capacity of the right and left visual half systems and at revealing the degree of lateralization in motor responses to right and left visual field stimuli. Tests concerned more specifically with language and with motor control will be reported separately.

From *Brain*, 1965, **88**, 221–236. Reprinted with permission of the publisher and authors. Aided by the National Institutes of Health, U.S. Public Health Service, Grants No. M3372 and No. 2G86, and the Frank P. Hixon Fund.

TESTING METHODS

Projection of visual information confined to one or the other hemisphere was effected by presenting stimuli within the right or left half visual field while the subject was fixating a central point. All stimuli presented in the left half-field thus went to the right hemisphere and vice versa. Inadvertent projection of test information into the wrong hemisphere caused by eye movement away from the fixation point was controlled by tachistoscopic presentation of the stimuli at 1/10 to 1/100 sec. combined with close observation of the subject's gaze. Several variations of the general testing procedure were tried, including the use of goggles equipped with time shutters, ocular electrodes, and different tachistoscopic techniques.

The test conditions most extensively utilized were the following: The subject was seated at a table with his eyes approximately 6 ft. in front of a translucent white viewing screen 4 × 4 ft. with its centre at subject's eye-level. A small asterisk figure at the centre of the screen was used to facilitate fixation. The stimulus patterns, mounted in pairs or singly on 2 × 2 slides, were rear projected on to the screen from a distance of 10 ft. by an automatic projector equipped with a tachistoscopic shutter. A second projector, set on top of the first, maintained an even background illumination on the screen before and after each stimulus presentation. All patterned stimuli were black on a white background. They appeared 4 in. high on the screen and were placed no nearer the mid-line than 5 in. In later tests of the past eight months the single large screen was replaced by two commercial viewers placed side by side with the screens 4 in. apart as indicated in fig. 1. Each viewer had its own automatic slide projector that could be controlled separately or flashed in synchrony with the other. For some of the tests a single unit was used with the subject fixating a point at the centre of the one screen. Each trial was preceded by explicit verbal instructions and/or overt demonstrations as to the nature of the test performance. One experimenter operated the projectors and watched the subject's gaze while another, sitting beside the table, recorded the results and checked the subject's general reactions. Because of the language handicap of the right hemisphere, all tests as a rule were run first with the right half-field and the right hand. It was easier for the patient to follow instructions for working on the left side after the test procedure had become familiar on the right side.

CASE HISTORY

The patient, a male war veteran, had been suffering intractable generalized convulsions for more than ten years prior to surgery. He had always been right handed and preoperatively had no marked sensory or motor impairments save a mild hypæsthesia on the left side. He was a high school graduate with an above-average I.Q. and considerable self-education. He used to read a lot, including Greek history and his favourite author, Victor Hugo, until the seizures became severe after which he settled for television and the newspaper headlines.

Fig. 1. Two automated projector-viewing systems with tachistoscopic shutters were arranged so they could be used separately, in alternation, or in synchrony to present stimulus material in either half visual field from 2 × 2 transparent slides.

Prior to surgery the patient had uncorrected visual acuity of 20/70 + 1 O.D. and 20/50 O.S. Extensive tests, including perimetry, showed no abnormality except some jerkiness of motion.[1] Tachistoscopic presentation of letters, numbers, geometric figures, and sentences showed that all stimuli were easily recognized and interpreted correctly in either visual half-field and/or correctly recorded by manual response with either hand. He also wrote moderately well with the left hand as well as the right, and his reading in general was normal.

The corpus callosum, hippocampal and anterior commissures were all completely sectioned in a single operation (Bogen and Vogel, 1962) by exposure and retraction of right frontal and occipital lobes. Some atrophy of the right frontal lobe was observed and the massa intermedia was judged to be absent. No generalized convulsions have occurred in the thirty months since

---

[1] The optometric tests were performed by Dr. G. Kambara.

the operation (Bogen and Vogel, 1963). No significant change in either temperament or I.Q. was noted. Three months after the operation, uncorrected acuity was unchanged. Ishihara colour cards were read correctly. He had always been cheerful by nature with a quick sense of humour and the same general temperament was retained after surgery. Other results of pre- and early post-operative testing were outlined in an earlier report (Gazzaniga et al., 1962, 1963).

OBSERVATIONS

Laterality in Visuomotor Integration

While the subject was seated before a table fixating on the central marker on a large upright screen, a bright spot of light $\frac{1}{2}$ in. in diameter was flashed in a prearranged pseudo-random schedule to different quadrants of the visual field. After each stimulus presentation, the subject responded immediately by pointing quickly to the spot where he had seen the light. When it was desired to test the use of a given hand, the subject's other hand was placed in his lap underneath the table.

Under these conditions, early post-operative testing revealed that when the stimulus fell in the right visual field, it could be localized with only the right hand and/or verbally. Stimuli in the left field could be located only with the left hand and not verbally. When both hands were left free for response above the table, the subject always used the right hand to point to stimuli that fell in the right field and the left hand for those that appeared in the left field. While one hand responded, the other usually remained quite motionless. Reaction time to all stimuli was nearly three times slower than normal. Earlier indications that the left hand might respond at times to stimuli in the right field (Gazzaniga et al., 1962) were not confirmed in the later testing. It is now believed that these earlier exceptions may have been due to failure to ensure adequate fixation on the centre of the screen. Tests similar to the foregoing, repeated at 24 months after surgery, show the patient now is able to use either hand to locate the visual target in either half-field, indicating an increased control of the secondary hand. Responses executed with the primary hand from each hemisphere remain markedly superior to those of the secondary in speed, accuracy and general coordination. Verbal recognition or description are still lacking, however, for the left field stimuli.

The results showed, in brief, that when visual stimuli entered one hemisphere, manual responses utilizing the arm governed primarily from the same hemisphere went off appropriately while responses with the other limb were absent in the early months and never became as good as those of the primary arm. Later testing revealed a definite improvement in motor control over the secondary arm. Throughout all these and other tests, it was only those stimuli that fell in the right visual half-field that were acknowledged and described verbally.

Retrieval Tests for Pattern Discrimination

A series of retrieval tests were designed whereby the subject was obliged to select from a group of five figures on 5 × 3 in. cards placed on a table in front of him, the one that corresponded to the pattern flashed tachistoscopically on the screen. Generally a new set of 5 cards was placed in front of the subject before each trial. Most sets contained the correct card and one blank card, plus three other incorrect cards. Geometric symbols, numbers, single words and short phrases were used; in some trials a simultaneous verbal description was requested while others involved only the manual response. The stimuli were flashed on the screen in either or both visual half-fields on a randomized schedule so that the subject could not anticipate where the next stimulus would appear. The subject then tried to pick out from the series of 5 cards in front of him the pattern, word or sentence most like the projected figure.

In this situation the right hand responded correctly with virtually 100 per cent accuracy to all stimuli presented in the right field, regardless of their nature. The retrieval score with the right hand for the same set of stimuli flashed to the left field, however, failed to rise above chance. When stimuli were presented to the left field, the left hand was able to seek out the correct card at a level $2\frac{1}{2}$ times better than chance. The left hand made no response or responded only at a pure guess level when the stimuli were presented to the right visual field. In cases where stimuli were presented in the left field only, the subject, when questioned, would commonly deny having seen anything and often seemed puzzled that he should be asked to pick up a card. When he was asked what figure he had chosen, just after a correct pattern had been retrieved with the left hand following left field stimulation, the usual reply was, "The blank one."

When stimuli were flashed simultaneously to both fields and each hand responded to its respective stimulus, the *per cent* of correct retrieval by either the left or right hand did not drop. Nor were there other indications of perceptual distraction, conflict or interference between the hemispheres under these conditions. Verbal recognition remained specific to right-field stimuli here as before.

During the first post-operative year the intermittent apraxia of the left hand often prevented appropriate responses by this hand to stimuli seen in the right visual half-field. During the second year there was increased ability of the patient to control his left arm so at the present date $2\frac{1}{2}$ years after the operation the patient is able to respond with the left hand when discriminating stimuli are projected into the right visual field. There has been only slight, if any, improvement, however, in the ability of the right hand to respond correctly in discriminating stimuli in the left field.

Stimulus Preference Tests for Pattern Discrimination

When using the left hand to select one of 2 test objects or patterns, the subject frequently displayed persistent preferences for one over the other. This applied to tactile as well as to visual discriminations. Such left-hand preferences appeared also when no visual field restrictions were imposed and the subject was using the left hand to select objects with both eyes open. Presented with a choice of 2 objects or cards, the left hand picked one and consistently retrieved it, regardless of right-left position and other variables. This preference could be reversed by deliberately taking the subject's hand and placing it on the other stimulus and then rewarding this choice. As testing of this kind progressed, it became possible after some weeks to reinforce correct responses by reward signals instead of actual rewards, such as tapping a pencil on the table to indicate a correct choice. When an original preference had been reversed, there was a tendency for the subject to revert to the initial preference at the end of a short rest interval of 2 to 6 minutes; but a given preference did not carry over with any consistency from one week to the next.

These left-hand preferences were sufficiently consistent to make feasible their use in finding out more about the visual discrimination capacity of the relatively inaccessible right hemisphere. Discrimination tests were run with procedures similar to those above but with a second, more portable system in which miniature projector units were positioned 3 feet in front of the patient's eyes on a 2 × 3 ft. black background supporting board (fig. 2). These units flashed $\frac{3}{4}$ in. geometric figures on a 1 in. ground glass screen at 0.1 sec. A pair of these screens was located in the left visual field and a single one in the right field positioned at points approximately 10 degrees lateral to and on a level with the fixation point. The subject again sat at a table in front of the units where he could easily point to the specific stimulus of his choice. A centre hole at the fixation point in the background board allowed the experimenter to observe the patient's eyes and to present stimuli only when the subject's gaze was firmly centred. The visual patterns consisted of a variety of simple geometric figures such as squares, triangles, circles and the like.

In each trial a pair of different geometric symbols was flashed to the left visual field, side by side (4 in. apart) in a horizontal plane. Simultaneously and at a corresponding point in the right field, either a cross or a circle was flashed. The right-left positioning of the 2 figures in the left field was switched randomly in a standard discrimination procedure. The subject was instructed verbally and by demonstration to have the left hand point to the preferred stimulus in the left half-field. His left-hand responses were made immediately in a proficient, adept and somewhat automatic manner. Following his manual response to the left field, he was also asked which of the two stimuli had appeared in the right field.

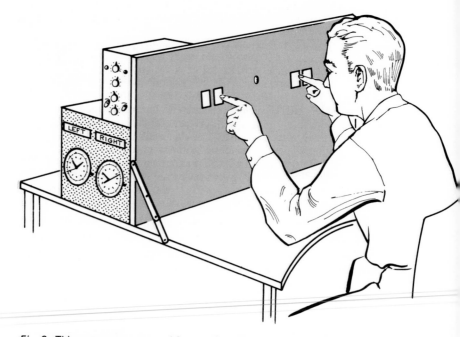

Fig. 2. This apparatus was used for reaction time and was modified for other tests as described in the text. The stimuli were projected on the response panels in either or both visual fields.

The characteristic outcome was as follows: (*a*) Over a series of trials, the left hand would repeatedly point to one of the two left-field patterns, regardless of its right-left position; (*b*) the subject was able, on the same trial, to report accurately which of the two stimuli had been flashed simultaneously in the right visual field; and (*c*) when questioned, the subject consistently denied any knowledge of the stimulus flashed to the left field.

Tests for Lateral Specialization of Visual Function

The patient had always been right-handed and had never had occasion to write or draw with the left hand, so far as he or his family could recall. Following the commissurotomy, when he copied sample figures that suggested spatial perspective like the Necker cube, his performance with the left hand was consistently better than that with the right (fig. 3).

In order to get the left hand to perform, the subject was seated at a table and the performance was started with the use of the subject's right hand and

Fig. 3. Samples of the performance of Case I with right and left hand in copying example figures, each trial being limited to three minutes.

| | Example | Left Hand | Right Hand |

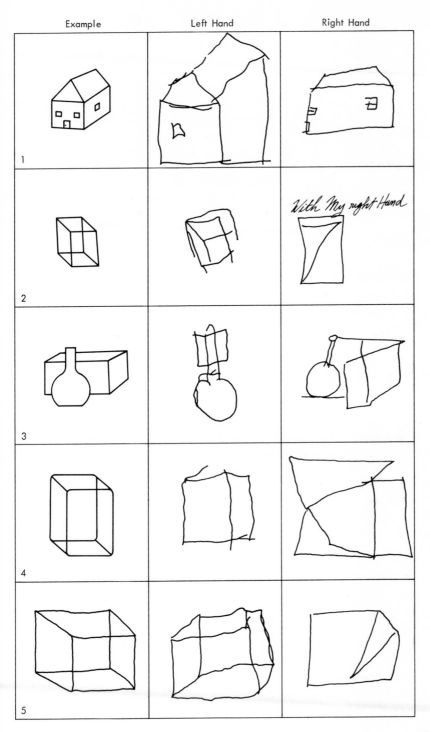

With My right Hand

verbal instructions. After the test procedure had become familiar, the hands were shifted with the aid of verbal instruction and "do this" demonstration. Subsequent changes were then made from one hand to the other and a three-minute period was allowed each hand for each drawing. Performance with the left hand was handicapped in that the hand would often tighten and go out of control before the three-minute period was up. Most commonly it would slowly swing upward from the paper to a raised position above the left shoulder.

When attempts were made in a recent session to assist the right hand in drawing a Necker cube, by demonstrating the strategy of first drawing two overlapping squares and then connecting the four corners, he was still unable to carry out the task with the right hand. However, immediately after the right-hand failure, his left hand drew the complete cube without copying from any example and without using the demonstrated strategy.

The subject was always able to reconstruct standard patterns in a block design test and to assemble complex object puzzles with the left hand. Those patterns that were correctly reconstructed with the right hand were always extremely simple and done so only after much practice. The inability of the right hand puzzled the patient and when it was apparent from his facial expression that he knew the right hand had performed incorrectly, the left hand folded behind him and sometimes restrained by the experimenter, would make spontaneous movements as if to reach out and correct the error. When free use of both hands was permitted, the patient usually was unable to arrange the blocks and/or picture parts correctly, mainly because the right hand would always try to help and would consistently undo the superior accomplishments of the left.

Reading

There was no complaint by the patient of visual impairment during the first several months after surgery even though as evident from the above, he was unable to read or to describe objects, pictures or symbols presented in the left-half visual field. His reading in tachistoscopic tests after the operation, so far as the right half-field was concerned, seemed roughly normal in speed and comprehension. He continued to look at the evening newspaper and to watch television without comment.

Approximately 25 weeks after surgery, however, he began to complain of difficulty in sustained reading. As he described it, printed words tended to fade out until they became indistinguishable and he was obliged to stop and rest for some minutes after which he was able to continue for another short period. When asked to read aloud during a testing session, he did moderately well for about half a page, and then began to slow, to stumble, and had to stop. If the first word on a line was short, he would generally not include it in his verbal recitation. However, his answers to questioning regarding the content of what he had covered indicated good comprehension. With large print and simple material such as found in a book for 6-year-olds he was able to continue a little longer but the same problem persisted.

In March 1963 the uncorrected acuity was 20/70 + 1 O.D. and 20/50 O.S. Following correction, and if the head was turned to the left, acuity improved to 20/25 O.D. Perimetry with a variety of targets still showed a left homonymous hemianopia for tests that required a verbal response. Normal tests, including the Lancaster red-green and orthoptic survey, showed normal stereopsis (as also found by Bridgman and Smith, 1945).

By about the 7th month, the subject had clearly abandoned efforts to read anything more than the newspaper headlines and the short phrases and words encountered in television. Tests of his reading ability run again at 18 and 30 months indicated little if any change from the condition at 6 months. In addition to this impairment, if short phrases or long compound words were printed out on a piece of paper, such as " ham and eggs," and presented to him briefly, with the last word or word segment being pointed to by the experimenter for a verbal response, the patient would verbalize the last word and claim that was all there was on the paper.

Intermodal Transfer

The patient was taught to distinguish with the left hand such objects as wooden ovals, pyramids or a door latch or electric plug, while wearing a blindfold (fig. 4f). The patient was consistently unable to give a verbal description of an object that he was manipulating with the left hand. However, as soon as the object and the blindfold were removed, he had no trouble in pointing out, with his left hand, the correct object seen in a chance position among 6 other objects of similar size. After training and presentation to the left hand, responses carried out with the right hand were no better than chance and vice versa for objects not audibly named.

Other discriminations of the same sort of objects were made on the basis of unrestricted vision without tactile contact and with the left hand responding by pointing at the chosen object. When the patient was then blindfolded, tactile recognition of the object palpated among a series of others was immediate with either hand.

In general, intermodal transfer of this sort occurred readily within one hemisphere but never between the hemispheres.

Confirmatory Findings on a Second Case

Many of the foregoing tests have now been applied to a second patient more recently recovered from the same kind of brain surgery done for the same reasons and with therapeutic results equally good to date. This is a woman 30 years old without history of prior brain injury. I.Q. tests before surgery gave scores in the 70–80 range, but were difficult to assess because of preceding seizures and heavy medication. The post-surgical recovery was excellent and

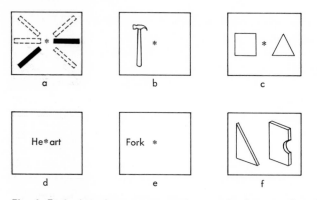

Fig. 4. Each plate shows representative samples from a series of stimuli used in different visual tests as described. The point of fixation for samples *a–e* is identified by an asterisk. *a*, Split-bar test. Subject compares directional orientation of lines in right and left fields. One of 3 positions on left is paired with one of 3 on right in random order. Subject responds verbally, draws with right, left, or both hands, or points to matching samples. *b*, Object-retrieval test. Objects pictured in left or right fields are retrieved from among an assortment of other objects using different somatic-visual-cortical field combinations. *c*, Double field presentation of geometric figures, objects, scenes, numbers, colours, etc., is combined with verbal plus manual pointing, drawing and writing responses of one or both hands. *d*, Triple word test. Commissurotomy patients never identify the whole word, only right and left parts separately, and only the right vocally. *e*, Name-object retrieval test. Subject's visual and auditory comprehension of verbal material in minor hemisphere is shown by correct non-verbal responses (like pointing at correct one of a number of objects, signalling correct one of several definitions read by experimenter, etc.). Spoken or written answers even by left hand don't rise above pure guess level. *f*, Inter-modal finds the corresponding object by vision using left or/and right hands. Similar tests were run in a reverse order.

more rapid than in the preceding patient, with no mutism or akinesis of the left arm after the 2nd day. The severe apraxia to verbal commands that has persisted in the preceding case was apparent here only in the early postoperative weeks. The patient's temperament, I.Q., swimming strokes and many other general features of behaviour appeared to have suffered little if any impairment. There were complaints, however, of reduction in vitality, initiative and memory that cannot be ascribed entirely to commissurotomy until possible involvement of the fornix is ruled out. Unlike Case I (Gazzaniga *et al.*, 1963), this person was able to localize verbally or by pointing with either hand, cutaneous stimulation across the mid-line on the torso and proximal extremities suggesting greater bilaterality in the cerebral representation of each cutaneous half-field. To what extent this is a reflection of natural individual variation rather than prior brain damage, remains a problem. The body map for cutaneous sensibility was much like that of Case I, however, when the tests involved more complex discriminations beyond that of mere localization of simple point stimuli. Postoperative testing through the 40th week included determinations of visual acuity and extent of visual fields, verbal and manual responses to tachistoscopically presented visual stimuli, retrieval, matching, transfer, preference block design and reading tests plus other tests of motor and somatosensory function. The testing sessions, carried out in the laboratory or in the patient's home, averaged about two hours every second or third week and totalled some hundred hours. The results in this second case are basically similar to those obtained in the first patient and can be most easily presented in terms of the differences that have appeared.

As in the first patient, all tests indicated a complete separation of the perceptual, cognitive and mnemonic activity of the left and right hemispheres in all the visual tests. Anything seen, comprehended or remembered as a result of lateralized input restricted to one hemisphere, could not be used to aid in any direct way responses that emanated from the other hemisphere. In even so simple a performance as nodding the head "yes" or "no" to indicate whether red and green colours flashed to left and right fields were the same or not, there was no sign of cross integration. The same was true in attempts to tell whether broad lines or bars running from left to right field through the fixation point were straight or broken at the middle (fig. 4a). So far, we have found no evidence that what is perceived in the right half-field has any influence on the perception or comprehension of what is seen in the left half-field.

The most marked difference between the two cases was seen in the ability of the second case by the sixth postoperative month to use either hand in responding to unilateral cerebral input or to verbal instructions. When a perceptual or cognitive activity was centred or confined to one hemisphere, motor expression was usually better with the favoured or primary hand but fair to good response was also possible in many performances with the secondary hand ipsilateral to the working hemisphere. There was no difference between ipsilateral and contralateral combinations in reaction time to a simple flash of light in either half-field. This good control and use of the secondary hand in many activities tended to obscure the earlier evidence of hemispheric independence. For example, sketches of the Necker cube that in early months could be performed only with the left hand, indicating specialization of the right hemisphere, would be carried out with either hand by the seventh month after the operation.

Even so, when separate and different stimuli were projected to each hemisphere simultaneously, the patient tended to respond in a manner indicating that for each hemisphere, the contralateral hand was definitely favoured over the ipsilateral one. For example, when stimulus pairs (fig. 4c) were presented tachistoscopically and the patient was asked to pick out the "seen" stimulus from a series of sample cards, she characteristically picked only the "triangle" when she was working with the right hand. When responding with the left hand, she regularly ignored the figure in the right field and chose the one that appeared in the left half-field, in this case, the square.

The patient could write and execute printed commands only with the right hand during the early months after the operation. Subsequently, the control of the left hand by the left hemisphere improved, until the left hand could also be used for these purposes though generally not so well as the right. Hand use, *per se*, thus became much less valuable as a criterion of which hemisphere was active than it had been in the first case or during the first several months in the present case and it became necessary to rely more and more on speech for this purpose.

High to perfect scores were obtained for the discrimination and comprehension of patterned stimuli presented to the right hemisphere (fig. 4b, e) in a variety of retrieval and matching tests that included words and numbers with non-verbal responses. Her performance in this respect was strikingly superior to that of Case I with known damage in the right hemisphere. Though able to comprehend written material in either field, Case II showed no ability at all to put together a longer word or a compound word that fell half in one field and half in the other (fig. 4d). With such a word as " heart " for example, with the fixation point falling between " he " and the " art, " she would describe only the word " art." Other results involving symbolic capacities of the hemispheres will be reported elsewhere.

DISCUSSION

It is evident in the foregoing that surgical disconnexion of the hemispheres, with the resultant separation of the cortical representation for right and left halves of the visual field and for right and left limbs, produced in both cases clear-cut functional disturbances that correlated directly with the anatomical separations effected by the surgery. Performances in which the visual inflow was restricted to one hemisphere, and the response involved only the hand for which the primary cortical representation was in the same hemisphere, were little affected, whereas those performances requiring interaction or direct cooperation between the two hemispheres showed marked disruption. Activities that involved speech and writing were well preserved but only in so far as they could be governed from the left hemisphere. It was clear that visual information did not transfer from one hemisphere to the other. Nor was there evidence that the perceptual activities of one hemisphere influenced the other, for both cases failed to achieve even the simplest sort of integration between the two visual half-fields.

The impairment of ability to make certain responses with either hand to material seen across the mid-line of the visual field, especially pronounced in Case I, indicates that in the human brain the corpus callosum in the intact condition plays a major role in the mediation of those responses in which the sensory input is directed to one hemisphere and the primary motor control lies in the other. This conclusion is contrary to a prevailing impression that in man the corpus callosum plays little or no part in such activities (Paillard,

1960). The present findings in this regard are also quite different from those obtained in split-brain cats where the visual input into one hemisphere could be used during a learning situation to guide the ipsilateral forepaw as well as the contralateral forepaw (Schrier and Sperry, 1959). Results more in line with the present have been obtained in split-brain monkeys where significant deficits have been observed in activities that pair an eye with the ipsilateral hand (Downer, 1959; Trevarthen, 1962; Gazzaniga, 1964). These comparative observations, though still meagre, suggest that the cortical control in each hemisphere for the ipsilateral upper extremity becomes proportionately less proficient as one ascends the evolutionary scale, while the corpus callosum becomes correspondingly more important in mediating such activity. This appears to be in part a matter of the relative importance of distal versus proximal movement in limb use, the latter being more subject to bilateral control by either hemisphere. At the same time, the severe apraxia seen in Case I and in some of the earlier reports where chronic lateralized cerebral damage was involved (Sweet, 1941; Bremer *et al.*, 1956; Geschwind, 1962) may have caused an unnatural dependence on the commissures and lead to some exaggerated conclusions regarding praxic functions of the corpus callosum.

The disconnected right hemisphere displayed subtle perceptual capacities as well as good comprehension for both the testing situation and at times the test stimulus itself. In this regard, results from Case II are especially clear in demonstrating that each of the separated cerebral hemispheres is capable of these higher mental functions. The upper limits of such function in the minor hemisphere, for the most part, remain to be determined.

The exact cause of the first patient's inability to read for a sustained period of time remains uncertain. A new set of eye-movement patterns and attention-forming mechanisms would be called for to compensate for the inability to comprehend the print on the entire left half-field. Excess scanning movements of the eyes stimulated by the need of more information from the left field might lead to a distracting fluctuation of attention between the two hemispheres. That a similar reading difficulty has not appeared in Case II suggests that pre-surgical brain damage may be a critical factor in the first case. In general, however, it remains a problem as to what extent the observed differences between the patients should be ascribed to pre-existent brain damage and how much to natural individual differences in brain organization. Cerebral dominance and lateral specialization including language functions along with the unsolved functions of the corpus callosum and other commissures would appear to be subject to a considerable range of individual variation.

One of the interesting questions regarding lateral specialization in the human cerebral cortex concerns the nature of the specialized functions allocated to the so-called minor or nondominant hemisphere. A number of studies based mainly on patients with unilateral cortical damage suggest that the perception of certain kinds of spatial relationships, the recognition of faces and certain non-verbal auditory functions like timbre and tonal memory, are among those that are more highly developed in the minor hemisphere (Hécaen et al., 1951; McFie and Zangwill, 1960; Piercy et al., 1960; Milner, 1962; Piercy and Smith, 1962). Commissurotomy cases, in which both hemispheres remain essentially intact but separated, offer obvious advantages for the testing of such lateral specialization. To a considerable degree, the properties of each hemisphere are reflected independently in the performance of the appropriate hand, especially in the first patient and during the first months in the second case. The superior performance of the left hand over the right in the block design test, drawing and other simple tasks that incorporated spatial relationships observed in both patients offers striking support of the previous inferences that this aspect of visual activity is represented principally in the right hemisphere. Again it would seem that the corpus callosum in the normal brain must play a critical role in serving to integrate this component of visual function with others specific to the left hemisphere.

In regard to the foregoing, it is also of interest to note that while both patients were incapable of reconstructing Necker cubes, block designs and the like with the right hand, they were capable of matching the test stimulus by simply pointing with this hand or indicating the correct design among a sampling of five related patterns. This shows that the primary perceptual capacity of the left dominant hemisphere is capable of discriminating between correct and incorrect reconstructions. Since it is also true that both patients have no motor problems with the right hand, the difficulty in reconstruction in these visual tests must lie somewhere in between these two systems. The further tentative conclusion may thus be drawn from these cases that the lateral specialization lies more in the motor executive or expressive sphere than in the sensory-perceptual components of the performance.

These same problems and the analysis would appear to apply to the speech mechanism as well. Tests now in progress suggest that the disconnected right "non-speech" hemisphere may have a similar capacity to comprehend and to match written or spoken words at a rather high level but yet not be capable of expressing the comprehension through speech.

The total picture of the cerebral disconnexion syndrome as exhibited by Case II above, comes considerably closer to that depicted in the Akelaitis-Van Wagenen series (Akelaitis, 1941, 1943, 1944; Van Wagenen and Herren, 1940) than does that of our first case. This is attributable in the main to the greater motor control in each hemisphere for the ipsilateral side. Absence and impairments of right-left integration in gnostic functions, however, become strikingly apparent with application of critical tests. All the data are consistent with the earlier conclusion that surgical disconnexion of the hemispheres results in a splitting and doubling of most of the gnostic or psychic properties of the brain (Sperry, 1961a, 1961b). The normal unity of perceptual awareness in the primate brain may be inferred to be dependent to a large degree on the cerebral commissures, especially the corpus callosum. The functional separation of right and left mental spheres that is produced by cutting the commissures was strikingly evident in a number of the above testing situations, to the point as described where left and right hemispheres were attempting conflicting solutions to the same task.

SUMMARY

(1) This is a report of two cases of surgical disconnexion of the cerebral hemispheres in man effected by a complete transection of the corpus callosum and the anterior and hippocampal commissures, with separation of the massa intermedia.

(2) In this paper we discuss principally the responses of these patients to tests of visual functions.

(3) Performances in which the visual inflow was restricted to one hemisphere and the response involved only the hand for which the primary cortical representation was in the same hemisphere were little affected, whereas those performances requiring interaction or direct cooperation between the two hemispheres showed marked disruption.

(4) Activities that involved speech and writing were well preserved, but only insofar as they could be governed from the left hemisphere. It was clear that visual information did not transfer from one hemisphere to the other.

(5) The observations gave some support to previous views concerning lateral specialization of function in the human cerebral cortex as between the major and minor, or non-dominant, hemisphere.

REFERENCES

AKELAITIS, A. J. (1941) *Arch. Neurol. Psychiat., Chicago*, **45**, 788.

AKELAITIS, A. J. (1943) *J. Neuropath., and Exp. Neurol.*, 226.

AKELAITIS, A. J. (1944) *J. Neurosurg.*, **1**, 94.

BOGEN, J. E., & VOGEL, P. J. (1962) *Bull. Los Angeles Neurol. Soc.*, **27**, 169.

BOGEN, J. E., & VOGEL, P. J. (1963) *Surg. Forum*, **14**, 431.

BREMER, F., BRIHAYE, J., and ANDRÉ-GALISAUX, G. (1956) *Schweiz. Arch. Neurol. Psychiat.*, **78**, 31.

BRIDGMAN, C. S., & SMITH, K. U. (1945) *J. comp. Neurol.*, **83**, 57.

DOWNER, J. L. DE C. (1959) *Brain*, **82**, 251.

GAZZANIGA, M. S. (1964) *Exp. Neurol.*, **10**, 148.

GAZZANIGA, M. S., BOGEN, J. E., and SPERRY, R. W. (1962) *Proc. nat. Acad. Sci.*, **48**, 1765.

GAZZANIGA, M. S., BOGEN, J. E., & SPERRY, R. W. (1963) *Neuropsychologia*, **1**, 209.

GESCHWIND, N., & KAPLAN, E. (1962) *Neurology*, **12**, 675.

HÉCAEN, H., DE AJURIAGUERRA, J., & MASSONNET, J. (1951) *Encéphale*, **40**, 122.

MCFIE, J., & ZANGWILL, O. L. (1960) *Brain*, **83**, 243.

MILNER, B. (1962) In "Interhemispheric Relations and Cerebral Dominance." Baltimore, p. 77.

PAILLARD, J. (1960) In American Physiological Society "Handbook of Physiology," Sect. I, Vol. III, p. 1679.

PIERCY, M., HÉCAEN, H., & DE AJURIAGUERRA, J. (1960) *Brain*, **83**, 225.

PIERCY, M., & SMITH, V. O. G. (1962) *Brain*, **85**, 775.

SCHRIER, A. M., & SPERRY, R. W. (1959) *Science*, **129**, 1275.

SPERRY, R. W. (1961*a*) *Fed. Proc.*, **20**, 609.

SPERRY, R. W. (1961*b*) *Science*, **133**, 1749.

SWEET, W. H. (1941) *Arch. Neurol. Psychiat.*, *Chicago*, **45**, 86.

TREVARTHEN, C. B. (1962) Thesis, California Institute of Technology.

VAN WAGENEN, W. P., & HERREN, R. Y. (1940) *Arch. Neurol. Psychiat.*, *Chicago*, **44**, 740.

Successful Interocular Transfer of Pattern Discrimination in "Split-Brain" Cats with Shock-Avoidance Motivation

Jeri A. Sechzer

ABSTRACT. Interocular transfer of pattern discrimination was studied in "split-brain" cats with section of the corpus callosum and optic chiasm. Each cat learned a pattern discrimination under food-approach and under shock-avoidance motivation. Under food-approach motivation no split-brain cats showed transfer from the trained to the untrained eye. However, the same split-brain cats, trained with shock-avoidance motivation, all showed significant interocular transfer of the pattern discrimination. The success or failure of interocular transfer of pattern discrimination is strongly influenced by the method of training employed. This transfer is mediated by an extracallosal, subcortical pathway which is activated by shock-avoidance but not by food-approach motivation.

Successful transfer of a learned pattern discrimination from one eye to the other depends upon either the corpus callosum or the optic chiasm, for only when both of these are sectioned does such interocular transfer fail (Myers, 1955, 1956, 1959; Sperry, Miner, & Myers, 1955). Brightness discrimination,

From *Journal of Comparative and Physiological Psychology*, 1964, **58**, 76–83. Reprinted with permission of the publisher and author. This investigation was carried out while the author held a postdoctoral fellowship at the Institute of Neurological Sciences supported by Grant 2g-281 and Grant MH-03571 from the National Institute of Mental Health and received support from the Office of Naval Research NONR 551(39) while the author was a research fellow in the University of Pennsylvania Department of Physiology. I am especially grateful for the assistance and cooperation of Thomas H. Meikle, Jr. throughout this research, including his aid in neurosurgical techniques and development of the apparatus. Gratitude is expressed to Eliot Stellar and James M. Sprague, under whose direction this dissertation was carried out, to Philip Teitelbaum for his helpful criticism of the manuscript, and to Alan Laties for the preparation of histological sections of the retinas reported in this study.

however, will still transfer from one eye to the other even after section of both the optic chiasm and the corpus callosum (Meikle & Sechzer, 1960). This finding points to an extracallosal pathway mediating the interaction of the two hemispheres in brightness discrimination.

The question asked in the present investigation is: Are there extra-callosal pathways that could mediate the interocular transfer of pattern discrimination? In raising this question, it is interesting to note that all previous work has been done under food-approach motivation. Would the use of shock-avoidance motivation, involving the pain pathways, bring in extracallosal mechanisms and thus facilitate the transfer of pattern discrimination?

Thus the present study was carried out to determine whether the same "split-brain" cats that fail to transfer a learned pattern discrimination from one eye to the other with food-approach motivation will transfer this discrimination at high levels when it is learned with shock-avoidance motivation. The positive results reported here offer evidence for bilateral interaction of visual function without dependence upon either the corpus callosum or the optic chiasm.

METHOD

SUBJECTS.   Two normal cats served as controls Ss and six experimental cats had both the optic chiasm and the corpus callosum sectioned.

NEUROLOGICAL AND VISUAL TESTING.   Prior to the surgical procedures all Ss were tested neurologically as previously described by Sprague, Levitt, Robson, Liu, Stellar, and Chambers (1963), to make sure that no abnormalities could be observed especially in visually guided behavior.

OPERATIVE PROCEDURE.   Under aseptic conditions the optic chiasm was sagittally sectioned by the transbuccal approach after the method described by Myers (1955). This was followed in 21–35 days by aseptic mid-sagittal section of the corpus callosum. The anesthetic agent for all Ss was pentobarbital sodium (36 mg/kg body weight) administered intraperitoneally. A 2–4 week postoperative period intervened before training was started.

APPARATUS.   All cats were trained and tested in a semidarkened, discrimination apparatus that was used for food-approach as well as shock-avoidance motivation procedures. As can be seen in Figure 1 this apparatus consisted of a 36 ×12 ×12 in. transparent plastic box with a metal grid floor through which an electric shock could be delivered. A removable wooden partition divided the apparatus into a start box and alley. The end of the alley consisted of two translucent milk-plastic doors placed side by side. One door had four black vertical striations while the second door had four black horizontal striations. The areas of the patterns were identical and of equal luminance, differing only in orientation. One of the striated doors was arbitrarily selected as the positive stimulus. The negative door was locked from behind while the positive door remained unlocked. The position of the positive and negative

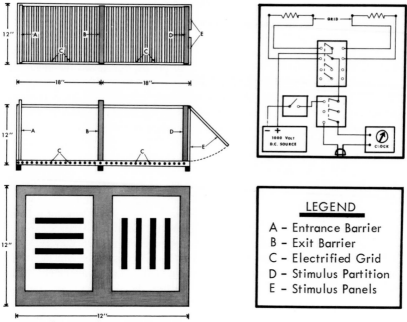

Stimulus Panels and Partition

Fig. 1. Apparatus used for shock-avoidance and food-approach training procedures.

stimuli was randomly alternated from right to left in accordance with the Gellermann sequence (1933). In order to prevent the second eye from seeing during this training period, visual input was restricted to one eye with a soft, rubber, monocular mask similar to that described by Myers (1955).

In order to compare food-approach motivation with shock-avoidance motivation each cat was trained in one procedure first, and then the polarity of the stimuli was reversed during training and testing with the second procedure. Thus, five split-brain cats and one normal control cat were trained monocularly and tested for transfer to the second eye with the shock-avoidance procedure first and then the food-approach procedure. To find out whether the order of procedure made any difference in the results and because of the necessarily conflicting nature of the reversed polarity of these stimuli, one split-brain and one normal cat were trained and tested for transfer to the second eye with the food-approach procedure first followed by the shock-avoidance procedure.

During the first procedure some cats were presented with horizontal striations as the positive stimulus and some with vertical striations as the positive stimulus. These stimuli were then reversed in polarity at the onset of the second procedure.

SHOCK-AVOIDANCE MOTIVATION. As the first step in training, each animal was allowed to explore the apparatus in an illuminated room. During this time an occasional electric shock was delivered to the cat through the metal grid floor as the cat proceeded down the alley. This helped to determine the minimum shock level required to make the cat run down the alley and escape through one of the doors onto a table. The cat was then picked up and returned to the start box for the onset of the next trial. During this part of the procedure, both doors were unlocked and devoid of the horizontal and vertical stimuli. The cat was not masked. Once the shock level was determined for each cat and the preliminary training completed, the cat was habituated to the monocular mask. Training with the striated stimuli was begun.

Each cat was trained to go through the correct, unlocked door within a 5-sec. interval in order to avoid receiving shock. The cat was placed in the start box at the beginning of each trial. At the onset of the trial, the wooden partition was raised and, at the same time a steady light was turned on, illuminating the patterned doors at the end of the alley. After 5 sec., an intermittent shock was presented for approximately .5 sec. once every 5 sec. until the cat escaped through the correct door. At this time both light and shock were terminated. Since a correction method was used, avoidance could be accomplished in one of two ways. If S pushed the incorrect door, found it locked and then went through the correct, unlocked door before the end of the 5-sec. interval, the response was not scored as a correct discrimination even though it was an avoidance. If S went through the correct door on the first choice, without error, within the 5-sec. interval, the behavior was scored as a correct discrimination, avoidance response. Thirty trials a day were usually given until a criterion of 90% or more correct responses were obtained for 2 consecutive days plus 9 or 10 correct responses on the first 10 trials of the third day.

At this point, interocular transfer was tested. The initially trained eye was masked and the naive eye exposed. Twenty transfer-test trials were given with the untrained eye. In order to keep the transfer-test procedure consistent with the end of the training procedure, when the cat was avoiding 100% of the time, no shock was given on the 20 transfer-test trials regardless of the animals' performance. Other than this, the 20 transfer-test trials with the untrained eye were exactly the same as the training trials with the first eye. If interocular transfer was not demonstrated, training with the second eye was begun with shock as required, and continued until performance reached criterion.

FOOD-APPROACH MOTIVATION. During this procedure, the positive stimulus for training and testing was the negative stimulus used in the shock-avoidance procedure. Thus if a cat was trained in the shock-avoidance procedure with horizontal striations as the positive stimulus and vertical striations as the negative stimulus, training with the food-approach procedure was carried out with vertical striations positive and horizontal striations negative.

The cats received food only during training and testing. A small piece of spleen was placed on a table behind the doors so that it was necessary for a cat to go through one of the doors in order to obtain its food. The initial training was done with unmarked doors and without the monocular mask.

Once the desired responses were obtained, the mask was put on, and training on the striated doors was started with the first eye. Each cat was trained to go through the correct door in order to get food. The cat was placed in the start box prior to the onset of each trial. The doors, with their respective positive and negative stimuli, were illuminated constantly with a steady light source. At the onset of each trial, the wooden partition was raised, and the cat proceeded down the alley, going through the correct door to eat the food placed on the table. Correction for errors was permitted as in the shock procedure. This was important, not only to keep the two procedures the same, but also to make sure that all cats received the same amount of food each day. A correct response was scored only when the cat chose the correct door on the first choice. Thirty trials a day were given until criterion was reached, 90% or more correct responses for 2 consecutive days and 9 or 10 correct responses on the initial 10 trials of the third day, just as for the shock-avoidance procedure. Interocular transfer was then tested. The trained eye was masked and the naive eye exposed. Twenty transfer-test trials were given with the untrained eye. In order to keep the 20 transfer-test trials consistent with those at the end of the training procedure, the cats received food at the completion of each transfer-test trial. If interocular transfer was not complete, training with the second eye was continued until performance reached criterion.

ANATOMICAL PROCEDURE. Two split-brain cats (SB No. 4 and SB No. 7) were sacrificed under anesthesia, and the brains were perfused with saline followed by 10% formalin. Gross examination was done during removal of the brains from the cranium. Parlodian sections were prepared and alternate sections were stained by Weil and thionin techniques.

Retinal sections of the eyes of each of the two cats were prepared and stained with thionin for additional determination of the completeness of the optic chiasm section.

RESULTS

Neurological Testing

The neurological testing carried out with the control cats and with the experimental cats prior to surgery showed no abnormalities. The only deficit which appeared after surgery was a bitemporal hemianopia (blindness in both temporal visual fields) as was expected from optic chiasm section.

Transfer Testing

The over-all results of this study are given in Table 1, which demonstrates that, regardless of the order of testing procedure, no split-brain cats trained with food-approach motivation showed any interocular transfer; whereas all of the same split-brain cats, when trained with shock-avoidance motivation, showed high levels of interocular transfer.

Table 1 Individual Performance Under Shock-Avoidance and Food-Approach Procedures

| | SHOCK-AVOIDANCE PROCEDURE | | | | | FOOD-APPROACH PROCEDURE | | | | |
| | | | SECOND EYE | | | | | SECOND EYE | | |
Ss	TEST CONDITION[a]	TRIALS WITH FIRST EYE	% CORRECT IN FIRST 20 TRIALS[b]	TRAINING TRIALS	% SAVINGS	TEST CONDITION[a]	TRIALS WITH FIRST EYE	% CORRECT IN FIRST 20 TRIALS[b]	TRAINING TRIALS	% SAVINGS
					NORMAL CATS					
C-1	1-V	350	90	0	100	2-H	460	70	160	65
C-2	2-H	170	75	50	71	1-V	180	95	0	100
					SPLIT-BRAIN CATS					
SB-4	1-V	1320	80	100	92	2-H	1210	30	1150	5
SB-7	1-H	1196	80	230	82	2-V	1540	53	1610	−4
SB-24	1-H	1090	70	80	93	2-V	850	35	960	−12
SB-30	1-V	630	60	200	68	2-H	1410	40	1340	5
SB-31	1-H	1104	80	140	87	2-V	2220	30	2040	8
SB-25	2-V	930	10	360	61	1-H	740	40	720	2

[a] Numeral indicates whether procedure was first or second for individual animal; V and H indicate positive stimulus for that procedure.
[b] No shock administered.

The two normal control cats showed significant interocular transfer in both the food-approach and the shock-avoidance tests. However, as Table 1 indicates, transfer to the second eye was less in the second procedure regardless of whether it was shock-avoidance or food-approach. This limitation of transfer in the second procedure was presumably due to the conflict produced by the reversal of the stimuli, as similarly reported by Myers (1959). Figure 2 shows the details of the performance of Normal Control Cat C-2.

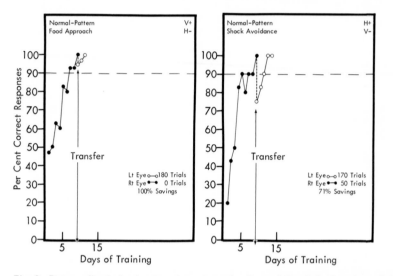

Fig. 2. Pattern discrimination learning curves for Normal Cat C-2, showing original learning and successful transfer to the second eye under food-approach and shock-avoidance motivation. (Closed circles indicate left eye training; open circles indicate right eye training.)

The results of a split-brain cat (SB No. 25), trained first with food-approach motivation and then with shock-avoidance motivation, are shown in Figure 3. With food-approach motivation, training with the first eye took 740 trials (about 2–3 times the normal rate) to reach criterion with horizontal striations positive. On the transfer-test trials, the cat performed at a chance level of 40% with the second eye. There were no savings in relearning, and complete retraining of the second eye was necessary. This retraining took 720 trials, indicating complete failure of interocular transfer.

Training with shock-avoidance motivation was then carried out in this split-brain cat with vertical striations as the positive stimulus. It took 930 trials for this cat to reach the 90% criterion level with the first eye. On the transfer-test trials, the cat performed at a 10% level with the second eye, indicating almost complete preference for the horizontal striations learned previously under food-approach conditions. On the next day, training with the second eye was begun. Due to the long latencies in performance, shock was

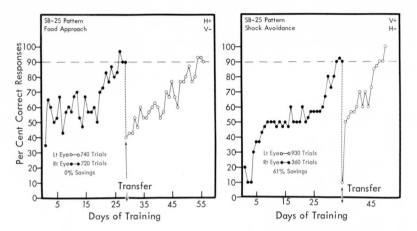

Fig. 3. Pattern discrimination learning curves for Split-brain Cat SB No. 25, showing failure of transfer to the second eye under food-approach training and successful transfer under shock-avoidance training. (Symbols as in Figure 2.)

given early in the test session. Performance on the second day increased to 50%. After this, the cat's performance steadily improved until criterion was reached within 360 trials, a savings of 61% in relearning with the second eye. This degree of savings is evidence that a high level of interocular transfer had occurred in spite of the conflict due to the reversal of the stimuli in the second training procedure. This savings with shock-avoidance training is especially significant when compared to the 0% savings shown with food-approach training. In addition, it is only 10% less than that of the Normal Cat C-2, trained in the same sequence.

Figure 4 is representative of a split-brain cat (SB No. 24), trained first with shock-avoidance motivation and then food-approach motivation. With shock-avoidance training carried out first, there is thus no conflict condition present as was true of the previous split-brain cat (SB No. 25). For this procedure, horizontal striations represented the positive stimulus. It took 1,090 trials (about 3–4 times the normal rate) for this cat's performance to reach criterion with the first eye. On the transfer-test trials with the second eye, performance was 70%. The next day, training with the second eye was started, shock being given when latencies were above 5 sec. Training with the second eye took only 80 trials to reach criterion levels, demonstrating a 93% savings in relearning or almost complete interocular transfer.

Training with food-approach motivation was carried out next. Training took 850 trials with the first eye, with vertical striations as the positive stimulus, and 960 trials or 110 trials longer with the second eye. Thus this split-brain cat demonstrated total failure of interocular transfer under conditions of food-approach motivation, while under shock-avoidance conditions transfer was almost complete.

The remaining four split-brain cats, trained with shock-avoidance motivation first and food-approach motivation second, confirm these results (see Table 1). Three of these split-brain cats performed at 80% on the first 20 transfer-test trials with the second eye, and demonstrated an 82–92% savings in relearning with the second eye. The fourth cat performed at 60% on the transfer-test trials with the second eye and showed a 68% savings in relearning. In all cases, subsequent training with food-approach motivation showed total failure of interocular transfer.

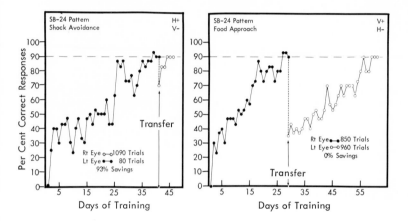

Fig. 4. Pattern discrimination learning curves for Split-brain Cat SB No. 24, showing successful transfer to the second eye under shock-avoidance training and failure to transfer under food-approach training. (Symbols as in Figure 2.)

Anatomy

Four of the six operated cats reported here are still being tested in other studies. Examination of the brains of the two remaining split-brain cats (SB No. 4 and SB No. 7) showed complete section of the optic chiasm and the corpus callosum. Pertinent histological evidence confirming complete optic chiasm section of both of these cats was obtained by examination of the retinas (see Figure 5 and Figure 6). Almost total absence of the nasal retinal ganglion cells is seen while the few remaining cells are abnormal. The temporal retinal ganglion cells on the other side are normal.

Our previous work has shown failure of interocular transfer of pattern discrimination under food-approach motivation only when there is complete section of the optic chiasm and at least the posterior portion of the corpus callosum. Therefore, it is assumed, in the present study, that the failure of transfer under food-approach motivation means successful section of the optic chiasm and at least the posterior corpus callosum. The histological analysis of all the operated animals described here will be reported in subsequent publications.

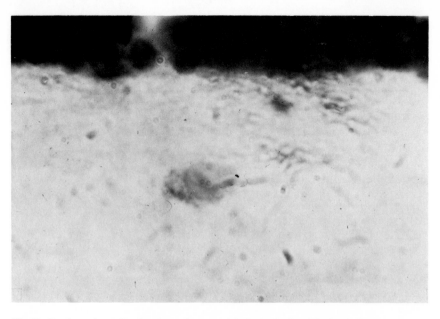

Fig. 5. Section of nasal retina from the eye of Split-brain Cat SB No. 4. (In the ganglion cell layer no normal ganglion cells are found. An occasional shrunken ghost cell, as shown above, is seen. Thionin 450X.)

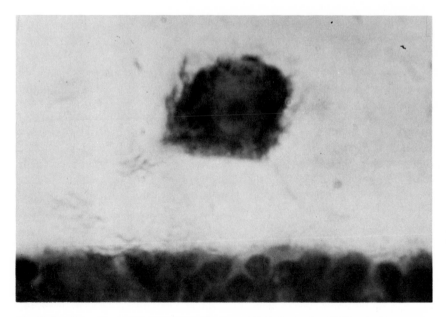

Fig. 6. Section of temporal retina from the eye of Split-brain Cat SB No. 4. (The ganglion cell layer is normal. Typical normal ganglion cell is shown above. Thionin 450X.)

DISCUSSION

That there is a high level of interocular transfer of a pattern discrimination in split-brain cats in a shock-avoidance situation demonstrates that bilateral interaction of a complex visual function can occur after section of both the corpus callosum and the optic chiasm. It is concluded that this transfer is mediated by an extracallosal, subcortical pathway which is activated by shock-avoidance but not by food-approach motivation. At present, two alternative mechanisms can be suggested.

First, in keeping with the historic concept that pattern discrimination is critically dependent upon the striate cortex, one possible explanation of these present findings would require the assumption of an extracallosal commissure, connecting the two cerebral cortices. Although no definite anatomical pathway for this mediation is known as the present time, support for this hypothesis comes from experiments by Rutledge and Kennedy (1960). Stimulating the cortex of one hemisphere and recording the electrical response of the opposite cortex, these investigators have demonstrated interhemispheric communication in the cat after section of the corpus callosum, presumbably via a multisynaptic, subcortical system.

A second, alternative, explanation of the successful interocular transfer of pattern discrimination in split-brain cats involves the role of subcortical visual areas. This alternative is based upon the idea that under shock-avoidance conditions, pattern discrimination can take place subcortically as well as cortically, and that transfer might occur through one or more subcortical commissures perhaps in the same way as the transfer of supra-threshold brightness discrimination seems to occur.

In support of this hypothesis, anatomical and electrophysiological evidence by O'Leary (1940), Bishop and Clare (1955) Barris, Ingram, and Ranson (1955), and Doty (1961), suggests a possible mechanism for the role of subcortical visual areas in the acquisition and retention of pattern discrimination.

Further evidence for believing that the midbrain may be involved in the transfer of pattern discrimination under shock-avoidance conditions is the fact that pain is represented in the midbrain (Delgado, 1955, Spiegel, Kletzkin, & Szekeley, 1954). In the present study, shock (pain) was delivered bilaterally as a reinforcing stimulus, thereby activating centers below the cortex, probably via the spino-tecto-thalamic tracts which terminate in the midbrain and thalamus. Anatomical studies of Nauta and Kuypers (1958) and Anderson and Berry (1959) show direct termination of the spino-tecto-thalamic tracts in the superior colliculi and adjacent tegmentum. Both Hayhow (1958) and Barris *et al.* (1935) showed direct termination of the optic pathways in the superior colliculi. Evidence from the anatomical studies by Altman and Carpenter (1961) demonstrates indirect input of optic pathways to the tegmentum via the tecto-reticular tracts. Thus by comparing the anatomical termination of the spino-tecto-thalamic tracts with that of the optic tracts, it can be seen that both pain and visual pathways reach the superior colliculi and adjacent tegmentum directly or indirectly. This evidence suggests that these two modalities, pain and vision, can interact in subcortical centers, and this interaction may help explain why pain (shock) is an effective stimulus in facilitating interocular transfer of pattern discrimination in split-brain cats.

Behavioral studies have also implicated subcortical areas in the acquisition of pattern discrimination. Blake (1959) showed that bilateral removal of the superior colliculi in cats resulted in complete loss of a previously learned pattern discrimination with inability to relearn the problem within the same number of trials originally required. Although Sperry *et al.* (1955) had previously reported little or no deficit in the acquisition of pattern discrimination in cats with bilateral removal of superior colliculi, recent work by Myers (1961) has shown that bilateral aspiration of the colliculus results in a mild and transient deficit of a previously learned, difficult pattern discrimination. Furthermore, when these lesions extended only slightly into the tegmentum, lying ventral to the superior colliculi, profound decrements in performance were observed. In addition, Meikle and Sprague (1962) have reported that unilateral aspiration of the superior colliculus results in visual neglect and deficient following of objects in the contralateral visual field, and in deficient tactile placing in the contralateral limbs, with reduced distractability to auditory and tactile stimuli on the contralateral side. Finally, Sprague, Chambers, and Stellar (1961) have reported that midbrain lemniscal lesions in cats resulted in increased thresholds to painful stimulation in addition to visual neglect and inattention. Taken together, these results suggest that the midbrain may be involved in pattern discrimination and other complex functions as well, and may be concerned with the interaction of the visual modality with other modalities, including pain.

In the light of the foregoing analysis of the functions of central visual mechanisms, several testable hypotheses may be derived from the fact that there is interocular transfer of pattern discrimination in split-brain cats. First, the visual cortex may not be essential for pattern discrimination under shock-avoidance conditions. Second, there must be extracallosal commissures that can mediate the interocular transfer of pattern discrimination. Third, the confluence of pain and visual pathways known to occur in the superior colliculi and adjacent tegmentum may be essential to the interocular transfer of pattern discrimination in split-brain cats, trained under shock-avoidance motivation.

REFERENCES

ALTMAN, J., & CARPENTER, M. B. Fiber projections of the superior colliculus in the cat. *J. comp. Neurol.*, 1961, **116**, 157–178.

ANDERSON, F. D., & BERRY, C. M. Degeneration studies of long ascending fibre systems in the cat brain stem. *J. comp. Neurol.*, 1959, **111**, 195–230.

BARRIS, R. W., INGRAM, W. R., & RANSON, S. W. Optic connections of the diencephalon and midbrain of the cat. *J. comp. Neurol.*, 1935, **62**, 117–153.

BISHOP, G. H., & CLARE, N. H. Organization and distribution of fibers in the optic tract of the cat. *J. comp. Neurol.*, 1955, **103**, 269–304.

BLAKE, L. The effect of lesions of the superior colliculus on brightness and pattern discrimination in the cat. *J. comp. physiol. Psychol.*, 1959, **52**, 272–278.

DELGADO, J. M. R. Cerebral structures involved in the transmission and elaboration of noxious stimulation. *J. Neurophysiol.*, 1955, **18**, 261–275.

DOTY, R. W. Remarks on the optic tectum and functional significance of the topographical aspects of the retino-cortical projection. In R. Jung & H. Kornhuber (Eds.), *The visual system: Neurophysiology and psychophysics.* Berlin: Springer-Verlag, 1961. Pp. 215–217.

GELLERMANN, L. W. Chance orders of alternating stimuli in visual discrimination experiments. *J. genet. Psychol.*, 1933, **42**, 206–208.

HAYHOW, W. R. The cytoarchitecture of the lateral geniculate body in the cat in relation to the distribution of crossed and uncrossed optic fibers. *J. comp. Neurol.*, 1958, **110**, 1.

MEIKLE, T. H., JR., & SECHZER, J. A. Interocular transfer of brightness discrimination in split-brain cats. *Science*, 1960, **132**, 734–735.

MIEKLE, T. H. JR., & SPRAGUE, J. M. Aspiration of superior colliculus in cats. *Amer. Ass. Anat.* 1962, **142**, 258.

MYERS, R. E. Interocular transfer of pattern discrimination in cats following section of crossed optic fibers. *J. comp. physiol. Psychol.*, 1955, **48**, 470–473.

MYERS, R. E. Function of corpus callosum in interocular transfer. *Brain*, 1956, **79**, 358–363.

MYERS, R. E. Interhemispheric communication through the corpus callosum: Limitations under conditions of conflict. *J. comp. physiol. Psychol.*, 1959, **52**, 6–9.

MYERS, R. E. Perceptual effects of tectal lesions. *Federat. Proc.*, 1961, **20**, 336.

NAUTA, W. J. H., & KUYPERS, G. J. M. Some ascending pathways in the brain stem reticular formation. In H. H. Jasper, L. D. Proctor, R. S. Knighton, W. C. Noshay, & R. T. Costello (Eds,) *Reticular formation of the brain.* Boston: Little, Brown, 1958. Pp. 3–31.

O'LEARY, J. L. A structural analysis of the lateral geniculate nucleus of the cat. *J. comp. Neurol.*, 1940, **73**, 405–430.

RUTLEDGE, L. T., & KENNEDY, T. T. Extracallosal delayed responses to cortical stimulation in the chloralosed cat. *J. Neurophysiol.*, 1960, **23**, 188–196.

SPERRY, R. W., MINER, N., & MYERS, R. E. Visual pattern perception following subpial splicing and tantalum wire implantations in the visual cortex. *J. comp. physiol. Psychol.*, 1955, **48**, 50–58.

SPIEGEL, E. A., KLETZKIN, M., & SZEKELEY, E. G. Pain reactions upon stimulation of the tectum mesencephali. *J. Neuropathol. exp. Neurol.*, 1954, **13**, 212–220.

SPRAGUE, J. M., CHAMBERS, W. W., & STELLAR, E. Attentive, affective and adaptive behavior in the cat. *Science*, 1961, **133**, 165–174.

SPRAGUE, J. M., LEVITT, M., ROBSON, K., LIU, C. N., STELLAR, E., & CHAMBERS, W. A neuroanatomical and behavioral analysis of the syndromes resulting from midbrain lemniscal and reticular lesions in the cat. *Arch. Ital. Biol.*, 1963, **101**, 225–295.

IV

ELECTRO-PHYSIOLOGICAL APPROACHES TO LEARNING AND MEMORY

The study of bioelectric activity has provided virtually all our information on how the nervous system processes sensory information and how it programs motor activity. Thus, it is reasonable to suppose that electrophysiology would provide insights into the mechanisms of information storage and retrieval in the nervous system. Two of the principal electrophysiological approaches to learning and memory are represented in this section, one involving electrical recording and the other involving electrical stimulation. The first approach is to study the effect of experience on the electrical activity of the brain. The second approach is to bypass the sensory pathways and present conditioned or unconditioned stimuli directly to the central nervous system by means of electrical stimulation.

Study of conditioning of electrical activity started with an apparatus failure. In the 1930s, Durup and Fessard (1935) were investigating the EEG desynchronization produced by a flash. They photographed cortical potentials on an oscilloscope with a camera synchronized to the flash. Occasionally the flash failed and the camera clicked. They noticed that the click alone produced the same local desynchronization of striate cortex as the light had. Since the click produced desynchronization only after repeated pairing with the light and soon failed to do so after repeated presentations without the light, Durup and Fessard realized that they had demonstrated classical conditioning and extinction of cortical arousal. In the decades that followed, virtually every type of classical conditioning of EEG (for example, delayed, trace, and differential conditioning) was obtained in both man and animals (see, for example, Jasper and Shagass, 1941 ; Morrell and Jasper, 1956). Furthermore, these conditioned electrical responses tended to precede conditioned behavioral responses in those experiments in which electrical and behavioral conditioning were studied simultaneously.

One difficulty with this technique is that although the conditioned cortical response was believed to be "representational" of the conditioned stimulus, it was a rather unspecific response. This problem was ameliorated by the use of an intermittent conditioned stimulus—termed a *tracer conditioned stimulus* because the evoked neural signals could be followed through the brain in the same manner as a radioactive tracer can be followed through a chemical process. Following this analogy, responses in the brain at the frequency of the tracer stimulus were termed *labeled responses*. The presence of labeled responses in a particular structure was believed by several groups of investigators to reflect signal information in that structure and the formation of the "temporary connections" underlying conditioning (see John, 1967).

The study by Chow, Dement, and John (see page 251) provides an ingenious test of the hypothesis that the labeled conditioned response carries information or is "representational." They trained cats to make an avoidance response to presentation of a flickering light. When the cats were well trained, the conditioning stimulus (CS) produced a repetitive discharge in striate cortex which preceded the behavioral response. In another situation, they paired a tone (now the CS) with the flickering light (now the UCS—unconditioned stimulus) until the tone elicited the repetitive cortical response formerly produced by the light. Then they returned the cats to the avoidance situation and presented the tone alone. Although the tone elicited the "labeled" response, it was not followed by an avoidance response, thereby suggesting that the labeled response was not "representational" and did not reflect a "temporary connection." Because of this and other difficulties with the interpretation of studies of conditioned EEG and of EEG correlates of behavioral conditioning and with the growth of microphysiological technique, many investigators turned to single-unit studies in their search for physiological mechanisms in learning.

Several workers have shown that the activity of single units can be modified by procedures analogous to classical conditioning (for example, Yoshii and Ogura, 1960; Kamikawa *et al.*, 1964). In one of the most interesting of these studies to appear, Morrell (see page 264) investigated plasticity of units in the visual cortex of the cat. Units in this area are known to respond to auditory and tactile stimuli (for example, Murata *et al.*, 1965) as well as to highly specific visual stimuli as shown by Hubel and Wiesel (1962). For about one-tenth of the units sampled, Morrell showed that the response pattern to visual stimuli could be modified by the immediately prior experience of the cell. What role, if any, these "plastic units" play in behavioral learning is still obscure, but, as Morrell points out, it has become clear that populations of plastic units seem to exist in many parts of the nervous system, in "specific" as well as "nonspecific" areas and in "higher regions" as well as relatively "low" ones. Morrell's study also illustrates an important fact about sensory coding. Polymodal cells are not necessarily nonspecific: the response pattern of Morrell's cells to visual stimuli was usually quite different from their response to auditory stimuli or to simultaneous visual and auditory stimulation.

The next selection, by Olds (see page 282), is a similarly brilliant demonstration of plasticity in the central nervous system. Olds succeeded in instrumentally (operantly) conditioning single units in awake rats. By presenting food to the rat following a burst of firing of certain units, he was able to increase their firing rate. In the beginning of these studies he encountered a fascinating obstacle. As he reinforced the firing of a particular unit, the incidence of a specific behavioral response of the rat increased—for example, looking at a light or making a particular leg movement. That is, it appeared that Olds was reinforcing a pattern of gross behavior that caused an increase in firing of the unit. He tried to eliminate this problem by presenting reinforcement only when the unit fired and the rat did not move. As he points out at the end of the selection, Olds seems to be attempting to reinforce the "willing" or intention of the brain to fire a particular unit. It is not clear how he will know when he has achieved this extraordinary goal.

The second approach to the electrophysiology of learning, presentation of the CS or UCS directly to the brain, is almost as old as the technique of brain stimulation itself (Zeigler, 1957). Here the aim seems to be to bypass the sensory and motor pathways and the complications of motivation and get directly to the "neural core" of conditioning. Most of these experiments involve classical conditioning, which is presumed to involve some interaction or "linkage" of the CS and UCS. If both the CS and UCS could be presented by direct brain stimulation, it might be possible to locate the site of this "linkage" by cutting the connections between the stimulation points.

In the first such successful study Loucks (1938) was able to obtain both limb and salivary classical conditioning with electrical stimulation of the cerebral cortex as the CS. More recent experiments by Giurgea and Doty using electrical stimulation as the CS are described in Doty's article "Conditioned reflexes formed and evoked by brain stimulation" (see page 292).

Demonstration that the UCS could be directly presented to the brain was much more difficult. In this paradigm, the CS is a peripheral stimulus such as a tone, and UCS is an electrical stimulus to the central nervous system that produces a motor response. Loucks (1935) tried very hard and failed to condition the leg flexion produced by direct motor cortex stimulation. Subsequently many other workers also tried and failed to condition a response produced by direct cortical stimulation. Finally, Giurgea, a Rumanian neurophysiologist, succeeded. In fact, he obtained excellent conditioning even when both the CS and UCS were electrical stimulation of the cortex. The crucial difference between Giurgea's and all the previous procedures was the intertrial interval. Previous workers had used intertrial intervals under two minutes. Giurgea's were from 3 to 5 min., and he found that even well-established CR's would extinguish when the intertrial interval was reduced to 2 min. Later, Giurgea visited Doty's laboratory in America, and some of their joint work in which both the CS and UCS are presented directly to the cortex is described in Doty's (1961) article reprinted in this volume (see page 292). Subsequent work has revealed that subcortical but not intracortical connections are crucial to conditioned reflexes established in this manner (Rutledge and Doty, 1962).

C.G.G.

REFERENCES

DURUP, G., & FESSARD, A. L'électro-encéphalogramme de l'homme. *Année Psychol.*, 1935, **36**, 1–32.

HUBEL, D. H., & WIESEL, T. N. Receptive fields, binocular interaction and functional architecture in the cat's visual cortex. *J. Physiol.*, 1962, **160**, 106–154.

JASPER, H. H., & SHAGASS, C. Conditioning the occipital alpha rhythm in man. *J. Exp. Psychol.*, 1941, **28**, 373–388.

JOHN, E. R. *Mechanisms of memory.* New York: Academic Press, 1967.

KAMIKAWA, K., MCILWAIN, J. T., & ADEY, W. R. Response patterns of thalamic neurons during classical conditioning. *EEG Clin. Neurophysiol.*, 1964, & **17**, 485–496.

LOUCKS, R. B. The experimental delimitation of neural structures essential for learning: The attempt to condition striped muscle responses with faradization of the Sigmond gyri. *J. Psychol.*, 1935, **1**, 5–44.

LOUCKS, R. B. Studies of neural structures essential for learning. II. The conditioning of salivary and striped muscle responses to faradization of cortical sensory elements and action of sleep upon such mechanisms. *J. Comp. Psychol.*, 1938, **25**, 315–332.

MORRELL, F., & JASPER, H. H. Electroencephalographic studies of the formation of temporary connections in the brain. *EEG Clin. Neurophysiol.*, 1956, **8**, 201–215.

MURATA, K., CRAMER, H., & BACH-Y-RITA, P. Neuronal convergence of noxious, acoustic and visual stimuli in the visual cortex of the cat. *J. Neurophysiol.*, 1965, **28**, 1223–1240.

RUTLEDGE, L. R., & DOTY, R. W. Surgical interference with pathways mediating responses conditioned to cortical stimulation. *Exp. Neurol.*, 1962, **6**, 478–491.

YOSHII, N., & OGURA, N. Studies on the unit discharge of brainstem reticular formation in the cat. *Med. J. Osaka Univ.*, 1960, **11**, 1–17.

ZEIGLER, H. P. Electrical stimulation of the brain and the psychophysiology of learning and motivation. *Psychol. Bull.*, 1957, **54**, 363–382.

Conditioned Electrocorticographic Potentials and Behavioral Avoidance Response in Cat

Kao Liang Chow,
W. C. Dement,
and E. Roy John

Conditioning of human electroencephalographic (EEG) responses by the Pavlovian procedure has been reported many times. The arresting or blocking of the occipital alpha rhythm in response to visual stimuli has been used as the unconditioned response (UR) to form various types of Pavlovian conditioning (2, 3, 8), and has been employed as the conditioned response (CR) to demonstrate inhibitory processes during extinction, delayed and differential conditioning (1, 6, 7). Recently, Morrell *et al.* (4, 5) reported conditioning of electrical responses of the brain in unanesthetized monkeys. They used flickering light as the unconditioned stimulus (US). Depending on the frequency of the flicker, the UR was either a desynchronization or "activation" of the occipital rhythms (flicker frequency about 500 per sec.), or a photic driving, *i.e.*, repetitive discharge having the same frequency as that of the stimulus (flicker frequency about 6–12 per sec.). By pairing a low-frequency flicker light as the US and a tone as the conditioning stimulus (CS), they demonstrated successive stages in the formation of conditioned electrical responses.

From *Journal of Neurophysiology*, 1957, **20**, 482–493. Reprinted with permission of the publisher and authors. This study was supported by research grants B-801 from the National Institute of Neurological Diseases and Blindness of the National Institutes of Health; the Fund for Neurobiology, Inc.; and the Wallace C. and Clara M. Abbott Memorial Fund of the University of Chicago.

At the beginning of conditioning, the tone elicits a generalized desynchronization of the whole cortex. Later the CR is a localized occipital repetitive discharge with a frequency similar to the US. Finally, the tone initiates a localized desynchronization of the occipital area.

In all these studies, the conditioned electrical potentials were assumed to indicate the formation of some sort of temporary connections in the brain. By eliminating the behavioral changes in a conditioned reflex, such potentials provide a simpler phenomenon than the behavioral learning process. The latter presumably also depends on the creation or alteration of neural connections. Whether the conditioned electrical response of the brain is comparable to or a part of behavioral learning, however, has yet to be determined. If both are expressions of the same neural processes and the brain potentials either initiate or accompany the learned behavior, then cortical conditioning in animals may provide a more direct means for experimental analysis of the neural substrate of learning than has hitherto been available.

The present study attempts to clarify the relationship between such " cortical conditioning " and overt behavioral conditioning. Specifically, we have inquired whether a sensory stimulus which, through the cortical conditioning process, has acquired the ability to elicit central electrical responses characteristically evoked by a second sensory stimulus, has simultaneously acquired the ability to elicit overt behavioral responses that have been associated, through conventional conditioning techniques, with that second stimulus. As the overt behavioral response for this investigation we chose conditioned avoidance of a flashing light (flicker). For the cortical conditioning, the procedure of Morrell and Jasper (4) was adopted.

First, cats were trained to react, by crossing from one to the other compartment in a double grill box, to a low-frequency flicker which was always followed by electric shock. ECG records taken at the completion of this training indicate that the flicker invariably provoked repetitive discharge or photic driving in addition to the behavioral crossing.

Second, while these animals were restrained in a holder, a conditioned electrocorticographic (ECG) response was established by presenting paired tone and flicker repeatedly. After such conditioning, the tone itself would elicit either localized photic driving or localized desynchronization of the occipital region.

Third and finally, the cats were placed in the double grill box again and the tone alone was presented. Both ECG and behavioral responses were recorded to determine whether the tone by itself would cause ECG changes alone, or behavioral crossing alone, or ECG changes preceding behavioral crossing. Only the last result would suggest the possibility that conditioned ECG potentials are sufficient to initiate the behavioral avoidance response.

METHODS

APPARATUS

A. PHOTIC STIMULATOR. The flicker was produced by a specially constructed photic stimulator which provided either constant light or flicker. Frequency of flicker was continuously variable. No audible clicks accompanied the light flashes. The light source was a 24-inch fluorescent tube encased in an aluminum reflector. Intensity may be controlled by placing suitable masks in front of the tube. The apparatus consisted of a variable speed motor driving a microswitch by means of a cam. The microswitch interrupted the current across the tube. The current was rectified, filtered, and supplied by a high-voltage transformer which in turn was connected to a 115 V., 60-cycle source.

B. TONE GENERATOR. The tone was generated by a permanent magnet 10-inch loudspeaker activated by 115 V., 60-cycle alternating current through a rheostat and transformer. A noiseless mercury switch in the adjacent room initiated and terminated the stimulus.

C. DOUBLE GRILL BOX AND ELECTRIC SHOCK. The double grill box was a rectangular box, $16 \times 42 \times 20$ inches, made of plywood on three sides. The top had an opening 24×6 inches, fitted with transparent lucite which served as a window to admit light from the photic stimulator resting on it. The front panel of the box was made of lucite sheet and the bottom was of 0.25 inch brass rods spaced 1 inch apart from each other. A central partition divided the box into two equal compartments. Through a 15×10 inch rectangular opening in the partition, the animal could move from one compartment to the other. The bottom of each compartment was connected separately to the shock apparatus. By a simple switch arrangement, voltage may be applied to the brass grills of either one of the two compartments. The pattern of electrical connections of the individual rods in each grill were changed to insure effective shocks to the animal. The electric shock was delivered through a model 228 stimulator made by C. J. Applegate Company, which gives constant current, continuous shock ranging from 1 mA. to 6 mA. The whole box was shielded with fine wire mesh to facilitate ECG recordings.

D. ECG RECORDING APPARATUS. For ECG conditioning, the cat was restrained in the animal holder which consisted of a small wooden box into which the cat was fitted tightly and held immovable, with only its head exposed outside. A Grass model III four-channel EEG machine was used. One of the pens was connected to a photocell to register the flicker. On and off of tone was marked on the record manually. Both bipolar and monopolar recordings with the indifferent electrode at the vertex of the skull were used.

SUBJECTS AND PROCEDURE

Three adult cats served as subjects. All experiments were conducted with the cats in a dark room which contained the double grill box, fluorescent bulb of the photic stimulator, and the loud-speaker. The only illumination in this room was provided by the fluorescent light. The experimenters stayed in an adjacent room, in which the ECG machine and the controls for flicker, tone, and shock were placed. The animals were observed through a tiny glass window in the door between the two rooms. All the cats were treated according to the following schedule.

A. CONDITIONED AVOIDANCE TRAINING. An instrumental conditioning procedure was used. The cat was put into the double grill box. The fluorescent bulb of the photic stimulator was placed either on top or in front of the box. The fluorescent light was on continuously. To start a trial, the experimenter changed the continuous light to repetitive flashes with a frequency around 6 per sec., and kept this flicker on for 15 sec. At the end of this period, if the cat did not move into the other compartment of the box, the experimenter applied an electric current to the brass grill of the compartment which contained the animal. This shock was repeatedly applied until the cat crossed to the other compartment. The strength of the shock was adjusted to be just sufficient to force the animal to jump. The intensity of shock required to induce this reponse varied from 1 mA. to 4 mA. A correct response consisted of the animal moving from its initial position into the other compartment within the 15 sec. flicker period. Thus, flicker served as the CS for the cat to cross in order to avoid the shock. Fifteen trials were given in each session. The time interval between trials varied randomly from 10 to 50 sec. in order to avoid cyclic conditioning. Either one or two training sessions was given daily with only occasional omissions. The criterion of learning was 90 per cent correct responses in four consecutive sessions with a total of 60 trials. No ECG recordings were made during this training period.

B. OPERATION. After the animals reached criterion in the conditioned avoidance training, they were subjected to surgery under pentobarbital anesthesia with aseptic technique. A focal epileptogenic lesion was made and cortical electrodes were implanted. Needle electrodes, insulated except for the tip, were fixed with dental cement through holes drilled in the skull. The tip of the needle pricked through the dura and the superficial surface of the cortex. Four electrodes were implanted; one on each of the two sensorimotor regions and the two occipital areas. An indifferent electrode was cemented to the vertex of the skull. All these electrodes were led out through openings in the skin of the neck or top of the head, and attached to a harness around the cat's body from which they could be easily connected to the sockets of a flexible cable for ECG recordings. For the epileptogenic cortical lesion, a small opening was made over the right occipital region. After the dura was reflected, a generous amount of ethyl chloride was sprayed on the cortex. This method proved to be a very effective way to induce an epileptogenic focus that lasted up to three months. The reason for making such a lesion was that it facilitates the process of ECG conditioning and renders the established CR more stable.[1]

C. POSTOPERATIVE TESTING OF CONDITIONED AVOIDANCE RESPONSE. Beginning on the third day after operation, the cats were given three or four more sessions of conditioned avoidance training. These tests were necessary to insure that the animals still performed at the 90 per cent level and that the CR was not disturbed by the surgery.

---

[1] We are indebted to Dr. Frank Morrell who suggested this method of producing cortical lesions and demonstrated the technique of electrographic conditioning.

D. ECG CONDITIONING AND TEST OF TRANSFER. These two steps were conducted successively in one experimental session. All sessions were given in the evening. A 20-minute interval separated sessions when more than one was scheduled in the same evening. Cat No. 1 had two such experimental sessions; one was on the fifth and the other on the sixth postoperative day. Cat No. 2 had three sessions; the first was on the fifth and the second and third on the sixth postoperative day. Only conditioned localized repetitive discharge was established in these two cats. Cat No. 3 had four sessions; the first two were conducted on the sixth and the last two on the seventh and ninth postoperative days. Conditioned localized repetitive discharge was achieved with cat No. 3 during the first two sessions, and localized desynchronization during the last two sessions. The identical procedure was employed in each session. Thus, repeatable results were obtained for each cat. The successive steps used in each experimental session were as follows:

Cat in double grill box:

1. The conditioned avoidance response was tested by presenting flicker alone—5 trials.

2. The conditioned avoidance response was tested by presenting flicker alone and ECG was recorded at the same time—5 trials.

3. Tone alone was presented for 15 sec., during which period both behavior and ECG were recorded—5 trials.

Cat in animal holder with ECG recording:

4. Flicker of the same frequency as that used in the conditioned avoidance response was presented and the photic driving in ECG was recorded— 5 trials.

5. Tone alone was presented for 15 sec.—5 trials.

6. *ECG conditioning.* Paired tone and flicker were presented repeatedly. For each trial, the tone was turned on 2 sec. before the onset of the flicker and kept on throughout the duration of the latter. The flicker lasted 5 sec. Time intervals between trials varied from 15 to 30 sec. ECG was taken during the entire period. The criterion for conditioning was that the tone elicited either localized frequency specific, repetitive discharge, or localized desynchronization before the onset of the flicker stimulus, in two successive trials.

Cat in double grill box with ECG recording:

7. *Test of transfer.* As soon as the criterion for ECG conditioning was reached, the cat was moved quickly into the double grill box. Five trials of tone alone were given for 10 sec. to cat No. 1 and for 15 sec. to cats No. 2 and 3. ECG and behavioral changes were recorded.

8. Five trials of flicker alone were given finally to test that the conditioned avoidance response to flicker remained undisturbed.

RESULTS

Conditioned Avoidance Learning and Postoperative Retention

The learning scores of the three cats on the conditioned avoidance response were: No. 1, 360 trials and 198 errors; No. 2, 465 trials and 344 errors; No. 3, 420 trials and 172 errors. These scores did not include the criterion trials. For the cat, conditioning avoidance of flicker is more difficult than conditioning avoidance of sound. Our data on other cats indicated that they took about 150 trials to learn a conditioned avoidance response to a buzzer under otherwise identical conditions, or about one-third as many trials as with flicker. All three cats retained the conditioned avoidance response after the operation. They made a few errors when tested on the second or third day after operation, but reached 90 per cent correct performance in three consecutive sessions immediately afterwards. The unilateral irritative occipital lesion did not significantly affect the retention of this habit.

Pre-Conditioning Testing with Flicker Light Alone or Tone Alone

ECG tracings taken when the cat was in the double grill box before ECG conditioning indicated that the flicker light always elicited repetitive discharge or photic driving in the ECG. The cat's behavioral response to the flicker light, crossing from one compartment to the other in the grill box, *followed* such repetitive discharge. This result was obtained 43 times out of 45 trials given to the three cats (Table 1). Figure 1a shows the ECG tracings of the cat's response to flicker light before ECG conditioning. The ECG started with repetitive discharge and was disrupted by the cat's crossing from one compartment to the other. The arrow indicates the artifact caused by the cat's movements.

None of the cats showed locomotion and crossing behavior in the double grill box in response to the tone alone before the ECG conditioning. ECG recordings during such trials indicated a generalized desynchronization pattern in early trials which adapted to a normal resting record in later ones. Figure 1b illustrates ECG response of the cat in the grill box to tone alone before conditioning. Similar behavioral and ECG results were obtained in 45 trials given to the three cats in nine sessions (Table 1). An additional 45 ECG recordings to tone alone were obtained while the cats were restrained in the animal holder. Again, in these records, there were either general desynchronization or normal resting potentials. In no instance did the tone alone before ECG conditioning evoke repetitive discharge or localized desynchronization.

ECG Conditioning

The process of ECG conditioning in the cat resembled that described for the monkey (4). The tone was presented to the cat, restrained in the animal

Table 1 Summary of Data of ECG Conditioning and Test of Transfer[a]

CAT NO.	SESSION	PRE-CONDITION TESTING				ECG CONDITIONING TRIALS INCLUDING CRITERION	TEST OF TRANSFER, TONE ALONE		RETENTION TEST, FLICKER ALONE	
		FLICKER ALONE		TONE ALONE						
		C	D	C	D		C	D	C	D
1	1	5	5	0	0	21	0	4	5	5
	2	5	5	0	0	13	0	4	4	5
2	1	5	5	0	0	64	0	4	5	5
	2	5	5	0	0	15	0	2	5	5
	3	5	5	0	0	14	0	3	5	5
3	1	5	5	0	0	66	0	3	3	5
	2	5	5	0	0	61	0	4	5	5
	3	3	5	0	0	64	0	3	3	5
	4	5	5	0	0	35	0	2	4	5

[a] C, number of behavioral crossings in 5 trials; D, number of occurrences of photic driving in 5 ECG recordings. Sessions No. 3 and 4 in cat No. 3 were conditioned localized desynchronization experiments.

holder, 2 sec. before the flicker and lasted through the 5 sec. duration of the latter. After such combined stimuli were presented repeatedly to the cat, the tone by itself caused ECG changes prior to the onset of the flicker light. It elicited, first, generalized desynchronization of all cortical regions; second, localized frequency specific, repetitive discharge confined to the occipital region; and finally, localized desynchronization confined to the occipital region. All these conditioned ECG changes were not stable. They would be present in one trial, disappear for a few trials, and then reappear again. Also, the ECG might show localized desynchronization in one trial but reverse back to localized repetitive discharge in the next. For these reasons, the number of trials needed to reach the criterion did not truly represent the rate of conditioning, since the absolute end point had not been reached. In addition, the conditioned ECG potentials showed rapid extinction after a short time.

Localized repetitive discharge was conditioned seven times in the three cats. The number of trials needed, including the criterion trials, were shown in Table 1. These scores indicate various degrees of saving or retention of the conditioned response from one training session to the next in the same cat. Figure 1c shows the ECG record of a trial at the beginning of conditioning of cat No. 3, session 2. Figure 1d illustrates the conditioned generalized desynchronization. In Fig. 2a, 1 and 2 show two criterion trials. Figure 2b shows a bipolar recording of conditioned repetitive discharge in cat No. 1. Figure 2c illustrates bilateral conditioned repetitive discharge in the occipital

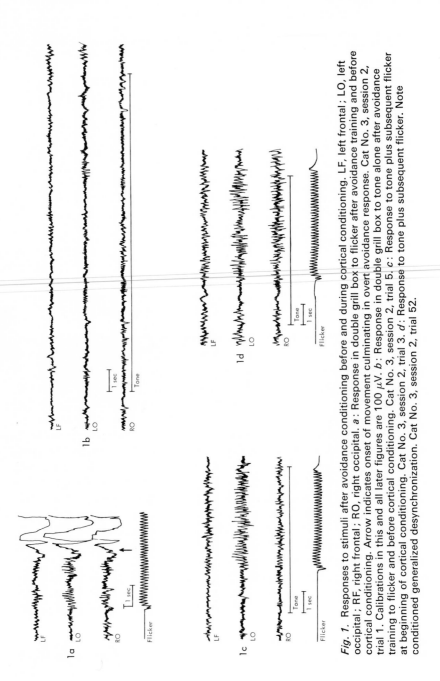

Fig. 1. Responses to stimuli after avoidance conditioning before and during cortical conditioning. LF, left occipital; RF, right frontal; RO, right occipital. *a*: Response in double grill box to flicker after avoidance training and before cortical conditioning. Arrow indicates onset of movement culminating in overt avoidance response. Cat No. 3, session 2, trial 1. Calibrations in this and all later figures are 100 μV. *b*: Response in double grill box to tone alone after avoidance training to flicker and before cortical conditioning. Cat No. 3, session 2, trial 5. *c*: Response to tone plus subsequent flicker at beginning of cortical conditioning. Cat No. 3, session 2, trial 3. *d*: Response to tone plus subsequent flicker. Note conditioned generalized desynchronization. Cat No. 3, session 2, trial 52.

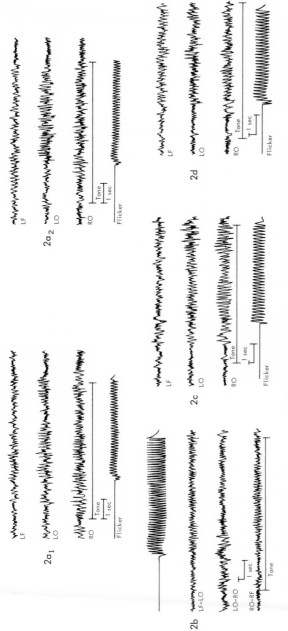

Fig. 2. Responses to stimuli after avoidance conditioning and cortical conditioning. Calibration, 100 µV. a_1, a_2: Criterion trials after cortical conditioning. Note onset of conditioned repetitive discharge to tone alone before onset of flicker in both occipital leads in a_1 and in right occipital lead in a_2. Cat No. 3, session 2, trials 60 and 61. *b*: Bipolar recording of conditioned repetitive discharge to tone after cortical conditioning. Note onset of discharge before presentation of flicker. Cat No. 1, session 2, trial 13. *c*: Bilateral conditioned repetitive discharge to tone alone before presentation of flicker. Cat No. 2, session 2, trial 15. *d*: Conditioned localized desynchronization in occipital region on presentation of tone alone. Cat No. 3, session 3, trial 64.

region of cat No. 2. In general, the conditioned repetitive discharges were more pronounced or confined to the right occipital area where the irritative cortical lesion was placed. Conditioned localized desynchronization was established twice, in cat No. 3 only. Figure 2d shows local desynchronization confined to the occipital region. Sometimes this local blocking appeared unilaterally. In such cases, it was restricted to the left occipital cortex, the side that had no irritative lesion.

Test of Transfer

After a conditioned ECG response was established, the cat was moved into the double grill box for the transfer test. Tone alone was presented to test whether the conditioned cortical potentials evoked by the tone would be accompanied by the conditioned avoidance behavior. Twenty-four out of the 35 such test trials showed local repetitive discharge, but in no trial with tone alone did the cat cross to the other compartment in the double grill box (Table 1). Figure 3a shows such a trial with tone alone for 15 sec. in cat No. 3. The conditioned repetitive discharge occurred in two brief bursts, and the cat remained quiescent during this period. Figure 3b shows a bipolar recording of cat No. 1, which was taken at the same session as 2b. The tone was on for 10 sec. and evoked a long period of repetitive discharge but no behavioral crossing. Figure 3c, taken at the same session as 2c, presents a 15 sec. record of tone alone in cat No. 2. All the conditioned repetitive discharge occurred only in short periods and did not last throughout the duration of the tone.

Ten test trials with tone alone were given to cat No. 3 in two sessions after a conditioned localized desynchronization was established. Similarly, the tone evoked localized blocking in 5 out of 10 trials, but did not stimulate the cat to cross the compartment in any of the test trials. Figure 3d shows the recurrence of the localized desynchronization in the occipital region during the 15 sec. test period.

Retention Test of Conditioned Avoidance Response

After the cats failed to manifest transfer of the conditioned avoidance response to tone alone, they were presented with flicker again to test retention of the conditioned avoidance response. Out of 45 such test trials in nine sessions, the cats crossed in the double grill box 39 times (Table 1). Thus, the failure of the cortical conditioning procedure to establish functional equivalence of the tone and the flashing light with respect to this overt behavioral response was not due to lack of retention of the conditioned avoidance response. Figure 3e shows the retention test trial 1 of cat No. 3, session 2. The arrow indicates when the cat started to cross.

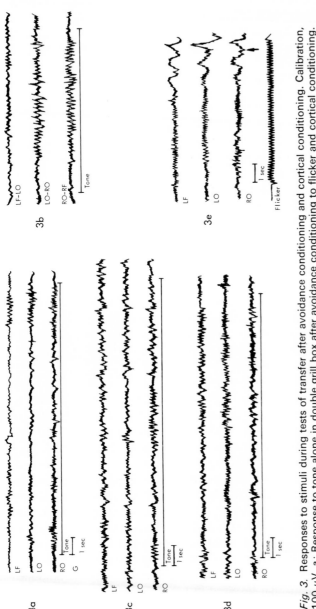

Fig. 3. Responses to stimuli during tests of transfer after avoidance conditioning and cortical conditioning. Calibration, 100 μV. *a*: Response to tone alone in double grill box after avoidance conditioning to flicker and cortical conditioning. Note that conditioned repetitive discharge occurs in two brief bursts rather than throughout period. Cat remains quiescent throughout. Cat No. 3, session 2, trial 3. *b*: Bipolar record of response to tone alone in double grill box after avoidance conditioning to flicker and cortical conditioning. Note long period of conditioned repetitive discharge during which cat did not manifest overt avoidance response. Cat No. 1, session 2, trial 5 (same session as 2*b*). *c*: Response to tone alone in double grill box after avoidance conditioning to flicker and cortical conditioning. Note that conditioned repetitive discharge occurs only in short bursts rather than throughout duration of tone. Cat remains quiescent throughout. Cat No. 2, session 2, trial 3 (same session as 2*c*). *d*: Record of conditioned localized desynchronization to tone alone in double grill box after avoidance conditioning to flicker and cortical conditioning. Cat remained quiescent during this period. Cat No. 3, session 3, trial 1. *e*: Record of response to flicker alone in double grill box after avoidance conditioning to flicker and cortical conditioning and test of response to tone in double grill box. Arrow indicates beginning of overt avoidance response, showing retention of response. Cat No. 3, session 2, trial 1.

DISCUSSION

The present results demonstrate that a conditioned ECG response cannot be readily transferred to a conditioned avoidance response. The establishment of partial equivalence between two different stimuli via cortical conditioning, using the more or less similar electrical responses to both stimuli as the indicator, is not sufficient to establish overt behavioral equivalence between these stimuli, using the manifestation of the conditioned avoidance response as the behavioral criterion.

To establish the conditioned avoidance response, flicker which elicited repetitive discharge in the ECG was repeatedly paired with a shock until the light by itself stimulated the cat to cross the compartment in a double grill box. To establish the cortical conditioning, a tone was paired repeatedly with flashing light (flicker) which elicited repetitive discharge in the ECG, until the tone by itself evoked either localized repetitive discharge or localized desynchronization in the ECG of a cat restrained in an animal holder. In spite of the existence of a common link (the flicker and its ECG potentials) between these two separate conditioned habits in the same cat, the tone alone would not initiate the behavioral crossing. This lack of transfer indicates that the conditioned ECG potentials were not sufficient for the occurrence of the avoidance behavior. This does not deny, however, the possibility of some other behavioral correlates of the conditioned ECG that were not apparent in our tests. Further, the conditioned ECG might influence behavior in a graded way which cannot be measured in our tests, in which an "all or none" behavioral response was required. If any latent effect of ECG conditioning occurred, then a cat with a pre-established, conditioned ECG potential should learn a conditioned avoidance response to tone faster than another cat without such ECG conditioning.

The process of ECG conditioning in the cats of the present study confirms that reported for the monkey. The conditioned ECG responses could be established within a few trials, and passed through three stages: generalized desynchronization, localized repetitive discharge, and localized desynchronization. These responses were not stable, and were easily extinguished. They appeared usually in short bursts during the presence of the CS rather than throughout its duration. These characteristics, plus the fact that the conditioned ECG responses were not followed by behavioral responses suggest that the former are not comparable to behavioral learning. One obvious difference is the larger number of trials needed in animal behavioral learning processes, and another is that a learned behavior is retained by the animal for a longer time. Thus, it remains in doubt whether the neural mechanism of temporal connection formation which is expressed in the conditioned ECG process is similar to that involved in behavioral learning. The former may not be a prototype, enabling more direct neurological study of the latter.

It should be noted that a unilateral irritative lesion facilitates ECG conditioning in our experiments. The cortical potentials of cats without such lesions are difficult or require more trials to be conditioned. In the monkey, a cortical lesion made by local application of alumina hydroxide cream hinders cortical conditioning (5). Moreover, the present results show that conditioned repetitive discharge tends to appear at the same side of the cortical lesion, but the conditioned local desynchronization, at the side opposite the lesion. The mechanisms responsible for these results and the functional significance of the conditioned ECG potentials await further investigation.

SUMMARY

Three adult cats were first trained to conditioned avoidance response in a double grill box. A flashing light (flicker) was the CS, and electric shock the US. The former evoked photic driving in the ECG and the latter forced the cat to cross over to another compartment in the box. After repeatedly paired presentation, the flicker by itself elicited both the ECG repetitive discharge and the behavioral crossing. These cats were then trained to a conditioned ECG response in an animal holder. A tone was the CS and the flicker light the US. The conditioned ECG response to tone alone was established through the following stages; first, generalized desynchronization; second, localized frequency specific, repetitive discharge in the occipital region; and finally, localized desynchronization in the occipital region. After the cats had both these conditioned responses they were put into the double grill box to test whether the conditioned ECG potential would be associated with behavioral response. Tone alone was presented and evoked only the ECG changes but not behavioral crossing. It was concluded that the conditioned ECG potentials were not sufficient to elicit overt behavior. The relation of the conditioned ECG response to behavioral learning is discussed.

REFERENCES

1. IWAMA, K. Delayed conditioned reflex in man and brain waves. *Tohoku J. exp. Med.*, 1950, **52** : 53–63.
2. JASPER, H. H., and SHAGASS, C. Conditioning the occipital alpha rhythm in man. *J. exp. Psychol.*, 1941, **26** : 373–388.
3. KNOTT, J. R., and HENRY, C. E. The conditioning of the blocking of the human electroencephalogram. *J. exp. Psychol.*, 1941, **28** : 134–144.
4. MORRELL, F., and JASPER, H. H. Electrographic studies of the formation of temporary connections in the brain. *EEG clin. Neurophysiol.*, 1956, **8** : 201–215.
5. MORRELL, F., ROBERTS, L., and JASPER, H. H. Effect of focal epileptogenic lesions and their ablation upon conditioned electrical responses of the brain in the monkey. *EEG clin. Neurophysiol.*, 1956, **8** : 217–236.
6. MORRELL, F., and ROSS, M. Central inhibition in cortical conditioned reflexes. *Arch. Neurol. Psychiat.*, Chicago, 1953, **70** : 611–616.

7. MOTOKAWA, K. Electroencephalograms of man in the generalization and differentiation of conditioned reflexes. *Tohoku J. exp. Med.*, 1949, **50**: 225–234.

8. TRAVIS, L. E., and EGAN, J. B. Conditioning of the electrical response of the cortex. *J. exp. Psychol.*, 1938, **22**: 524–531.

Effect of Prior Experience on the Firing Pattern of Visual Cortical Units

F. Morrell

SENSORY CODING IN SINGLE NEURONS

The mammalian visual system is especially well suited for an analysis of sensory coding. The elementary details of stage-by-stage connectivity have been intensively studied (55–66). An extraordinary degree of order and specificity has been found not only at lower levels but extending into the cortical regions and even beyond the primary receiving area (67). Single cells have been shown to be extremely selective in their stimulus preferences, and the required stimuli are generally quite complex (66, 67). Polysensory interactions at single units have been shown by Jung and coworkers (68) and by Murata *et al.* (69) to be a very common and pervasive feature of visual physiology.

Our investigation was designed to provide information on the following three questions:

From "Electrical signs of sensory coding". In G. C. Quarton, F. O. Schmitt, & T. Melnechuk, (Eds.), *The Neurosciences—A Study Program.* New York: Rockefeller University Press, 1967. Pp. 452–469. Reprinted with permission of the publisher and author, with whose approval certain material has been omitted. The work of the author reported herein was supported in part by USPHS Grant NB 03543 from the National Institute of Neurological Diseases and Blindness, NASA Grant NsG 215-62, and by USPHS Grant FR-70 from the General Clinical Research Centers Branch, Division of Research Facilities and Resources.

1. Do cells which respond to very specific and complex stimuli exhibit equally specific response patterns which constitute a neural signature for that stimulus?

2. In cells which respond to more than one stimulus configuration or more than one sensory modality, are there detectable differences in response pattern for each stimulus?

3. Are response patterns completely fixed or can they be modified as a result of experience?

The experimental animal was the curarized, unanesthetized cat. Prior to the experiment, the animals were fitted with an implanted nylon receptacle which could be opened when necessary for insertion of the microelectrode and with a cap of dental cement attached to the skull and specially molded to receive the ear bars of the stereotaxic instrument. The receptacle was 5–6 mm. in diameter and extended from the interaural line (Horsley-Clarke 0) anteriorly over the lateral gyrus. Thus, all penetrations were made in the zone designated as visual area III by Hubel and Wiesel (67). This area is considered analogous to Brodmann area 19 or parastriate cortex in man. During experimental sessions, an endotracheal tube was inserted for artificial respiration and the animal was immobilized with Flaxedil. The head was securely fixed in the stereotaxic apparatus by means of the cement cap; the body was kept warm and supported by elastic bands; and all injections were made through an indwelling femoral cannula. Thus, there were no pressure points, and great care was taken to assure that the procedure involved no stress for the animal. One-diopter contact lenses were fitted to each eye to assure a fixed focus and to protect the cornea from drying. Pupils were dilated with atropine.

Single-unit records were obtained with tungsten microelectrodes (70). After suitable amplification, the records were monitored on an oscilloscope and fed to a tape recorder for later playback and analysis.

All visual stimuli were projected on a viewing screen located 30 cm. in front of the eyes. Stimuli could be delivered to each eye separately. Stimulus duration was always 50 msec. Acoustic stimuli were 10 msec. clicks repeated for 50 msec.; tactile stimuli consisted of weak electrical shocks to the contralateral hind limb. All stimuli were delivered on a random schedule with a mean intertrial interval of 22.5 sec. A prepulse was put on tape 50 msec. before each stimulation.

Data analysis was performed on a LINC computer. It was programed to compute and display summed poststimulus time (PST) histograms (binwidth manually selectable) out to 250 msec. after stimulus onset or 300 msec. after the prepulse.

These experiments were carried out over a five-year period. During that time there were changes in experimental technique, recording apparatus, and even in strategy. Furthermore, each cell had a unique preferential or adequate stimulus (or stimuli), as well as a unique response pattern. Such particular preferences were sought out by the experimenters and were determining factors in the design of each experiment. Finally, variations in our ability to hold onto the unit and to maintain it in "normal" condition determined the duration of each experiment and the number of replications and controls which were possible in each case. Taken together, all these factors resulted in a lack of strict standardization of procedure from one experiment to the next. Nevertheless, as will be shown below, every effort was made to provide internal controls with which experientially determined changes in response pattern might be compared.

RESPONSE CHARACTERISTICS

Receptive fields were carefully plotted for each cell encountered, and the "preferred" stimulus configuration was determined. The latter was usually quite complex, consisting of edges, bars, or lines of various lengths and orientations. When the optimal stimulus was used, the mean cellular response was usually quite stable (as measured by PST histograms of sums of 20 trials) even though there was considerable trial-to-trial variability and scatter of

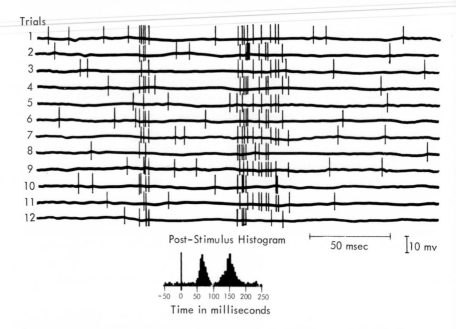

Figure 1. Single unit extracellular records of the first successive 12 trials of the 20 trials which were summed to form the PST histogram illustrated in the lower half of this figure. Each sweep was triggered by onset of stimulus. Preferred stimulus for this cell was a dark bar on a light background oriented on a line from 5 : 00 to 11 : 00, "stopped" on the left but extending out of the receptive field on the right. It was 4mm wide. Duration was 50 msec. Tracings were displayed on a storage oscilloscope by stepping down the vertical beam for each trial and were then photographed. The PST histogram displayed below was triggered by the pre-pulse which had been placed on the tape recording 50 msec before stimulus onset. It, therefore, illustrates

latencies and sometimes omission of some components. Figure 1 illustrates the first 12 trials out of the total of 20 used to compute the histogram shown in the lower part of the figure. There are obviously two bursts of activity evident when the tracings are displayed this way and, of course, two peaks in the histogram. By examination of single tracings, the early burst would not have been detected in trials 3, 5, 8, and perhaps 7.

A more complex response is shown in Figure 2, where trial-to-trial differences in latency are quite prominent. An inhibitory interval may be recognized in the histogram by the fact that after the first burst, the activity drops below the baseline of "spontaneous" activity (−50 msec.).

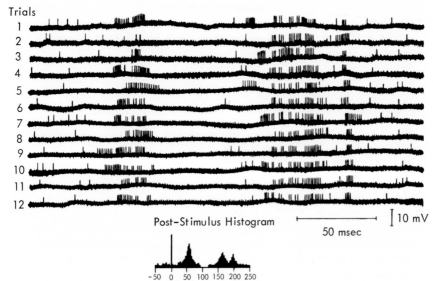

Figure 2. Single unit extracellular records of the first successive 12 trials of the 20 trials which were summed to form the PST histogram illustrated in the lower half of this figure. Three peaks are recognizable in the single tracings (except trial 2) although the "latency" varies from trial to trial. The "scatter" of these "latencies" may be visualized as the width or negatively accelerated slope of the histogram peaks. Note also how the histogram displays an inhibitory interval between the first and second peaks. The stimulus in this case was a dark corner in the right upper quadrant of the visual field.

---

the pre-stimulus level of activity (−50 msec to 0) as well as the cellular response to stimulation. When displayed simultaneously in this manner it is evident that there are two distinct bursts of activity (perhaps corresponding to onset and cessation of stimulation) which are reflected in the two peaks of the histogram. However, if the single traces had been examined separately, the early component might have been missed on trials 3, 5, 8 and, possibly, 7. Binwidth equals 5 msec in this and all other histograms displayed in this paper. The calibration bar at time zero in this and all other histograms equals 20 spikes.

A total of 890 cells of visual area III responded to preferred stimuli in the manner shown. A change of stimulus configuration—for example, from contralateral eye only to both eyes simultaneously—or changing the orientation of a line resulted in a different response pattern. Eight hundred and seventy-one of these cells also responded to tactile and acoustic stimuli with response patterns different from those elicited by visual stimuli. The preferred visual stimulus was then combined with other visual or other sensory stimuli yielding histograms having an extremely complex form rarely attributable to a simple linear summation of the firing pattern for each stimulus separately. Following this procedure (usually two blocks of 20 trials each), the original visual stimulus (test stimulus) was again presented alone. In the great majority of cells, response patterns were identical with those elicited prior to the paired trial experience. However, in 102 well-studied cells, the subsequent test stimulus evoked stable response patterns having a marked resemblance to those elaborated by the combined stimuli.

RESPONSE MODIFICATION IN "POLYMODAL" CELLS

Figure 3 demonstrates the histograms along with single-trace examples of the response to the visual stimulus (Fig. 3 L), to a shock to the contralateral hind limb (Fig. 3 S), to the two stimuli combined (Fig. 3 L + S), and to the visual stimulus alone after the paired trials (Fig. 3 L, lower). An appreciation of the true time course of this effect may be gained by viewing histograms of each successive sum of 20 trials for the entire stimulated output of a nerve cell throughout the period of its observation. Cell 63–294 delivered a moderately high-frequency, rather prolonged burst to a light line at about 2:00 in its receptive field (Fig. 4, trials 1–20). A second sum of 20 trials (trials 21–40) gives some indication of the stability of the histogram. The cell also responded to acoustic stimulation with a brief burst peaking somewhat earlier than the peak of the light-evoked discharge (trials 41–80). Stimulation with the light line was then resumed; the resultant histogram (Fig. 4, trials 81–100) showed that neither the interposition of acoustic stimulation alone nor the interposition of time itself had modified the response to light. Next, the light and click stimuli were presented simultaneously for two blocks of 20 trials each (trials 101–140), yielding PST histograms of very different composition than those for either stimulus individually. A reorganization or a completely new organization of response pattern emerged. Note that it took time; there are differences between the first (trials 101–120) and second (trials 121–140) sums of 20 trials of paired stimulation. Furthermore, following this experience, the light alone elicited a complex patterned discharge very similar to that elaborated by the combined stimuli (Fig. 4, trials 141–200). The reorganization thus established did not persist indefinitely but began to decay during

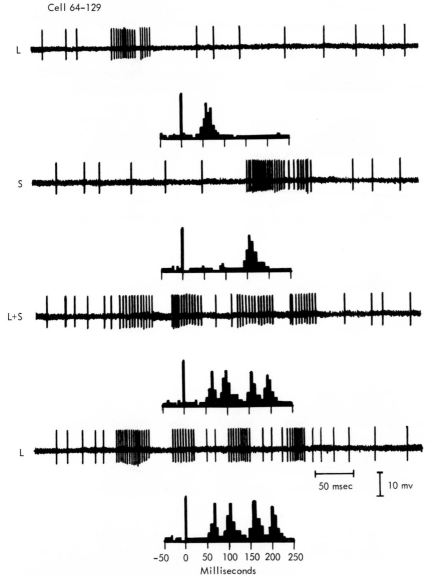

Figure 3. Experientially induced modification of response pattern. Cell responded to a dark horizontal bar at 3 : 00 (L) and also to electric shock to the contralateral hindlimb (S). Combining these two stimuli (L + S) resulted in a histogram very different from that which might occur from simple linear addition of the two separate responses. Furthermore, after 40 trials of such paired stimuli, the original visual stimulus (L) was presented alone. It elicited a pattern much more like that elaborated by paired stimulation than like that which it produced prior to pairing. The histograms are, again, sums of 20 trials. The single traces are those most representative of the overall pattern in each group of 20.

Cell 63-294

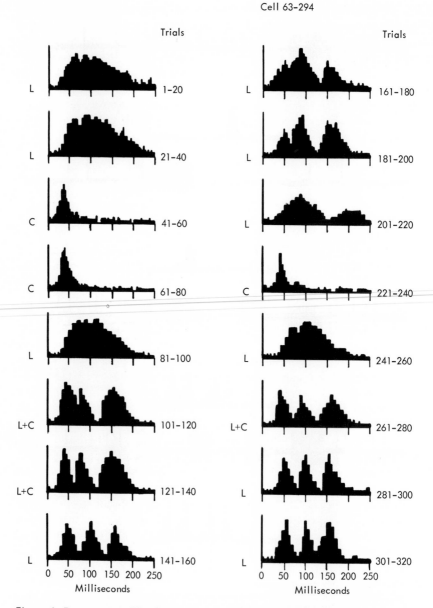

Figure 4. Response modification in a polymodal cell. "Preferred" visual stimulus
(L) for this cell was a light line at 2 : 00 in its receptive field. Click stimulus (C),
30 db above human auditory threshold in open field conditions, was also effective
although with a different pattern. This figure illustrates the PST histograms obtained
throughout the entire course of observation of this cell. L + C indicates "preferred"
visual and acoustic stimuli combined. Kind of stimulus is indicated on the left and
trial numbers to the right of each histogram in this and all subsequent figures.
Further explanation in text.

trials 201–220. An attempt to reestablish it by interposing a series of click-alone stimulation (trials 221–240) was unsuccessful, the subsequent testing with light (trials 241–260) yielding a histogram indistinguishable from that of the original response to light (trials 1–20). Note also that the response pattern to click (trials 221–240) was unchanged from that in the control period (trials 41–60). However, a series of 20 trials of combined light *and* click stimulation (trials 261–280) did have the effect of restoring the modified pattern, which then was persistently elicited by light alone (trials 281–320) for as long as the cell could be held.

RESPONSE MODIFICATION IN THE CASE WHERE NONPREFERRED STIMULUS IS INEFFECTIVE

Figure 5 illustrates sequential PST histograms in a cell which responded only to illumination of its receptive field in the contralateral eye (Fig. 5, trials 1–20) with a brief burst followed by an inhibitory interval. Ipsilateral eye stimulation (trials 21–60) produced no alteration in spontaneous firing rate or pattern. Yet when the two eyes were stimulated simultaneously (trials 61–100), a reorganization of firing pattern occurred, mainly consisting of the appearance of two late peaks and perhaps some increased scatter of the early component such that it encroached upon, and thereby shortened, the inhibitory interval. Now, however, when the preferred stimulus to the contralateral eye was reintroduced, the response pattern retained the two additional components contributed by or elaborated during paired stimulation (Fig. 5, trials 101–140). The new pattern began to decay during the third postpairing block (trials 141–160) and was gone by the fourth block (trials 161–180). Stimulation of the right eye alone was still ineffective (trials 181–200) and did not result in restoration of the modified response to the left or contralateral eye stimulus (trials 201–220). Stimulation of both eyes simultaneously again generated a complex histogram containing the two late components (Fig. 5, trials 221–240). Following this reinforcement, stimulation of the contralateral eye alone reproduced the modified pattern for the unusually long period of about 40 min., comprising four successive blocks of 20 trials each (trials 241–320) before the cell was lost.

The cells in Figures 4 and 5 both illustrate a differential specificity for the combined stimulus configuration. Stimulation by the nonpreferred member of the pair, whether it itself elicited a response as in the case of the click (Fig. 4) or did not as in the case of ipsilateral eye stimulation (Fig. 5), was not effective either in producing the response pattern due to paired stimulation or in restoring the capacity of the preferred stimulus to elicit the modified response.

Cell 64-104

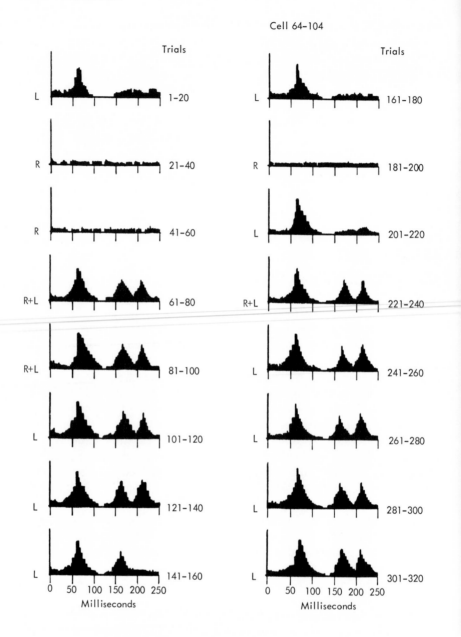

Figure 5. Response modification in the case where the non-preferred stimulus was ineffective. This cell responded to a light line 2 mm wide and 3 cm long only when the stimulus was presented to the left eye (L) ; stimulation of the corresponding receptive field area with the same stimulus to the right (ipsilateral) eye caused no alteration of spontaneous firing pattern (R, trials 21-60). However, simultaneous binocular stimulation produced a response pattern (trials 61-100) different from that to left eye alone (trials 1-20). PST histograms of successive sums of 20 trials are shown. Further explanation in text.

FURTHER DIFFERENTIAL SPECIFICITY

Another cell affords a striking example of differential specificity. PST histograms of cell 64–107 are shown in Figure 6. This cell had a response repertoire which was more varied than most. It responded best to a vertical bar of 3.6 cm. length moving from left to right or right to left across its receptive field. It responded also transiently to diffuse illumination of the room. But the most important characteristic of the cell was that response patterns to the vertical bar moving to the right and to the left respectively were different depending on whether the testing was done in the dark or in a dimly lighted room. Thus, one could distinguish four stimulus configurations to which the cell was differentially responsive; (1) visual stimulus moving to the right in the dark (VR-D), (2) visual stimulus moving to the left in the dark (VL-D), (3) visual stimulus moving to the right in the light (VR-L), and (4) visual stimulus moving to the left in the light (VL-L). The corresponding histograms are illustrated in Figure 6, VR-D, trials 1–20; VL-D, trials 21–40; VR-L, trials 61–80; VL-L, trials 81–100.

The cell also responded to an electric shock delivered to the contralateral hind limb (Fig. 6, S, trials 101–120) with a long latency. One of these four configurations, VL-D, was paired with the shock for two blocks of 20 trials each (trials 121–160). Following this experience, the VL-D–elicited response histogram was modified by the addition of a late component which resembled that contributed by shock stimulation (Fig. 6, trials 161–200). Testing of each of the other stimuli was then carried out. VR-D, trials 201–220, may be compared with its control, trials 1–20; VR-L, trials 221–240, may be compared with VR-L, trials 61–80; and VL-L, trials 241–260, with VL-L, trials 81–100. Finally, it was possible to restimulate with VL-D, trials 261–280, and note that the histogram modification was still present as compared with the control VL-D, trials 21–40. In this instance, the modification persisted for 60 min. after pairing, of which 30 min. were devoted to testing other stimuli and therefore not to stimulating with VL-D. It seems possible that the shorter duration of the effect seen in most cells (about 20–30 min.) may be a consequence of continuous testing, which, since it is unreinforced, may result in a process analogous to extinction.

SOME CONTROLS

Cell 64-126 (Figure 7) responded to acoustic (Fig. 7 C, trials 21–40) as well as visual stimulation (Fig. 7 L, trials 1–20). Combining the two stimuli resulted in a complex, rather rhythmic histogram which was certainly more than a linear transformation or addition of the two independent responses (Fig. 7, trials 41–80). On being tested with the preferred stimulus alone, the modified or new response persisted for some time (Fig. 7, trials 81–120) and then began to decay (Fig. 7, trials 121–140 and 141–160). After it had decayed, it was not

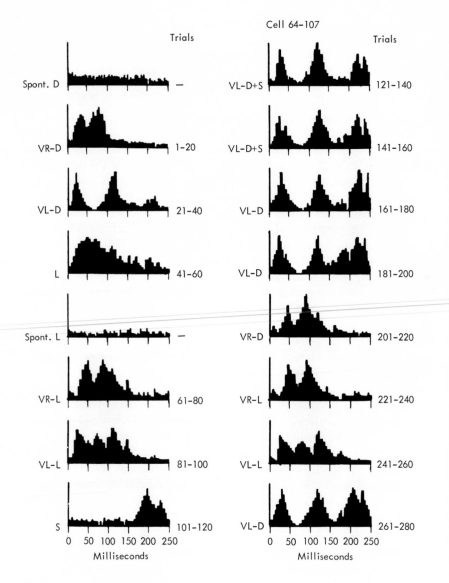

Figure 6. Further differential specificity. This cell had an extraordinarily rich response repertoire. It gave different response histograms to each of the following stimuli: a vertical bar 3.6 cm in length moving from left to right in a dark room (VR-D), the same stimulus moving in the opposite direction (VL-D), same stimulus moving from left to right with the room lights on (VR-L), and the same stimulus moving from right to left with the room lights on (VL-L). The cell also responded simply to diffuse illumination of the room (L) and to an electric shock to the contralateral hindlimb (S). One of these stimulus configurations (VL-D) was paired with shock (S). The others served as controls for specificity. Histograms labeled " Spont. D " and " Spont. L " represent sums of randomly chosen, 250 msec, segments of record when the cell was unstimulated either in the dark room (D) or with the room lighted (L). See text for further explanation.

Cell 64–126

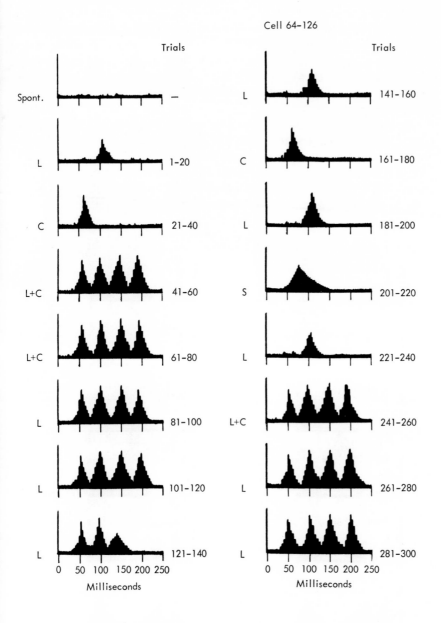

Figure 7. Cell was responsive to visual (L), acoustic (C) and tactile (S) stimulation. Illustrates PST histograms over the duration of experiment. Electric shock was used late in the experiment as a "novel" stimulus and did not result either in "dishabituation" or response restoration. Note that each of the three modalities of stimulation produced a different histogram. See text.

restored by exposure to the nonpreferred stimulus (Fig. 7, trials 161–180 and 181–200) or by exposure to an electric shock (Fig. 7, trials 201–220), introduced here as a novel stimulus, even though the shock succeeded in evoking a response from the cell. Again, only the specific pairing of the two stimuli restored the effect (Fig. 7, trials 241–260), which then persisted as long as the cell could be held.

In contrast, cell 65–203 fell into what we now designate as a *sensitization* group. It responded best to a light line directed toward 7:00 o'clock (preferred stimulus) but also to an electric shock to the contralateral hind limb (Fig. 8 S, trials 21–60). Combining the two stimuli yielded response histograms (Fig. 8, trials 61–100) which indeed seemed nothing more than a linear addition of the two responses independently. Nevertheless, the new response

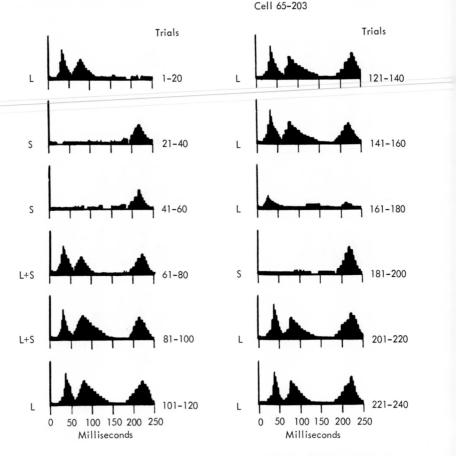

Cell 65-203

Figure 8. "Sensitization" cell. This cell was responsive to a light line directed toward 7 : 00 (L) but also to electric shock (S). The experiment differs from previous examples in that following decay of the modified response pattern (trials 101 through 180), presentation of shock alone, *without pairing,* resulted in restoration of the modified response histogram. See text.

persisted when stimulation was resumed with the preferred stimulus alone (Fig. 8, trials 101–160). The usual response decrement occurred to a level even lower than that of the control or original response. However, upon presentation of the shock alone, *not paired stimulation*—and even though the shock alone did not elicit the response pattern of the paired stimuli (Fig. 8, trials 181–200)—there was restoration of the modified-response pattern when tested by light stimulation alone (Fig. 8, trials 201–240).

DISCUSSION

The 102 cells which generated records of the type illustrated here stand in striking contrast to the great majority of the 769 cells wherein polymodal responses were also demonstrated. The response pattern elicited by pairing, in this latter group, did not show any persistence whatsoever when tested with either preferred or nonpreferred stimuli. Their response patterns were surprisingly constant and did not even show habituation or any appreciable variation over long time periods of several hours and many hundreds of stimulations, at least as measured by PST histograms of sums of 20 trials.

The complexity and specificity of the stimulus required to excite all of these cells, their receptive field patterns, ocular dominance distribution, and columnar organization emphatically confirm the observations of Hubel and Wiesel (67). The latter workers did not report a testing of polysensory convergence, but our observations on that score are in accord with those of Murata *et al.* (69) and Jung (68). In fact, Murata *et al.* (69) even examined their results by means of PST histograms, although they did not apparently look for evidence of modifiability.

The general stability of cellular responses in visual cortex makes those cells exhibiting response modification stand out clearly. Indeed, there was never any ambiguity over which cells would and which would not exhibit this property. Either the phenomenon was clearly present or the cell manifested no sign of modification even after hundreds of trials.

The distribution of modifiable cells was not random; it was quite specific. The cells were almost always encountered in groups, and such groups were invariably found in columnar penetrations of the microelectrode.

Given the data already on hand concerning polysensory convergence (see also Horn, 71), it is not really surprising that stimulation from other modalities might modify the response to preferred visual stimuli, although at best this might be expected in only a minority of cells or else there would not be as much constancy to our visual world as common observation insists there is.

Yet we have no way of judging whether the proportion we have found (roughly 10 percent) represents a realistic estimate of that portion of the population having "plastic" properties. There are indeed several reasons to consider that this estimate may be erroneously low. Thus, the recognition of pattern required the summed PST histogram method of data analysis. This, in turn, required that the same cell be held for several hours to provide all the necessary controls and comparisons. Needless to say, we may not have hit upon the appropriate or adequate stimulus in many cells. Moreover, if we lost a cell before adequate controls had been established, it was placed in the unmodified category. Thus, only cells in which adequate controls had been established were included in the modifiable group.

However tempting it may be, we do not yet believe it is wise or useful to label this phenomenon with the term *conditioning*, even though many of the criteria for conditioning are met and many subsidiary terms used in behavioral conditioning—for example, *extinction*. We understand this phenomenon described herein as a transient modification of response pattern which is specific to a particular past experience. The duration is limited but is of the same order of magnitude as the *consolidation* time (72) or short-term memory and of the heterosynaptic facilitation found by Kandel and Tauc in *Aplysia* (73). Behavioral conditioning requires the laying down of a permanent memory trace, and we do not have evidence that the microstructure of a cellular firing pattern is the physical substrate of enduring memory. It is quite unlikely that recognition or recall later on requires the cellular re-creation of these temporal patterns of discharge. Recognition and recollection do not require 250 msec. of time, as anyone who has worked with tachistoscopic presentation of signals can testify and as Lindsley *et al.* (74) have shown in an elegant physiological experiment.

These experiments have, however, provided answers to the questions set forth at the beginning of this section. There are clearly substantive differences in the response pattern of every single cell when it is activated by different stimuli. Thus, the fact that a cell may be responsive, for instance, to both a visual and an acoustic stimulus does *not* mean that modality information is lost. These cells must have their connectivity arranged in highly specific and organized ways so that fibers carrying acoustic information to two different cells in visual cortex may modify the output of these cells differentially. Similarly, Figure 7 illustrates that a single cell, even though capable of activation by visual, acoustic, and tactile stimuli, maintains stimulus-specific discharge patterns. These findings allow strong inference that the microstructure of the response as exhibited in PST histograms does, in fact, constitute the neural code for that particular experience. On the other hand, it is also true that the histograms exhibit varying degrees of *scatter* about the mode. On any single trial the response of a particular cell is probabilistic rather than absolutely deterministic with respect to both timing (see Fig. 2) and pattern (note omission of early component in some trials illustrated in Fig. 1). Therefore, on any given trial, the response pattern of a single cell cannot uniquely specify the nature of an experience. In relating these observations at the cellular level to the behavior of an organism, one must bear in mind the probability that information is processed in parallel in thousands of cells so that the organism need not depend on the reliability of any single element for identification of an experience. These parallel chains do not all have to carry exactly the same information and therefore, strictly speaking, may not necessarily be redundant. It is necessary only that the nervous system receive enough information about an experience to identify it, even if some aspects are left out or are distorted. Furthermore, it is likely that on first exposure to a stimulus, the nervous system specifies it less precisely than it does after many exposures. Ultimately, as was noted above, the code must be transformed from one based upon a discharge pattern through time to one which is more stable—that is, immune to electrical interference (75), more disseminated, and susceptible to very much faster " read-out."

The term *probabilistic* is used here merely to describe the nature of the observed relationship between input and output. It does not imply any particular conclusion about the fundamental nature of the *noise* in the system. It is quite possible that a completely deterministic system, but one in which many variables are unknown, would appear probabilistic to the limited viewpoint of a microelectrode sampling the output of one single cell. And, of course, these considerations do not exclude the possibility of some fundamental stochastic property operating on the process of synaptic transmission. All that can be said at this stage is that it is not necessary to introduce any fundamental indeterminacy in the system to account for all the available data.

At first glance it seems especially appropriate that cells exhibiting plasticity should be found in these higher reaches of the visual system. These cells all receive inputs from " hypercomplex cells " and are " higher-order hypercomplex," to use the terms introduced by Hubel and Wiesel (67). Since they were not randomly scattered but were organized quite specifically on a columnar plan, these cells would be in a position to make use of all the detailed information built into the connectivity of the visual system. They simply add another stage of complexity to the levels already described by Hubel and Wiesel.

Certain other considerations lead us to question the proposition that plasticity might be a property evolved in only higher-order cells. Thus, David Lindsley and K. L. Chow (76) have observed similar transient modifications of firing pattern in lateral geniculate neurons. This occurred in approximately the same proportion of total cells sampled (10 percent), and the cells were also grouped together. Similar observations have been made by Yoshii and Ogura (77) in reticular formation and by Kamikawa *et al.* (78) in the thalamus. Moreover, Weingarten and Spinelli (79) have shown changes in the receptive fields of retinal ganglion cells as a result of auditory and somatic stimulation, and Adkins *et al.* (80) have reported analogous observations in cuneate cells.

These related findings suggest rather that plasticity may be built in all along the neuraxis. There may be a specifically organized system of cells, developed during maturation, having a genetic endowment for the appropriate connectivity for intermodality interaction and short-term maintenance of change.

Whether the permanent traces which underlie learning take place in these cells or in still other more specialized ones with which these are presumably connected is a matter for future investigation.

ACKNOWLEDGMENTS

Dr. J. Engle, Jr., helped with portions of the studies on the visual system of the cat; Mr. Lud Kaspar aided in the technical aspects of the animal studies; David Hellerstein and William Bouris helped with computer programming. Most of all, I am indebted to Professor K. L. Chow for discerning criticism and stimulating discussion.

REFERENCES

[Editor's note: The text referring to notes 1–54 has been omitted with the author's permission, so the notes have been omitted too.]

55. S. POLJAK, 1927. An experimental study of the association callosal, and projection fibers of the cerebral cortex of the cat, *J. Comp. Neurol.*, Vol. 44, pp. 197–258.

56. S. A. TALBOT & W. H. MARSHALL, 1941. Physiological studies on neural mechanisms of visual localization and discrimination, *Am. J. Ophthalmol.*, Vol. 24, pp. 1255–1264.

57. J. M. THOMPSON, C. N. WOOLSEY, & S. A. TALBOT, 1950. Visual areas I and II of cerebral cortex of rabbit, *J. Neurophysiol.* ,Vol. 13, pp. 277–288.

58. S. W. KUFFLER, 1953. Discharge patterns and functional organization of mammalian retina, *J. Neurophysiol.*, Vol. 16, pp. 37–68.

59. M. H. CLARE & G. H. BISHOP, 1954. Responses from an association area secondarily activated from optic cortex, *J. Neurophysiol.*, Vol. 17, pp. 271–277.

60. R. W. DOTY, 1958. Potentials evoked in cat cerebral cortex by diffuse and by punctiform photic stimuli, *J. Neurophysiol.*, Vol. 21, pp. 437–464.

61. E. F. VASTOLA, 1961. A direct pathway from lateral geniculate body to association cortex, *J. Neurophysiol.*, Vol. 24, pp. 469–487.

62. R. OTSUKA & R. HASSLER, 1962. Über Aufbau und Gliederung der corticalen Sehsphäre bei der Katze, *Arch. Psychiat. Nervenkrankh.*, Vol. 203, pp. 212–234.

63. E. H. POLLEY & J. M. DIRKES, 1963. The visual cortical (geniculocortical) area of the cat brain and its projections, *Anat. Record*, Vol. 145, p. 345 (abstract).

64a. D. H. HUBEL & T. N. WIESEL, 1959. Receptive fields of single neurones in the cat's striate cortex, *J. Physiol. (London)*, Vol. 148, pp. 574–591.

64b. D. H. HUBEL & T. N. WIESEL, 1961. Integrative action in the cat's lateral geniculate body, *J. Physiol. (London)*, Vol. 155, pp. 385–398.

65. D. H. HUBEL & T. N. WIESEL, 1962. Receptive fields, binocular interaction and functional architecture in the cat's visual cortex, *J. Physiol. (London)*, Vol. 160, pp. 106–154.

66. D. H. HUBEL & T. N. WIESEL, 1963. Shape and arrangement of columns in cat's striate cortex, *J. Physiol. (London)*, Vol. 165, pp. 559–568.

67. D. H. HUBEL & T. N. WIESEL, 1965. Receptive fields and functional architecture in two nonstriate visual areas (18 and 19) of the cat, *J. Neurophysiol.*, Vol. 28, pp. 229–289.

68. R. JUNG, 1961. Neuronal integration in the visual cortex and its significance for visual information, *in* Sensory communication (W. A. Rosenblith, editor), Cambridge, M.I.T. Press, pp. 627–674.

69. K. MURATA, H. CRAMER, & P. BACH-Y-RITA, 1965. Neuronal convergence of noxious, acoustic, and visual stimuli in the visual cortex of the cat, *J. Neurophysiol.*, Vol. 28, pp. 1223–1239.

70. D. H. HUBEL, 1957. Tungsten microelectrode for recording from single units, *Science*, Vol. 125, pp. 549–550.

71. G. HORN, 1965. The effect of somaesthetic and photic stimuli on the activity of units in the striate cortex of unanesthetized, unrestrained cats. *J. Physiol. (London)*, Vol. 179, pp. 263–277.

72. J. A. DEUTSCH, 1962. Higher nervous functions: the physiological bases of memory, *Ann. Rev. Physiol.*, Vol. 24, pp. 259–286.

73. E. R. KANDEL & L. TAUC, 1965. Heterosynaptic facilitation in neurones of the abdominal ganglion of *Aplysia depilans*, *J. Physiol. (London)*, Vol. 181, pp. 1–27.

74. D. B. LINDSLEY, L. G. FEHMI, & J. W. ADKINS, 1967. Visually evoked potentials during perceptual masking in man and monkey, *Electroencephalog. Clin. Neurophysiol.* (in press).

75. F. MORRELL, 1963. Information storage in nerve cells, *in* Information storage and neural control (W. S. Fields and W. Abbott, editors), Springfield, Illinois, Charles C Thomas, pp. 189–229.

76. K. L. CHOW & D. F. LINDSLEY, unpublished observations.

77. N. YOSHII & H. OGURA, 1960. Studies on the unit discharge of brainstem reticular formation in the cat. I. Changes of reticular unit discharge following conditioning procedure, *Med. J. Osaka Univ.*, Vol. 11, pp. 1–17.

78. K. KAMIKAWA, J. T. MCILWAIN, & W. R. ADEY, 1964. Response patterns of thalamic neurons during classical conditioning, *Electroencephalog. Clin. Neurophysiol.*, Vol. 17, pp. 485–496.

79. M. WEINGARTEN & D. N. SPINELLI, 1966. Retinal receptive field changes produced by auditory and somatic stimulation, *Exptl. Neurol.*, Vol. 15, pp. 363–376.

80. R. J. ADKINS, R. W. MORSE, & A. L. TOWE, 1966. Control of somatosensory input by cerebral cortex, *Science*, Vol. 153, pp. 1020–1022.

Operant Conditioning
of Single Unit Responses

J. Olds

In the course of experiments on the mechanisms of operant reinforcement, the question repeatedly arises as to what is reinforced when an originally infrequent behavior is made to occur more often by the application of a rewarding stimulus following each of its occurrences. The behavior as an ephemeral event is over by the time the reinforcement occurs and it is clear that some arrangement of structures within the organism which controls the emission of the behavior is the reinforced entity. The question is whether the arrangement is diffuse or localized and whether the reinforcing event occurs at some particular subdivision of this central organization. One might imagine that the organization would be represented by electrical activity which could be recorded with macro- or microelectrodes and that electrical methods would eventually allow detailed study of the process providing we could find a way of localizing the critical steps.

We have sought by studying whether action potential sequences could be brought under operant control to take some steps toward the discovery of anatomical areas and electric signs of the reinforcement process. The questions involved in the initial phases of this study were first whether some neural patterns could be differentiated out of their behavioral matrix so that they could be brought under voluntary control even when restrictions were placed on the normal voluntary behavior patterns of the subject, second whether any neural responses were sufficiently linked to processes under voluntary control to permit success in experiments of this type, third, whether some neural patterns would surpass others in "conditionability," *i.e.* in speed of conditioning and degree of "voluntary" control when conditioning was completed, and fourth whether particularly conditionable patterns would be correlated with formal, anatomical, or functional properties of the action potential sequences.

From *Excerpta Medica International Congress*, 1965, **87**, 372–380. Reprinted with permission of the publisher and author.

It seemed that the form of the pattern itself might be a sign of condition-ability. High frequency bursts might be refractory to conditioning because they indicated states of sleep. Single spikes might be refractory because they represented "idling" states of the neuron. Fast "random" activity might be amenable to conditioning because it represented participation of a unit in an ongoing process. Particular complex burst patterns or repeating interunit correlations might be conditionable if they were meaningful in the economy of the organism but not if their particular patterns were more or less chance affairs.

In the course of preliminary studies with the goal of making reinforcing feedback contingent on unit patterns alone, a variety of technical problems was solved, and the present report is of action potential sequences in hippo-campus and midbrain tegmentum that have been successfully conditioned by operant techniques. It gives the details of the methods that were finally evolved for this purpose. It has not yet been possible to divide action potential sequences on other grounds into those that are clearly amenable to manipula-tion by operant techniques. However, the evolution of a standard procedure, and the successful conditioning of a variety of action potential patterns has indicated clearly the direction for these further tests.

METHODS

The subjects were rats; they were tested in a small circular plastic cage. Selected patterns of action potential sequences caused the discharge of a pellet dispenser and thereby presented the subject with a 45 mg. pellet. This discharge of the pellet dispenser is hereafter referred to as "reinforcement" (in accordance with the terminology of operant conditioning).

Fixed microelectrodes of relatively large size (67 microns diameter) were made of enameled nichrome wire following the method of Strumwasser (1958)[4]. Nine of these were implanted in each rat under guidance of single unit recording; a larger uninsulated ground electrode was also implanted which extended from the top to the base of the brain. About half the im-planted probes yielded action potential recordings for indefinite periods after implantation. The method had the advantage of keeping the electrodes in the "same" place for long periods. Wires were considered to be sufficiently flexible to "ride with the brain" and sufficiently blunt to be stopped by cell membranes. The large size rendered micron movements relatively unimportant so far as the output pattern was concerned. The fact that several unit responses of different sizes could be recorded simultaneously from the same probe was regarded as an advantage because it will eventually permit the study of several units within a small area. Also the fixed method of implantation permitted recording from several microelectrodes simultaneously. The microdrive previously used had been so large as to preclude the study of more than one probe at a time. A difficulty was that responses were of small size, ranging from 2 to 4 times the noise level. This necessitated electronic analysis for purposes of rapid feedback of reinforcement.

A swivel system utilizing double brushes on opposite sides of commutator rings allowed recording of unit responses without generation of noise during turning of the commutator. The swivel was mounted on a counterbalanced arm placed about 12 inches above the animal. Noisefree "microdot" cables coupled the microelectrodes to the commutator.

A system of electronic analysers (Fig. 1) was used for three purposes: (1) to detect and count the action potentials, (2) to detect movement and muscle artifacts, and (3) to detect rapid trains of action potentials and on the basis of these to trigger the positive reinforcement mechanism. The waveform analyser responded to all signals above a certain amplitude. If these signals fell to the baseline within a prefixed period after achievement of the triggering amplitude, the signal was identified as an action potential (a "unit" response). If the signal fell to the baseline too soon or too late the

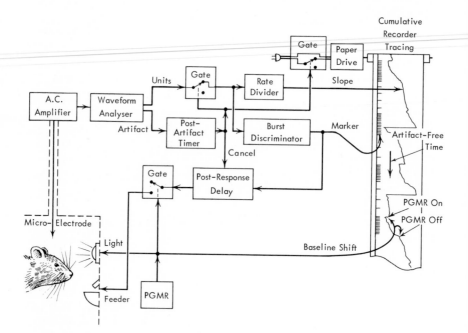

Fig. 1. Operant conditioning apparatus for single unit responses (see text for discussion). On the cumulative recorder tracing, the rate of the unit response is converted into the slope of the line, the spikes to one side of the tracing indicate occurrences of the operant response, i.e. the selected burst of unit activity. When these occurred during "programmer on" intervals they caused the food magazine to be discharged presenting the animal with a pellet. "Programmer on" intervals are marked by a sharp displacement of the tracing to the left (baseline shift). The tracing itself does not record all time but moves only during artifact-free periods; when artifact occurs, all systems are cut off.

signal was classified as an artifact. When unit identification was made, the device yielded one output; when an artifact identification was made, the device yielded a different output. The "time window" used to discriminate unit responses from artifacts was variable so that it could be set by hand to match a particular unit response. An amplitude window was also used to categorize unit responses as is regularly done in spike height analysers.

Artifact output when it occurred was led off two ways: (a) to a retroactive cancellation device which provided that the animal would not be reinforced if there were movement artifact within $\frac{1}{2}$ sec. after the correct response; (b) through a post-artifact delay which stopped all recording and unit counting and also "stopped time" so far as the recorders were concerned for a 2 sec. period after each artifact. This assured that the animal would not be reinforced if there were movement artifact within 2 sec. before (or $\frac{1}{2}$ sec. after) the correct response.

Unit response identifications when they occurred were also led off two ways: (a) through an electronic counter (or rate divider) to a cumulative recorder where the rate of the unit response was recorded automatically as the slope of a line; the electronic counter was used as a rate divider because rates were often too high for the automatic stepping solenoid of the cumulative recorder; (b) into a "burst discriminator" which yielded an output pulse whenever a particularly high response rate occurred. This device consisted of a second electronic counter and a timer. A particular unit response started both counter and timer whenever it found the burst discriminator in a reset position; $\frac{1}{2}$ sec. after the first response, the timer reset the counter. If the counter reached a preset number prior to reset, a burst identification output occurred. The present number was selected empirically at the beginning so that the average interval between burst output pulses was 15 minutes. This was done during a pretest period of four hours during which there were no reinforcements.

After the preliminary period, the burst output was used to trigger the food magazine and the action potential sequence which met this criterion was considered to be the "correct" or "operant" response. Two gates intervened after the burst output. One was a $\frac{1}{2}$ sec. post response delay device which permitted retroactive cancellation when artifact followed too soon after the correct response. The other was the on-off timer which provided during the final phase of the experiment that the animal would be reinforced for the selected action potential sequences during only 2 min. out of every 10. During the 2 min. "on" period an indicator signal provided a cue that the reinforcement mechanism was engaged.

The correct action potential sequences (selected by the burst discriminator) were also recorded by means of an event marker on the cumulative recorder paper. During some experiments, the burst output was used to drive the stepper of the cumulative recorder (Fig. 2 and 3) and action potentials which occurred in slower sequences were not recorded. In current

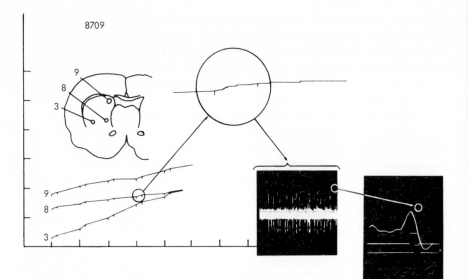

Fig. 2. Operant patterns for three neurons recorded from caudate or internal capsule in rat #8709. These are patterns that appeared after conditioning was complete. In this case, only the operant responses (*i.e.* the high frequency patterns) are recorded on the tracings. The space between each pair of spikes on the tracing indicates light-on periods, and the upward deflection of tracings that occur at these points represent "major accelerations" which indicate that the operant response is under control. The upward deflections are actually composed of many small upward steps (see circled area) and each upward step represents the occurrence of 20 unit responses within a $\frac{1}{2}$ sec. period (see first black rectangle where the whole baseline is a $\frac{1}{2}$ sec. period). Unit identifications are shown by dots above spikes in first rectangle; one of these spikes is spread out in the second rectangle where the whole baseline is a 5 msec. period. The tracing just below the action potential represents the Schmidt trigger which is activated as the potential reaches near maximum; it starts two timers of which only the second one is shown (in the lowest tracing); if the Schmidt trigger "de-triggers" during the period of the second timer, this correlation of events activated the unit identifier (see dot below the top tracing).

experiments, the unit response rate itself is recorded by means of the stepper and those bursts which satisfy the criterion (of the burst discriminator) are recorded as spikes on an event marker at one side of the tracing (Fig. 1). After the programmer is engaged, the "on" periods are also recorded on the tracing by means of an abrupt baseline deflection (seen at "programmer on" and "programmer off" points of Fig. 1).

A variety of test sequences has been used. All involved pretraining of the animal to respond by eating when the food magazine was discharged. After pretraining there was a four hour preliminary period for setting the wave-form analyser, analysing unconditioned rates of action potential sequences, and setting the burst discriminator so that it responded about once every 15 minutes. After this there was an extended period (of at least 48 hours) during which the output pulses generated by the burst discriminator triggered the food magazine. If a pronounced increment in the occurrence of the selected action potential sequences resulted, then the final stage of the experiment was initiated. In this, the programmer was engaged and the animal was tested for about 4 days to find whether there would be a shift of the operant response (*i.e.* in the selected action potential sequence) so that the action potentials would in the end occur mainly during the 2-min. reinforcement intervals.

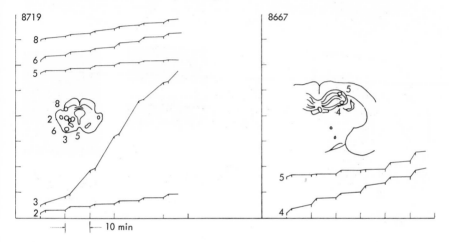

Fig. 3. Operant patterns for units in tegmentum (left) and hippocampus (right).

RESULTS

It has not been possible to modify action potential patterns of firing significantly by reinforcing the animal after single spikes which occurred in isolation, or after rapid bursts of from 3 to 6 spikes as occur in pyramidal neurons during sleep (Evarts, 1964[1]), or by reinforcing the animal after long enduring gaps in the action potential activity. It is not clear, however, that our experiments have been sufficiently sustained to permit a conclusive statement that success in these directions might not be attained later.

There has been repeated success in modifying rates by reinforcement of rates in the order of 8 or more responses per $\frac{1}{2}$ sec. interval (see Figures 2–4).

Successful experiments occurred when action potentials were derived from a variety of structures including the reticular activating system and other tegmental areas, the hippocampus, and parts of the basal ganglia. Repeated failures occurred with probes in some forebrain and midbrain areas. It is not clear whether this turns mainly on a basic difference in organization or on the difficulty encountered in holding satisfactory recordings over long periods of time when probes were placed in the refractory regions. It happens that the areas yielding positive experiments were the areas yielding most satisfactory long run recordings.

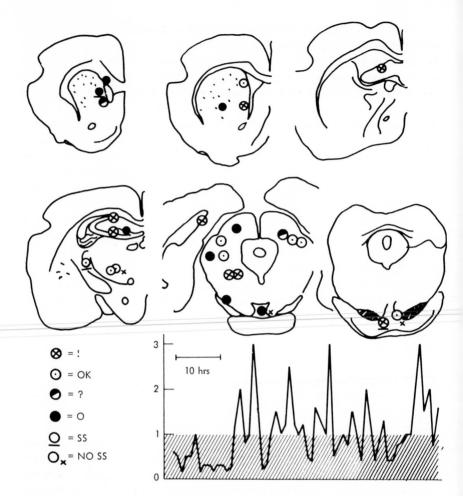

Fig. 4. Map of probe placements. The factor by which acquisition scores exceeded extinction scores during the fifth 24 hour period of program testing is indicated as follows : circles containing crosses—acquisition rate = 10 times extinction rate ; internal dot—acquisition rate = 3 to 9 times extinction rate ; half-filled circles—acquisition rate = 1 to 2 times extinction rate ; filled circles—no difference. Six probes in animal 9918 were first used for recording in unit conditioning tests and later for stimulating in tests for self-stimulation ; of these the three underlined points yielded positive reinforcement ; stimulation of the three X'd points however failed to yield self-stimulation behavior. Self-stimulation and unit conditioning were observed together with probes in reticular nucleus of thalamus and in pons. Other data suggest this would happen also in hippocampus. Data are graphed to show the course of conditioning for one of the successful experiments (probe in pons). The data indicate the number of operant responses per minute during acquisition divided by the correlated extinction response rate.

In one animal, six probes were tested in sequence: three in the mammillary peduncle area of tegmentum, one in hippocampus or fimbria, one in the thalamus (in or near the reticular nucleus), and one in the dorsal anterior part of the caudate area. Action potentials derived from the 3 tegmental leads were tested first for one week each, and then potentials from the foreb rain leads in the order listed. After the first 6 weeks, during which attempts were made to condition one pattern derived from each of these probes, the whole experiment was repeated so that each probe was tested a second time. Clear evidence of conditioning was obtained with action potentials derived from two of the three tegmental probes, and with action potentials from hippocampus and thalamus. There was rather clear evidence of a failure with the probe in dorsal caudate. The evidence from one of the tegmental probes was unclear. The data must be interpreted with caution, however, because of the possibility that previous experience played a large role in the psychological aspects of these experiments. When a subject is repeatedly conditioned in the same cage to make a number of different responses in succession, it must be remembered that there is only one animal. During the early experiments in a series utilizing a single subject, there is a growing familiarity with the cage which may aid in later acquisitions; there is also accretion of habits which may be incompatible with later acquisitions. Therefore the negative cases need a variety of special checks before we can begin to make definite statements.

In many, if not all the cases which we have studied to date, rapid changes in action potential sequences have occurred at some point during almost each day or night even without conditioning. For this reason it was not possible to view an initial pronounced increment in rate as significant evidence for conditioning. It might have been possible to follow such a change over a longer period to find whether it would be sustained but this would still have left doubt because in the first place a very long interval would have been necessary to establish initial variability before a significant change could have been established, and in the second place a change owing mainly to a gradual shift in geometrical relation of probe to neurons would have been significant but relatively uninteresting.

It turned out that the alternation between programmer "on" and "off" periods provided a relatively rapid method for circumventing both of these problems. Therefore, the important evidence for conditioning came not in the preliminary training period but in the gradual shift of the action potential pattern until eventually it seemed to be controlled by the programmer's signal light. Change over time in this degree of control provided the important evidence. Initial control of this action potential by the light was of course not evidence of conditioning.

It was not unusual for action potentials to be somewhat slowed by the signal light in early phases of the experiment (see Fig. 4, graph). This was perhaps because many behavior patterns of the rat are inhibited to some degree when the environment is lighted. If the subject had had considerable pretraining in the testing environment there was sometimes a sudden shift after a limited number of reinforcements. In one, not unusual case, it required only 3 reinforcements to produce a dramatic shift so that for the next several hours almost all "response increments" occurred during light-on intervals. During the 4 preceding hours all such increments had occurred during the light-off periods.

After the first such signs of conditioning, there was often a waning of the effect owing, it appeared, to (i) satiation of the animal, (ii) arrival of daylight, and (iii) possibly the gradual movement of the probe in relation to neurons which would have presented the animal with a changed problem. However, during succeeding days, the control of the action potentials by the signal light was often regained and sometimes it would be almost completely stable by the end of the 4th day of programmed testing.

DISCUSSION

In behavioral reinforcement there are two primary variables: the reinforcing object or stimulus and the reinforced response. Application of the reinforcing object immediately after the chance occurrence of the reinforced response causes a modification in the incidence of the latter in the subject's behavior repertory. The goal of a series of studies in our laboratory (Olds and Olds, 1961[3]; Olds, 1962[2]) has been to find some set of neural interactions which could be said to be involved more or less directly in the reinforcement process, some synapses or ephapses perhaps where the afferents could be said to be on the "reinforcing" side and the efferents on the "reinforced" side of the relationship.

We have attempted to discover the extent and structure of systems involved on the reinforcing side of the process by utilizing the self-stimulation method (Olds, 1962[2]). In the series of studies described here and previously (Olds and Olds, 1961[3]), we have tried to study the extent and structure of systems involved on the reinforced side. By a gradual process of mapping and elimination it may eventually be possible to find where and how the two systems meet. This goal is not as yet to understand, but to find places where the critical interactions may be observed.

What has been achieved is a method for identifying neural processes which are manipulable by means of operant reinforcement. Neuron responses needed to be conditioned in order to validate the method and this, we believe, can be shown to occur. An anticipation is that some subset of the "conditionable neurons" will be critically involved in operant conditioning. The problem which lies ahead is that of finding a way to identify from the elements in the larger class the subset that is involved in critical phases of conditioning.

Why are not all the "conditionable" neurons candidates for being members of the subclass? Mainly becuase a variety of patterns should be "conditionable" that have nothing especially to do with conditioning. For example, sensory systems whose stimuli could be readily modified by orienting responses; or proprioceptor systems should be readily conditioned insofar as the skeletal responses that produce them can be readily conditioned. Also motor systems involved in the final control of skeletal and voluntary behavior should be relatively conditionable. Some sensory systems whose stimuli are not readily modified by orientation should be refractory; and similarly homeostatic effector systems should likely be ruled out. But still a great number of responses not at the critical phase of the conditioning processes should be "conditionable."

In free behavior tests, the correlates of obvious skeletal responses might be most easily conditioned, including perhaps pyramidal and extrapyramidal components and sensory systems responding to proprioceptive feedback. Systems related to postural adjustments and sensory systems responding after orienting responses might also be conditioned but would perhaps be somewhat more refractory as animals are not used to "looking at" things in order to discharge a food magazine. If neuronal correlates of some integrative or intentional central process occurred prior to the energizing of specific motor systems (and these would be closer to the goal of our search) these might also be conditionable; it is not clear, however, whether they could be detached with ease from their motor consequences.

The problem is first to map this larger system of conditionable elements and then to find a way to divide it up into systems that are more and less likely to be critically involved. The system will of course be divided on histological grounds and because the probes can be stimulated it will be divided on functional grounds. Tests of this sort will provide clues that should lead toward identification. Also, this will allow identification of overlapping or tangential relations between the "reinforcing" and the "reinforced" systems.

Other methods of searching for the critical subsystem involve placing limitations on behavior. In the tests described above, for example, a restriction system was used to limit movement. Most movements caused special electronic detectors to be discharged and these precluded reinforcement; therefore the "operant responses" were forced into relatively movement-free intervals. In such restricted behavior tests it seemed that the order of conditionable substrates would be changed: units following obvious skeletal behaviors were largely excluded. Units following postural adjustment and units related to orientable stimuli were not ruled out. Units following intentional processes, however, might be most easily conditioned if they could be detached from their behaviors. After preliminary analysis of the parts of the brain yielding "conditionable responses" has been made, we hope to extend this method of behaviour limitation utilizing paralysis and perhaps even isolated cerebral preparations to exclude still further the chance of interference from sensory feedback systems.

REFERENCES

1. EVARTS, E. V.: Temporal patterns of discharge of pyramidal tract neurons during sleep and waking in the monkey. *J. Neurophysiol.*, 1964, 27 (152-171).
2. OLDS, J.: Hypothalamic substrates of reward. *Physiol. Rev.*, 1962, 42 (554-604).
3. OLDS, J., & OLDS, M. E.: Interference and learning in paleocortical systems. In: *Brain Mechanisms and Learning*, Delafresnaye, J. F., editor, Blackwell Scientific Publications, Oxford, 1961 (153-187).
4. STRUMWASSER, F.: Long-term recording from single neurons in brain of unrestrained mammals. *Science*, 1958, 127 (469-470).

Conditioned Reflexes Formed and Evoked by Brain Stimulation

Robert W. Doty

Early in 1870 Hitzig reported that electrical stimulation applied across the head from ear to ear produced movements of the eyes. Since these movements occurred even in the blind, it was reasoned that they did not arise from subjective following of objects whirling in the visual field pursuant to the accompanying sensation of vertigo. Further work (Fritsch and Hitzig, 1870) failed to discover the labyrinthine basis of these movements; instead, logical analysis of the facts available led to the then remarkable proof that the cerebral cortex was electrically excitable. The science of the nervous system was thus provided with one of its most powerful tools. By application of electrodes to the human brain and the elicitation thereby of a variety of

From *Electrical Stimulation of the Brain* by D. E. Sheer (Ed.) (Austin; University of Texas Press, 1961), pp. 397–412. Reprinted with permission of the publisher and author, with whose approval certain material has been omitted. The original research reported here was supported by grants B-663 and B-1068 from the National Institute of Neurological Diseases and Blindness, National Institutes of Health, and a grant from Foundations' Fund for Research in Psychiatry.

sensations, emotions, moods, and memories, direct proof is obtained that neural processes are the basis of human experience.

However, the discovery of differentially excitable zones within the cortex, together with the description of the exceptional cells (Betz, 1874) within this "motor" zone, supported a compartmentalized view of the function of the cortex. The study of the cerebral cortex, which had begun with phrenology, soon returned to it. But to achieve a nervous system which itself integrates across all sensory and motor boundaries and is permanently altered by its own activities, a more dynamic view is required. Evidence for the required flexibility was not long in coming. Soltmann (1876) proposed that some portions of the nervous system could assume the function normally served by others, since removal of "motor" areas from puppies did not produce the expected deficit upon maturation. Brown-Sequard (1884) reported (though the conditions of the experiment are not clear) that, following stimulation of the "motor" cortex, movements of the face, neck, and tail could be obtained from the occipital cortex. In 1897 Ewald, the first to use chronically implanted electrodes, claimed that "there is no point on the cerebral cortex from which, in the fully normal and unrestrained dog, muscle movements cannot be obtained" (see Talbert, 1900). The truth of this statement has now been most carefully and convincingly documented by Lilly (1958) and Hughes (1959) on the monkey and cat.

Thus movement is a general function of systems entered by stimulation at the cortical level. The threshold and degree of elicited movement depend upon the state of the system. More unexpectedly and more interestingly, the elicited movement can in certain circumstances be shown to depend upon the concurrent or preceding excitation of other regions of the nervous system; and seemingly permanent alterations of the excitability characteristics of a given cortical region, as shown in the present chapter, can be so achieved.

Wedensky (1903) stimulated homotopic points on the two hemispheres and noted a reciprocal interaction such that an "antagonistic" point was facilitated whereas the threshold at the homologous point was depressed. In a synopsis of these findings he appears to regard this as a property of cortical systems; the closeness to later Pavlovian concepts of cortical action is of historical interest. Actually, the phenomena are probably best explained as interactions at the spinal level.

Of less historical but more practical import is the work of Baer (1905). Using chronically implanted electrodes, he confirmed Brown-Sequard's contention that "nonmotor" cortical points in dogs could be altered to produce movements if their excitation was concurrent with, or followed stimulation of, the anterior "motor" cortex. In an exceptionally clear case he could elicit movements of the head, trunk, and rear leg from the "visual" cortex with currents which had been completely ineffective when tried at thrice the strength prior to prolonged direct-current stimulation of the cruciate area. These effects subsided within fifteen minutes.

For more enduring alterations a learning situation is employed. Loucks (1933, 1935, 1938) was the first to succeed here; he produced discrete foreleg movements persistently from " visual " cortex stimulation after this stimulation had been repeatedly paired with shock to the limb. There are, of course, many complexities here, both of engram formation and motivation. But the point is clear: the effects produced by stimulation of the higher central nervous system are subject to lasting alteration by prior, associated activity. Furthermore, by such regulated intrusions into the normal actions of the brain it is possible to manipulate both engram and motive to ultimately reveal something of their neural nature.

TECHNIQUES

The electrode assemblies used in our experiments for chronic cortical stimulation have been described elsewhere (Doty *et al.*, 1956) and scarcely differ from those developed by Ewald (1898) and Talbert (1900) save that acrylic plastic is utilized in place of ivory. They are 7-mm.-diameter buttons bearing pointed platinum electrodes. The buttons are inserted into a trephine hole in the skull and held in place with screws. The dura is removed so that the electrodes rest on or within the cortex. The implantation procedure is simple, electrode orientation is exact, and access to the underlying cortex for surgical procedures is readily achieved. There is, however, a disadvantage in that connective tissue and bone regrowth tend to extrude the button from the skull in some animals over a period of months. Therefore, in cases where electrode orientation and subsequent surgery are not critical, the Delgado type of cortical electrode might be preferable.

[A section describing the electrode assembly and its implantation has been omitted.]

For stimulation of the cat cortex, 1-msec. rectangular current pulses are feedback-regulated to maintain constancy regardless of impedance changes. This regulation is a great convenience and makes threshold comparisons much more accurate by eliminating the variable capacitative waveforms found when current is obtained from a constant-voltage stimulator. Constant-current stimulators were not available for the work described later on subcortical stimulation or for cortical stimulation at two points. Stimulus frequency was 50/sec. for cortex and 300/sec. subcortically, with 0.2-msec. pulses in the latter case. All stimulation is delivered through closely approximated electrodes, the animal is never grounded, and all stimulating and monitoring circuits are isolated from ground. Such precautions are deemed essential to preclude any possibility of action of stimulating currents at points remote from the electrodes. All stimuli are monitored on cathode-ray oscilloscopes.

The " unidirectional " pulses to the cortex, seldom more than 1 ma. and delivered through platinum electrodes, seem to produce no particular tissue damage as judged histologically (Doty *et al.*, 1956) and by constancy of behavioral threshold over a period of months (Doty and Rutledge, 1959). This is not the case when a combination of nichrome electrodes and more intense currents is used, as in some of our stimulation of subcortical structures. Here a necrotic cyst about 1 mm. in diameter may form about the electrode tips, especially in cases where self-stimulation is induced.

To establish conditioned reflexes (CR's) to cortical stimulation as conditioned stimulus (CS) paired with shock as an unconditioned stimulus (US), we restrained cats in a hammock (Doty *et al.*, 1956) and gave them 20 combinations per day at about 1-minute intervals. They were trained to a criterion of 12 avoidances of the US in a single session. Without further training to the initial CS, tests were made for generalization to a second type of CS, which was also reinforced. Generalization was considered positive if CR's to the new CS occurred during the first session and if criterion was reached in about one-fourth the number of trials required for the CS used initially (Doty and Rutledge, 1959).

Earlier experiments showed that in working on marginal gyrus near the midline there is some danger of the animal receiving the CS via the trigeminal innervation of the meninges (as well as through intended cortical excitation). This could completely invalidate many of the conclusions reached in such work and hence must be very stringently controlled. Such a potential source of error does not seem to exist on the cat cortex farther laterally, but even here the control procedure of trigeminal neurotomy is performed in critical experiments.

Section of the fifth nerve in the cat is an exceedingly difficult surgical problem. The internal carotid artery, though small, makes a ventral approach impracticable, and lifting of the brain in a "subtemporal" approach provides little better access and would damage cortical electrode sites. Stereotaxic procedures seem much too inaccurate for this critical brain-stem region, where total destruction of the fifth nerve must be achieved without damaging the brachium conjunctivum, the vestibular inflow, etc. Thus the approach must be made through a 7- to 8-mm.-diameter opening rongeured in the occipital bone. The head should be held so that the cerebellum tends to fall medially away from this opening. The operator stands in front of the animal with light laterally from above. The cerebellum is slowly compressed with a pledget of cotton, and cerebrospinal fluid is continuously aspirated with a small polyethylene sucker. A large vein in the tentorial angle is followed down to its point of crossing to the brain stem. The fifth nerve is just beneath this vein and usually crossed by other veins. The nerve is first incised with a cataract knife and then hooked through with a Darling capsulotome. Only rarely is this accomplished without tearing some veins in the area. Even severe hemorrhage can be stopped, however, by repeated applications of room-temperature saline and gentle pressure. Cellulose sponge is not left within the skull, though the opening is covered with it. A period of ten days is needed, possibly for reorganization of vascular supply, before the second nerve can be safely cut. Bilateral section in one stage produces severely debilitated animals if hemorrhage is encountered. Subsequent to a bilateral denervation the animals must usually be assisted in eating for the remainder of their lives. Corneal ulceration always occurs but is not severe if general health is maintained.

CORTICAL STIMULATION AS *CS*

In a series of well-conceived and carefully executed experiments, Loucks (1933, 1935, 1938) demonstrated that after repeated coupling with a US, stimulation of the marginal gyrus in the dog could produce conditioned salivary or flexion responses. The modifiability of the response produced by cortical stimulation was even more dramatically evidenced in the cruciate area. Here stimulation initially produced movement of the right hind leg; but, after conditioning, movement of the left foreleg also occurred, even when the hind legs were paralyzed (Loucks, 1935).

Such experiments revealed that practicability of using central electrical excitation to analyze the neural processes involved in learning. Rutledge and I have tried to take advantage of this circumstance. Our validation and confirmation of Loucks appears elsewhere (Doty *et al.*, 1956; Doty, 1959), together with a consideration of the potential value of such experiments and the control of possible artifacts.

Perhaps the most interesting thing about cortical stimulation producing CR's is that it works. There are many reasons why it might not. The connections of the stimulated neurons might be inappropriate or too restricted, or their induced, synchronous activity might be so abnormal as to be ineffective. Electrical stimulation can block vision or voluntary movement in man (Penfield, 1958). And Chow (personal communication) has been able to show that bilateral stimulation of temporal lobes in monkeys can produce a localized afterdischarge during which certain visual discriminations are abolished. Electrical stimulation might even produce the spreading depression of Leão which Bureš has used to interfere with conditioning (Bureš and Burešová, 1959).

The question of induced electrical abnormalities for most of the work to date can be answered only by inference. Yet even when abnormalities are induced, as in the following example, they do not necessarily interfere with elaboration of CR's. Cat 58–24 had lesions aimed at transecting the thalamus in the stereotaxic planes A 7.5 to A 9.5, with destruction of medial diencephalic and hypothalamic nuclei on the right plus section of the posterior three-fourths of the corpus callosum. Stimulation from electrodes in the right anterior ectosylvian gyrus, probably corresponding to somatosensory area II (see Malcolm and Smith, 1958), produced Jacksonian seizures with current above 0.25 ma., thus indicating an exceptionally low seizure threshold (at least as compared with more dorsal and posterior cortex). At 0.2 ma. an after-discharge consistently appeared during which the left foreleg flexed in a series of minor twitches for 2 to 10 seconds, and whiskers and eyelids occasionally participated as well. Nonetheless, this stimulation was fully effective in producing flexion CR's of the right foreleg, which were then customarily followed by the left forepaw twitches.

This is an exceptional case, however, and usually no overt sign of the cortical stimulation is seen, especially after the first few presentations (Doty et al., 1956; Doty, 1959), until conditioned "emotional" reactions such as pupillary dilatation and cringing begin to appear. The current for cortical stimulation is set sufficiently high (0.8 ma. if seizures do not intervene) to be above the threshold for CR elicitation in the great majority of animals, yet usually below threshold for induced movement. The threshold for CR elicitation has not been found to correlate with electrode depth or location specified histologically and by sensorially evoked potentials. Indeed, the threshold, as judged by sampling different cortical regions in the same animal, seems to be a characteristic of the individual animal rather than the electrode location (Doty and Rutledge, 1959).

Only rarely does the suspicion arise that the cortical stimulation might be peculiarly incapable of engram formation or activation. In these cases an animal which has been trained to respond to several modalities of CS (e.g., tonal, photic, or cortical stimulation at one or more points) may in the identical situation fail to respond, for hundreds of trials, to stimulation at a particular cortical region. Again, an example may be useful. Cat 57–3 took 123 trials before two CR's had been made, and 371 trials to a criterion of fifteen CR's in 25 trials to a photic CS. On the first day's test with a tonal CS, seven CR's were made; and criterion performance was attained the following session, after a total of 49 trials. It then took 93 trials before two CR's were made to stimulation of the left middle ectosylvian gyrus at 0.7 ma., and criterion was obtained only after 250 trials at 0.9 ma. The threshold for performance at a level of 60 per cent or better to this direct cortical CS was then found to be 0.3 ma. Since the cortical stimulation is ultimately effective in such cases (the dramatic difference between milliamperes of current used during training and the ultimate threshold in the example is typical), the long period of ineffectiveness in these highly trained animals poses a very interesting problem. Is the excitation ineffective because it induces abnormal activity, or because it is not conducted to the right places in the right manner. There is some hope that this type of situation can be produced at will, in which case its detailed study, especially by electrical recording, will become feasible.

For the majority of the experiments it may be stated that no area of the cat cortex so far examined, including marginal, postlateral, posterior, and middle suprasylvian, and posterior, middle, and anterior ectosylvian gyri, has been found from which foreleg flexion CR's cannot ultimately be produced. Stated in different terms, the right foreleg can be caused to flex discretely by stimulation at any chosen cortical point. Obviously the neural circuitry is not nearly so simple as the latter statement might imply. Experiments with generalization show that once CR's have been established to stimulation of one cortical region, they may in a great many cases, with very little additional training, be elicited by stimulation of other cortical regions or by peripherally presented stimuli. If an animal is trained to stimulation of one marginal gyrus and this region is then removed and time is allowed for degeneration, stimulation of the other marginal gyrus produces CR's the first time tried. If the callosal fibers connecting one middle ectosylvian gyrus with the other are severed and the animal is trained to stimulation of one gyrus, it then responds immediately to stimulation of the other (Doty and Rutledge, 1959).

Thus the alteration of the nervous system which leads to foreleg flexion upon CS presentation is by no means restricted to the cortical zone stimulated. There are negative cases, particularly between certain heterotopic cortical regions, as exemplified in Cat 57–3, where such ready generalization does not occur. But so far these negative cases have only served to emphasize the meaningfulness of the positive cases. Nor can it be held that the cortical stimulation produces only some vague, undifferentiated activity which would be similar regardless of region, since it is possible to train cats to differentiate the location or the frequency of the cortical stimulus. The best explanation would appear to be one which puts the neural alteration someplace in the effector system. As Sperry (1955) has suggested, a change in level of excitability of a particular system would render it prone to be triggered by slight additional sensory input. The excitability of the "foreleg flexion system" is certainly increased by the experimental setting. Most cats come to a state in their training where occasional "spontaneous," indiscriminate flexions are made with no relation to the CS, simply as a consequence of being in the training apparatus. During the course of conditioning it is also possible to demonstrate that excitability of the flexor system of the limb being conditioned (and that limb only) is greatly enhanced during CS presentations almost 100 trials prior to the appearance of the first flexion CR's (Doty and Rutledge, 1959). Thus, in this type of conditioning, shifts in excitability within the motor system produce an organization not unlike that already known for certain complex brain-stem reflexes, such as deglutition, which are triggered into preset activity upon appropriate stimulation (Doty and Bosma, 1956).

Developing the paradigm, deglutition can, similarly to the conditioned flexion reflexes, be triggered by many inputs—e.g., from the amygdala, the precentral motor cortex, and the trigeminal, glossopharyngeal, superior laryngeal, and recurrent laryngeal nerves. And, as can be the case with differentiation in conditioned reflexes, the highly integrated motor pattern of such synergies as deglutition may best be triggered by specific temporal, and probably spatiotemporal, organizations of afferent input (Doty, 1951). From the pharyngeal region the motor organizations of sneezing, coughing, gagging, swallowing, or vomiting must be differentially elicited by afferent patterns selectively channeled to systems of motor control. Are these not, then, " phylogenetic engrams "? In terms of input and output organization, they are suggestively similar to the " individualized reflexes," i.e., conditioned reflexes, of Pavlov.

Considering the engram in the type of CR studied here to be principally an alteration in the threshold of a pre-existing foreleg flexion system, the question can then be asked, By what paths must the CS attain this motor organization to be effective? Obviously, on the basis of the foregoing data on generalization, the paths of access are multiple but not entirely unlimited. Starting from a chosen point of origin, the question can, however, be approached in a different fashion by surgical elimination of available paths. Rutledge and I have undertaken a rather arduous series of experiments of this type. For CS applied at the marginal gyrus, the unilateral lesions have included (in individual cases) severance of the white matter beneath the stimulated zone, circumsection of the gray matter around it, or destruction of most of the lateral geniculate nucleus and part of the internal capsule. With CS applied at the middle ectosylvian gyrus and the corpus callosum partially or totally sectioned, subcortical lesions have been placed to destroy the medial geniculate nucleus or to transect and destroy much of the medial diencephalon (as in Cat 58–24). While the experiments are still incomplete, two conclusions seem justified at this time.

First, as might be expected, none of these lesions has permanently abolished CR's in response to the cortically applied CS (nor to a tonal CS used to test the general state of the animal). Secondly, direct subcortical projection from the stimulated zone seems more important than elaboration of the CS over intracortical paths. In eight cats in which the cortex was circumsected about the stimulating electrodes, a procedure which inevitably traumatizes the stimulated region, an average of only 80 trials of retraining was required. On the other hand, section of the white matter for a distance of 9 to 15 mm. beneath the cortical electrodes without disturbing them necessitated, for twelve cases, an average of 200 trials of retraining with suprathreshold stimuli. The average for initial training of thirty-five animals, with excitation of this area as CS, was 185 trials; and generalization to homotopic marginal gyrus in eleven animals averaged 73 trials. Thus, though stimulation was applied to the selfsame area, there was no generalization between stimulation in the intact and undercut conditions; complete retraining was ordinarily required.

There are obviously many extensions of this approach by which it should be possible to destroy a behaviorally effective pathway and then, having limited the egress of the applied stimulus, follow the redevelopment of the effect along preselected routes. The isolated neural networks studied by Burns (1958) are shown here to be capable of conducting excitation of behavioral significance. The rate of conduction can be a limiting factor, since on one animal it could be repeatedly demonstrated that a CS of 0.2 ma. was effective in producing a CR within 3 to 4 seconds, but not within the 2 seconds customarily elapsing between CS onset and US. It required 1.0 ma. for CR's with the latter latency. When the undercutting extends for only 5 to 6 mm., the initial postoperative effectiveness of the CS is diminished but not lost.

It is tempting to regard the ineffectiveness of the CS after undercutting as a failure to activate the engram system. Inappropriateness of connection or pattern of activity would thus be implied, much as with the failure of generalization exemplified by Cat 57–3. However, it is also possible that excitation is not being conducted through the cortical neuropil during the month or so of retraining. The fact that animals in this experimental setting generalize to another CS in 75 per cent of the tests (Doty and Rutledge, 1959) favors the latter view—i.e., if the excitation were conducted, CR's should be expected. Time alone may thus be an important factor in the reorganization of such partially denervated cortex; and, though only minimal changes appear in cyto-architecture, development of supersensitivity of denervation could conceivably be important.

[A section on self-stimulation of subcortical structures has been omitted. An account of similar work is H. C. Nielson, R. W. Doty, and L. T. Rutledge, Motivational and perceptual aspects of subcortical stimulation in cats. *Amer. J. Physiol.*, 1958, **194**, 427–432.]

FORMATION OF CONDITIONED REFLEXES INDEPENDENT OF MOTIVATION

Though it is common experience that temporal or spatial juxtaposition of events tends to form a lasting association between them, and though " associationism " has played a prominent role in psychological theory, it has been difficult to find unassailable experimental demonstrations of this effect. Prima facie, the conditioned reflex is formed purely on the basis of temporal association between CS and US; indeed, the co-originator of this experimental procedure, Bekhterev (1911), termed it an " associative reflex." However, in the usual conditioning procedure there is a strong motivational factor, and it is generally held that this factor of motivation, " drive-reduction," etc., is an essential element in the learning process. A review of the evidence for this position is not pertinent here save to point out that the findings of Loucks (1935) that CR's could not be established to " motor " cortex stimulation as US unless a food reward was introduced, played a prominent part in establishing this thesis.

In experimentation with human subjects the situation is too complex to be certain that associations can be formed free of motivation. Animal experiments with sensory-sensory conditioning are likewise complex and suffer not only from the possibility of stimulus generalization but also from the necessity of proving the association by training the animals in a motivational situation. Several electrophysiological experiments, such as those of Jasper and Shagass

(1941), Morrell and Jasper (1956), and Buser and Rougeul (1956), show neural alterations in which a motivational component is clearly lacking, but so too is any immediate behavioral connotation. The alterations of excitability studied by Brown-Sequard (1884) and Baer (1905) are perhaps pertinent but ephemeral. So too is the effect reported by Rusinov (1953) in which a discrete flexion of a rabbit's forepaw can be obtained by an intense auditory stimulus for some twenty minutes after application of a small polarizing current to the appropriate area of "motor" cortex. All these experiments, however, possess elements suggestive of conditioned reflex activity without a motivational component.

The evidence of Brogden and Gantt (1942) is more convincing. They employed stimulation of the cerebellum as US, and a bell or light for CS. After a number of pairings the CS, in certain animals, came to evoke movements very similar to those induced by cerebellar stimulation. Kriayev (see Giurgea, 1953) apparently demonstrated a similar effect using stimulation of the "motor" cortex. The experiments of Giurgea carry this approach still farther and establish unequivocally the fact that, contrary to the negative results of Loucks, stimulation of "motor" cortex can be used as US in establishing CR's. Nikolaeva (1957) has reported similar experiments with cats without remarking their uniqueness.

Giurgea (1953, 1955) began his experiments in 1951 in the laboratories of P. S. Kupalov, seeking experimental confirmation of the latter's hypothesis of "shortened conditioned reflexes." Thus both CS and US were applied to the cortex electrically—the CS to the occipital area, the US to the sigmoid gyrus. Dogs were used in all experiments. Six to ten pairings were given per day at 3- to 5-minute intervals. The cortical stimulation was a 50/sec. alternating sinusoidal current of about 1 to 5 volts. It was applied through permanently implanted electrodes of 0.3-mm.-diameter silver wire about 3 to 4 mm. apart, resting on the dura mater. Results with the first animal are typical of about thirty studied so far. This first experiment is exceptional only insofar as massed trials were used, i.e., 42 and 21 trials on the first two days, respectively. The cortical US in this animal produced an abrupt inclination of the head down 90°, then a slower rotation up to the right with the right cheek up and a turning of the forequarters to the right. For the first 18 stimulations of the occipital cortex there was no reaction. On the 19th pairing there was a slight shaking of the head to the CS. On the 24th, 26th, and 30th trials there was a very slight rotation of the head to the right; on the 31st the same, but to the left. On trials 35 to 42 the CS evoked a definite movement of the head to the right in seven of the eight presentations. The following day this CR of turning the head to the right occurred in 18 of 21 trials; in one of these it was almost identical with the UR.

Continuing this type of experiment in Bucharest, Giurgea and his colleagues discovered the following facts about this phenomenon: It is not dependent upon meningeal stimulation, for such CR's can be established after destruction of the Gasserian ganglion on the pertinent side (Raiciulescu *et al.*, 1956). After establishing such a CR to stimulation of parietal-occipital cortex as CS, generalization was obtained to a photic CS and to a tonal CS (Giurgea and Raiciulescu, 1957). A subcortical mechanism is involved, since CR's of this type were established in two animals when the CS and US were delivered to different hemispheres following total, histologically confirmed section of the corpus callosum (Raiciulescu and Giurgea, 1957; Giurgea *et al.*, 1957). The electrical activity recorded from electrodes in the US area does not appear to be changed by this procedure and is within normal limits of low voltage, fast activity very shortly after a US is applied (Giurgea and Raiciulescu, 1959). If the CS is applied at intervals of 2 minutes or less, in most but not all animals the CR disappears (Giurgea, 1953, 1955), although the UR is unaffected. This disappearance phenomenon is similar to that seen in the usual type of Pavlovian conditioning; in the Russian school it is considered to be a manifestation of overactivity producing a Wedensky-type inhibition in complex neural circuits. It is termed "supraliminal inhibition" ("hyperliminal" would probably be a better term). This disappearance of the CR with frequent presentation of the CS probably explains the failure of Loucks (1935) to obtain this type of conditioning, since all his intertrial intervals were 2 minutes or less, usually 30 to 60 seconds.

In the spring of 1958 Giurgea spent three months in our laboratories at Michigan, where we were able to duplicate his basic observations and examine more fully the absence of motivational effects in these phenomena. The following summaries of experiments on four dogs represents our joint effort in this regard (Doty and Giurgea, 1958):

Dog Alpha was an alert, active male of 13 kg. Stimulation with any combination of six electrodes in the postcruciate area produced extremely stiff, unnatural movements. A mild tic of the right shoulder at an irregular rate averaging 1/sec. was noted postoperatively and persisted throughout the animal's survival. It might have arisen from three small cotton balls neglectfully left between dura and cortex when achieving hemostasis at the time of electrode implantation. There was no electrical abnormality, however, in records taken from the adjacent electrodes.

Stimulation at 1.8 ma. of an area immediately posterior to the left postcruciate sulcus was used as US; it produced a lifting and extension of the right hind leg, a slight lifting and curling of the tail, and rotation of the head to the midline and down. The necessity for such high currents probably indicates poor contact of electrodes with the cortex because of the thickness of the skull. The CS of 1.1 ma. was applied to the left posterior suprasylvian gyrus. Pairing was begun on the ninth postoperative day. For 38 of the 42 times the CS was presented during the first five days of training, there was no response whatever. On the other four occasions there was equivocal head movement and alerting. The CS current was increased and maintained at 2.2 ma. during and after the sixth training session. The CS thenceforth produced an opening of the eyes and turning of the head to the right—a movement so consistent that there seems little doubt it was "inherent" to this stimulated area. On the 30th post-operative day, after 108 pairings and a hiatus of 11 days in the sessions, the first distinct "CR's" were made. The CS current had now been reduced to 1.0 ma., and during the first six presentations of this 14th session it elicited eye opening and turning of the head to the right. On the last four trials, however, the head turned to the left against this "inherent" movement and was brought to the midline and down, thus reproducing a portion of the UR. This latter movement to the CS was seen in a high percentage (up to 100 per cent in a particular session) of presentations during the subsequent sessions; it had a threshold of about 0.3 ma. and could be elicited by 0.4 ma. applied to another pair of electrodes in the same posterior suprasylvian area. Movement of the leg or tail to the CS was never seen.

The animal was then given a CS of 3/sec. clicks, with the same US. In the first session, the first five trials produced no response; the last three produced some equivocal head movement. In the next session and from then on to a total of 81 trials in 13 sessions, the clicking CS evoked "CR's" almost identical with those seen to posterior suprasylvian CS. A different UR was then tried— an abrupt, stiff, high lift of the right foreleg which was frequently accompanied by a slight lift of the left hind leg and elevation of the proximal tail. A 9/sec.-click CS was used for 85 trials. At first the previously established "CR" was obtained, but this became modified to a side-to-side movement of the head with the nose pointing slightly down.

Considerable training was required to teach this dog to eat in the experimental situation and to press a lever for food rewards. Ultimately it was shown that the animal would press indefinitely, e.g., 50 times for 12 food rewards, with cortical stimulation at CS or US areas being coupled with each press. The US currents produced several aborted seizures and caused slowing of the response rate only insofar as they unbalanced the animal by the sheer violence of the induced movement. No overt reaction occurred to the posterior supra-sylvian stimulation at 1.1 ma. during lever-pressing. A single tap on the side of the cage accompanying a lever press for food could abolish pressing for five minutes, and if repeated brought this behavior to a complete halt.

Dog Beta was a 7.5-kg. male, a dachshund-beagle type. The slightest discomfort or forceful restraint, such as merely taking hold of the animal by the scruff of the neck, brought forth vigorous and persistent yelping and whining. A US of 2.0 to 2.5 ma. applied to the right postcruciate gyrus produced a brisk, high, natural-appearing flexion of the left hind leg uncontaminated by other movement. Prior to pairing, the CS to the right marginal gyrus was very carefully studied; it produced no overt sign even at intensities of 2.2 ma.

Pairing was begun on the sixth postoperative day, with a 1.8- to 2.0-ma. CS. The first sign of movement to the marginal gyrus CS occurred on the 45th pairing during the sixth session. This was a tossing of the head and other indefinite movements—such as stepping or shifting of weight—which became very common throughout subsequent trials. The first CR occurred on the 66th pairing during the ninth session on the 22nd postoperative day. It consisted of two 10-cm. flexions of the left hind leg without other movement during the CS.

These flexions, and all others scored as CR's, were lifts of the leg which were held for about one second. They were distinctly different from the stepping movements and restlessness which occurred to the CS much more often. The limb was usually replaced prior to the UR. These CR's also occurred after both hind legs had been freed of the restraining harness. During extinction these CR's were occasionally so identical with the UR that the experimenters jumped to check the equipment thinking the postcruciate gyrus had been stimulated through error. The threshold for eliciting this CR with marginal gyrus CS was 0.95 ma.; for "restlessness," it was 0.6 ma. The CR occurred 74 times in 171 presentations (including extinction) after its first appearance.

Stimulation of the right posterior ectosylvian gyrus had never been paired with the US; yet, when tested during the 17th session and after 120 marginal gyrus CS's, it produced head bobbing and a little stepping at 1.3 and 1.8 ma. Tests on the fifth postoperative day had yielded no response from this area at 2.2 ma. Full CR's were subsequently obtained by ectosylvian stimulation.

Extinction of the CR was then attempted, by presenting the marginal gyrus CS at 2-minute intervals and giving 15 trials per day. Extinction was not obtained by this method. The protocol for the 84th presentation at 1.6 ma. reads: "Immediate flexion of the left hind leg, brief and about 5 cm. Replaced; then a 12-cm. maintained lift enduring at least 2 seconds—just like a UR in vigor, intensity, and duration." At this stage of extinction, posterior ectosylvian stimulation produced a CR on only one of twelve presentations during five sessions; the others yielded no response. Stimulation at the base of the brain in the left temporal polar gyrus produced a "pointing" reaction during which the nostrils flared and the animal remained immobile with head and eyes fixed to the right; but there was no evidence of CR's in five presentations. There was no response to 3/sec. clicks.

Trouble with the electrode connector precluded testing in a lever-pressing situation. However, there was little need for such a test. This animal daily ran to the experimental room and jumped into the cage to be harnessed. There was no evidence of pain or any emotion during any of the training sessions. The animal's ability to evidence such factors was further demonstrated at the end of the experiment, when stimulation through the faulty connector produced immediate pain reactions.

Dog Gamma was a clumsy and lively 16-kg. male. The thickness of the skull made electrode placement difficult, and no uncomplicated movements could be obtained from stimulation in the postcruciate area. Subcortical stimulation of 0.4 ma. was thus used as US. It was applied to electrodes 1.5 mm. above the right pyramid at the level of the caudal tip of the mammillary bodies, 3.5 mm. lateral to the midline in the external medullary lamina, field H_1 of Forel. It produced a forceful extension of the neck and rotation of the head up over the right shoulder, wider opening of the eyes, flaring of nostrils, and occasionally a lifting of the right lip. The CS was applied to the left posterior ectosylvian gyrus at 2.2 ma.; it produced no response or indication of effectiveness for 68 pairings in ten sessions. The CS was then tried at 4.8 ma. without producing any overt effect; and from this it was concluded that the electrodes were not contacting the cortex.

A 4-second CS of 12 clicks was then paired with the field-of-Forel US. This CS produced very little orienting, and there was essentially no response during the first session. Nonspecific movements and whining occurred to the CS in the second session. The first CS of the third session, which was the 16th trial, elicited a turning of the head up and 130° right. Similar CR's occurred for six of the seven presentations that day. With progression of the pairings, the CS came to evoke a mounting state of agitation in which the animal whined, yelped, and pulled at the harness on every presentation. CR's of extension and rotation of the head and neck to the right occurred on 48 of the 96 presentations after the first CR was made. The CR was usually superseded by agitation prior to the UR. The CR, and in great measure the agitation as well, was extinguished in three sessions, totaling 22 presentations of CS alone.

This animal pressed the lever most avidly for food. Presentation of the click CS and other sounds caused considerable inhibition when coupled with pressing, but did not halt pressing entirely. Hesitation also developed at first during postcruciate stimulation, producing a hind leg lift, but subsequently did not alter pressing behavior. Coupling 0.2 ma. stimulation at the field-of-Forel point with each lever press had no effect; 0.3 ma. greatly reduced the pressing rate; and 0.4 ma. abolished pressing entirely.

Dog Epsilon, a 16-kg. male, was very lively and friendly but cowered and slunk along the floor when approached. For the first two of the eight months of work with this animal, it slouched in the restraining harness and adopted odd cataleptic-like postures. This behavior gradually subsided, and more normal posture was then maintained during the training sessions. The positions of the pertinent electrodes are shown in Fig. 1.

On the third postoperative day, stimulation of electrodes 5–6 at 1.6 ma., and 7–10 at 1.8 ma., gave no response. Pairing stimulation of 7–10 as CS with 3–4 as US was begun on the fourth postoperative day with 1.6 ma. and 0.8 ma., respectively. Orientation and slight turning of the head to the left was seen on the 1st and 11th CS presentations, but no other response occurred until the animal stood up and stepped forward on the 40th presentation during the sixth session. In the next sessions the CS frequently elicited a lowering of the head and a flexion of the right foreleg, though the UR was a lift of the left foreleg. The first flexion of the left foreleg to the CS occurred on the 81st presentation, during the 12th session, 16th postoperative day. On this occasion the head was lowered to the CS, and after some slight general movement there occurred a 4-cm. flexion of the right foreleg for 0.5 second. This was followed by a 15-cm. flexion of the left foreleg, which was held for 1.5 seconds and passed directly into the UR. With further pairing the right foreleg movements became less frequent and the left foreleg lifting more intense until it often equaled the UR in height and was held for 1 to 3 seconds. Movement of some sort now occurred to the CS about 95 per cent of the time; and CR's, though irregular in their predictability, occurred to 0.5-ma. and consistently to 0.7-ma. CS.

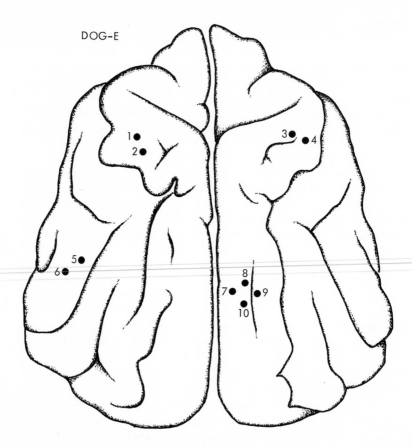

Fig. 1. Positions of stimulating electrodes on the surface of the brain of Dog Epsilon.

After 194 pairings and 58 left foreleg CR's, stimulation of 2.0 ma. through electrodes 5–6 was tried four times, paired with US to 3–4. On the second, third, and fourth presentations the right foreleg was lifted. Two sessions later the posterior ectosylvian stimulus was given at 1.6 ma. without being paired with a US. On the fifth such presentation the animal straightened his stance slightly and lifted the left foreleg for 2 seconds at a height of 10 cm. Differentiation was attempted without success, as shown in Table 1. Although some movement occurred to either the CS or the posterior ectosylvian stimulation on nearly every presentation, specific maintained elevations of the limbs were inconsistent.

Table 1   Initial Failure of Differentiation in Dog Epsilon

STIMULUS LOCATION	TOTAL DIFFERENTIATION TRIALS	LFL CR'S	RFL CR'S
Right marginal gyrus (US to right post-cruciate)	50	11	7
Left posterior ectosylvian gyrus (no US)	44	14	5

Stimulation of 1.2 ma. at electrodes 1–2 was then given 100 times by itself in twelve sessions, each time producing the right foreleg lift. . . . There were no spontaneous lifts of this leg during this period, though the left foreleg was occasionally lifted during some sessions. Stimulation at electrodes 5–6 with 1.0 ma. in 20 presentations through three sessions still produced five left foreleg CR's and no right foreleg lifts. The posterior ectosylvian stimulus was then paired with left postcruciate stimulation in a random temporal relation between the stimuli—i.e., " CS " might precede " US " by 15 seconds or follow by 75 seconds, etc. This was done 80 times in ten sessions; then, for nine sessions and 70 times, the " US " preceded the " CS " by 5 seconds. During these procedures the right foreleg was raised to the " CS " only once, on the 40th presentation, and the left foreleg twice. At first the stimulation at electrodes 5–6 produced stepping and a turning of the head down and to the right, but this subsided, so that in 39 of the last 70 presentations there was no response whatever to this " CS ".

Pairing was then begun for these stimuli in the usual temporal relation for conditioning. The effectiveness of the posterior ectosylvian stimulation in eliciting stepping and head movements promptly returned. At the 56th, 57th, and 58th pairings, postural preparation for the UR was made with a shift of weight from the right foreleg and tension of the right shoulder. This occurred irregularly from this point on. Such shifting and tension is here termed a " partial " CR. During trials 99 to 114 a sustained lifting of the left foreleg was elicited seven times. This had not been seen for more than a month of 30 sessions. The first right foreleg lift occurred at the 120th pairing; it had likewise been absent for 30 sessions. For a period of 19 days with 14 sessions, during trials 158 to 264, there were 45 sustained lifts of the right foreleg to stimulation at electrodes 5–6. The threshold for this effect was about 0.7 ma. During these 106 trials, 13 partial CR's of the right foreleg and 11 left foreleg CR's were also noted. At other times the CS usually produced stepping movements, most frequently of the right foreleg. Occasionally there was no response whatever.

Stimulation of 1.0 ma. was then applied alone to electrodes 7–10 for the first time in 79 days. The protocol reads: "Seemed to cause considerable arousal and a twisting movement of the head to the right with left ear up. The left foreleg was lifted 15 cm., flexing at the wrist, and held for about 5 seconds." This was a far more vigorous movement than any caused by stimulation at electrodes 5–6, and frequently thereafter lifts of 30 cm. were observed. On subsequent days it was shown that 1.1-ma. stimulation at electrodes 8–9 also produced this strong left foreleg CR, though stimulation at electrodes 1–2 had never been paired with this CS and was never used in this period. As stimulation at the marginal gyrus was resumed, the dog began to show great hesitation about entering the experimental room, and the behavior in the harness reverted to the slouching and catalepsis displayed when this animal was first introduced to the experimental situation. The stimulation at electrodes 7–10 had been given 18 times sporadically in ten days, and then 35 times at 1-minute intervals in three sessions, never coupled with postcruciate stimulation. There was no evidence of any "extinction" of the left foreleg response.

The effect of coupling stimulation with lever-pressing was then studied for one month. The same stimulation at electrodes 1–2, 3–4, and 5–6 which had served as US and CS had no effect on persistency of pressing. On the other hand, a few clicks, or a "crow call," or stimulation through electrodes 7–10 coupled with pressing could abolish the pressing completely. In such cases the animal returned to the slouching postures seen previously, hanging limply in the harness. Efforts in two sessions to establish habituation to clicks were unsuccessful, and no pressing could be elicited after clicks had been introduced.

Responses to direct currents applied between cortical electrode pairs 5–6 as CS and 1–2 as US were then studied 75 days after the previous pairings. The US at about 0.3-ma. d.c. sometimes produced a moderate flexion of the right foreleg; but more often it did not. After the 46th pairing, 50/sec., 1-msec. pulses were used again. For the first two sessions and 12 trials the CS at 0.23- to 0.3-ma. d.c. produced very slight alerting five times. In the seven trials of the third session the same CS four times evoked discrete 5-cm. lifts of the right foreleg, which were held for more than one second. Stepping movements of the right foreleg were common on occasions when specific lift CR's did not occur. After 84 pairings, 0.3-ma. d.c. was twice applied to electrodes 7–10 without overt effect. Then, through error, after the 91st pairing of 5–6 with 1–2, the 1–2 electrode stimulus was paired once with the CS at 7–10. Thenceforth, stimulation at 7–10, with 0.4-ma. d.c., produced four 4-cm. lifts of the right foreleg in five presentations. After a change to 50/sec. rather than d.c. stimulation for subsequent sessions, the stimulation at 5–6 with 0.9 ma. produced right foreleg lifts of 8 to 10 cm. enduring several seconds. The stimulation at 7–10 evoked either right or left foreleg lifts. After one pairing of stimulation at 3–4, the CS at 7–10 evoked left foreleg lifts on four of five presentations, while two stimulations at 5–6 continued to produce right foreleg lifts.

CONCLUSIONS CONCERNING NONMOTIVATED CR'S

Several general conclusions seem warranted by the evidence accumulated. The cortical stimulation used in establishing these conditioned reflexes has no motivational aspect in the usual sense of the word. This is not to say that this stimulation does not reach neurons of the hypothalamic or limbic systems. However, the effect of cortical stimulation of convulsive strength eliciting movements of exceptional forcefulness is so completely different from the total inhibition of lever-pressing produced by the most innocuous exteroceptive stimulation, that the neural organizations of these two types of stimulation must be profoundly different. That central stimulation in certain areas has strong motivational effects is well known and is illustrated for stimulation in the field H_1 of Forel in Dog Gamma. The avoidance of stimulation at the marginal gyrus shown by Dog Epsilon is probably explained on the basis of regrowth of trigeminal fibers into the connective tissue around the electrodes during the five months following implantation. This animal's sudden avoidance of the experimental situation when the stimulation was resumed also indicates that a factor of unpleasantness had developed which was not present initially. It is difficult to gauge the strength of this motivational factor, since auditory stimulation coupled with lever-pressing had the same effect as did marginal gyrus stimulation. The possibility of rewarding effects from the cortical stimulation used here seems rather remote and, if present, was not revealed by the lever-pressing tests.

The presence of another type of mild motivational factor can be dismissed on logical grounds. It could be argued that the CR's were a postural preparation to lessen the forcefulness of the UR. However, in the great majority of cases the leg was lifted several centimeters in the CR, then returned to the floor and in no way appeared to alter the course of the UR. It also seemed on occasion as though the CR was elicited with relative directness rather than via a synthesized movement, since, if posture was inadequate, muscles of the affected limb quivered and tensed but were ineffective in overcoming the postural setting. In animals Alpha and Gamma, where extreme muscular tension was most prominent, the CR's were least consistent and least like the UR. The confusion of limbs in Dog Epsilon, in which the CR often occurred in the "wrong" limb, resulting in abrupt postural reversal with the UR, gives further evidence that "purposiveness" and "preparation" are not adequate explanations for the CR's observed. Loucks (1938), however, reports a similar confusion for one animal in which marginal gyrus stimulation was used as CS and leg-shock as US, and Kellogg and Walker (1938) report the same for a peripherally presented CS under certain conditions. Thus this complication is common to this experimental situation but nonetheless hard to rationalize in motivational terms.

The more important question is, How are these "connections" formed so that stimulation in either hemisphere in widely differing sectors can induce movement of either limb (Dog Epsilon) or even a movement counter to that inherent to the area (Dog Alpha)? A primary requirement seems to lie in the temporal relation between the two stimuli. The long-repeated presentation of the US alone in dogs Gamma and Epsilon produced no change; nor did 150 pairings for Dog Epsilon in which the US in effect preceded the CS. Thus the observed phenomena are not mere artifacts developing as a consequence of stimulation per se. Since the complexities of motivation cannot here be called upon, it follows that higher neural action is so regulated that a "prior" excitation tends to evoke the same effect as a "subsequent" excitation with which it is repeatedly associated. Seemingly, the only logical place for this effect to occur is in alteration of the excitability of the particular system reached by "subsequent" excitation—an effector system by necessity in these studies. The evidence suggests this. It is characteristic of the animals in these and other (Giurgea, 1953, 1955) experiments that as the CR first begins to develop, minor stepping movements in the affected limb begin to appear in the absence of a CS, indicating that the motor threshold is probably lowered. The generalization to a new CS, seen particularly in Dog Epsilon and the earlier experiments of Giurgea and Raiciulescu (1959), and also in dogs Alpha and Gamma and to a limited degree in Beta, gives further evidence that the major alteration lies in the effector system.

Among the more serious difficulties with this concept is the confusion of limbs in Dog Epsilon. If it is the stimulated motor system which is undergoing a change in excitability, how is it that the system first responding was the contralateral analogue of the system stimulated? Speculative explanations might be found for this phenomenon, but there are indications that change is not limited to the effector system. There is a great alteration in the effectiveness of the CS in producing arousal, restlessness, and other non-specific movement unrelated to the UR, which is reminiscent of the augmentation of electrically measured arousal reactions seen during the course of "motivated" conditioning (Beck et al., 1958). This again does not arise simply from repetition but requires a particular temporal order of coupled stimulations. The evidence from Dog Epsilon, in fact, suggests that the repetition of the CS alone results in suppression of this arousal effect, much as in the process of habituation or the formation of a "primary inhibitory stimulus" (Szwejkowska, 1957), and makes subsequent use of this stimulation as a normal CS considerably more difficult. In the later experiments with Dog Epsilon the CS from one hemisphere tended, without pairing with the US, to produce CR's in the limb being activated by the US then commonly in use, thus indicating alteration more or less specific to the UR system. However, evidence was also gained that, by appropriate pairing, one limb could be raised to one CS, the other limb to the other CS. Here, as in all instances of differential responsiveness, simple "excitability change" in the effector system is not a sufficient explanation. A specificity is required which must ultimately come from the CS. Whether the specificity arises through altered receptivity imposed by the CS upon the effector system, or through intensification of afferent activity, or both, must be answered by experiment.

ACKNOWLEDGMENTS

I am extremely indebted to my colleagues Corneliu Giurgea, Lester T. Rutledge, and Cornelius Van Nuis, who share credit for the facts but not necessarily responsibility for the opinions expressed herein. I am also indebted to E. Roy John for bringing my attention to the writings of Brown-Sequard, Wedensky, and Baer.

REFERENCES

BAER, A. Ueber gleichzeitige elektrische Reizung zweier Grosshirnstellen am ungehemmten Hunde. *Pflüg. Arch. ges. Physiol.*, 1905, **106**, 523–567.

BECK, E. C., DOTY, R. W., & KOOI, K. A. Electrocortical reactions associated with conditioned flexion reflexes. *Electroenceph. clin. Neurophysiol.*, 1958, **10**, 279–289.

BEKHTEREV, V. M. *Die Funktionen der Nervencentra.* Vol. III. Jena: G. Fischer, 1911. Pp. 2014–2031.

BETZ, W. Anatomischer Nachweis zweier Gehirncentra. *Zbl. med. Wiss.*, 1874, **12**, 578–580, 595–599.

BROGDEN, W. J., & GANTT, W. H. Intraneural conditioning: Cerebellar conditioned reflexes. *Arch. Neurol. Psychiat.*, Chicago, 1942, **48**, 437–455.

BROWN-SEQUARD, M. Existence de l'excitabilité motrice et de l'excitabilité inhibitoire dans les régions occipitales et sphénoidales de l'écorce cérébrale. *C. R. Soc. Biol.*, Paris, 1884, 301–303.

BUREŠ, J., & BUREŠOVÁ, O. The use of Leâo's spreading cortical depression in research on conditioned reflexes. *Electroenceph. Clin. Neurophysiol.*, suppl. 13. Moscow colloquium on EEG of higher nervous activity, 1959.

BURNS, B. *The mammalian cerebral cortex.* London: Arnold, 1958.

BUSER, P., & ROUGEUL, A. Réponses sensorielles corticales chez le chat en préparation chronique. Leurs modifications lors de l'établissement de liaisons temporaires. *Rev. neurol.*, 1956, **95**, 501–503.

DOTY, R. W. Influence of stimulus pattern on reflex deglutition. *Amer. J. Physiol.*, 1951, **166**, 142–158.

DOTY, R. W. Brain stimulation and conditional reflexes. In M. A. B. Brazier (Ed.), *The central nervous system and behavior.* New York: Josiah Macy, Jr., Foundation, 1959, Pp. 241–306.

DOTY, R. W., & BOSMA, J. F. An electromyographic analysis of reflex deglutition. *J. Neurophysiol.*, 1956, **19**, 44–60.

DOTY, R. W., & GIURGEA, C. Conditioned reflexes established by coupling visual and motor cortex stimulation. *Physiologist*, 1958, **1**, 17.

DOTY, R. W., & RUTLEDGE, L. T. Generalization between cortically and peripherally applied stimuli eliciting conditioned reflexes. *J. Neurophysiol.*, 1959, **22**, 428–435.

DOTY, R. W., RUTLEDGE, L. T., JR., & LARSEN, R. M. Conditioned reflexes established to electrical stimulation of cat cerebral cortex. *J. Neurophysiol.*, 1956, **19**, 401–415.

EWALD, J. R. Ueber künstlich erzeugte Epilepsie. *Berl. klin. Wschr.*, 1898, **35**, 698.

FRITSCH, G., & HITZIG., E. Ueber die elektrische Erregbarkeit des Grosshirns. *Arch. Anat. Physiol.*, Lpz., 1870, **37**, 300–332.

GIURGEA, C. *Elaborarea reflexului conditionat prin excitarea directa a scoartei cerebrale.* Bucharest: Editura Academiei Rep. Pop. Romane, 1953.

GIURGEA, C. Die Dynamik der Ausarbeitung einer zeitlichen Beziehung durch direkte Reizung der Hirnrinde. *Ber. ges. Physiol.*, 1955, **175**, 80.

GIURGEA, C., & RAICIULESCU, N. Noi date asupra reflexului conditionat prin excitarea directa a cortexului cerebral. *Rev. Fiziol. norm. Pat.*, 1957, **4**, 218–225.

GIURGEA, C., & RAICIULESCU, N. Études électroencéphalographiques et neurophysiologiques sur les réflexes conditionées à l'excitation directe électrique du cortex cérébral. In. L. van Bogaert (Ed.), *Proceedings of the first international congress of neurological sciences. Vol.* 3. London: Pergamon, 1959.

GIURGEA, C., RAICIULESCU, N., & MARCOVICI, G. Reflex conditionat interemisferic prin excitarea directa corticala dupa sectionarea corpului calos. Studiu anatomo-histologic. *Rev. Fiziol. norm. Pat.*, 1957, **4**, 408–414.

HITZIG, E. Physiologisches und therapeutisches über einige elektrische Reizmethoden. *Berlin klin. Wschr.*, 1870, **7**, 137–138.

HUGHES, J. R. Studies on the supracallosal mesial cortex of unanesthetized, conscious mammals. I: Cat. Movements elicited by electrical stimulation. *Electroenceph. Clin. Neurophysiol.*, 1959, **11**, 447–458.

JASPER, H. H., & SHAGASS, C. Conditioning the occipital alpha rhythm in man. *J. Exp. Psychol.*, 1941, **28**, 373–388.

KELLOGG, W. N., & WALKER, E. L. "Ambiguous conditioning." A phenomenon of bilateral transfer. *J. comp. Psychol.*, 1938, **26**, 63–77.

LILLY, J. C. Correlations between neurophysiological activity in the cortex and short-term behavior in the monkey. In H. F. Harlow and C. N. Woolsey (Eds.), *Biological and biochemical bases of behavior.* Madison: University of Wisconsin Press, 1958, Pp. 83–100.

LOUCKS, R. B. Preliminary report of a technique for stimulation or destruction of tissues beneath the integument and the establishing of a conditioned reaction with faradization of the cerebral cortex. *J. Comp. Psychol.*, 1933, **16**, 439–444.

LOUCKS, R. B. The experimental delimitation of neural structures essential for learning: The attempt to condition striped muscle responses with faradization of the sigmoid gyri. *J. Psychol.*, 1935, **1**, 5–44.

LOUCKS, R. B. Studies of neural structures essential for learning. II: The conditioning of salivary and striped muscle responses to faradization of cortical sensory elements, and the action of sleep upon such mechanisms. *J. Comp. Psychol.*, 1938, **25**, 315–332.

MALCOLM, J. L., & SMITH, I. D. Convergence within the pathways to cat's somatic sensory cortex activated by mechanical stimulation of the skin. *J. Physiol.*, 1958, **144**, 257–270.

MORRELL, F., & JASPER, H. H. Electrographic studies of the formation of temporary connections in the brain. *Electroenceph. Clin. Neurophysiol.*, 1956, **8**, 201–215.

NIKOLAEVA, N. I. Summation of stimuli in the cerebral cortex. *Sechenov J. Physiol.*, USSR, 1957, **43**, 27–34.

PENFIELD, W. *The excitable cortex of conscious man.* Springfield, Ill: Charles C. Thomas, 1958.

RAICIULESCU, N., & GIURGEA, C. Reflex conditionat interemisferic prin excitarea electrica directa a scoartei cerebrale dupa sectionarea corpului calos. *Rev. Fiziol. norm. Pat.*, 1957, **4**, 336–339.

RAICIULESCU, N., GIURGEA, C., & SAVESCU, C. Reflex conditionat la excitarea directa a cortexului cerebral dupa distrugerea ganglionului lui Gasser. *Rev. Fiziol. norm. Pat.*, 1956, **3**, 304–308.

RUSINOV, V. S. An electrophysiological analysis of the connecting function in the cerebral cortex in the presence of a dominant area. *Comm. XIX Int. Physiol. Congr.*, Moscow. Izdatel'stvo Akademii Nauk SSSR, 1953, 152–156.

SOLTMANN, O. Experimentelle Studien über die Funktionen des Grosshirns der Neugeborenen. *Jb. Kinderheilk.*, 1876, **9**, 106–148.

SPERRY, R. W. On the neural basis of the conditioned response. *Brit. J. Animal Behav.*, 1955, **3**, 41–44.

SZWEJKOWSKA, G. The effect of a primary inhibitory stimulus upon the positive salivary conditioned reflex. *Bull. Acad. polonaise Sci.*, 1957, **5**, 393–396.

TALBERT, G. A. Ueber Rindenreizung am freilaufenden Hunde nach J. R. Ewald. *Arch. Anat. Physiol.*, Lpz., 1900, **24**, 195–208.

WEDENSKY, N. E. Die Erregung, Hemmung und Narkose. *Pflüg. Arch. ges. Physiol.*, 1903, **100**, 1–144.